The Craft of Log Building

The Craft of Log Building

A Handbook of
Craftsmanship in Wood

Hermann Phleps

Translated and adapted from
the original German by
Roger MacGregor

Lee Valley Tools Ltd.
Ottawa, Ontario

©1982, Lee Valley Tools Ltd.
ALL RIGHTS RESERVED
No part of this book may be reproduced in any form
including photocopying without permission in writing
from the publishers, except by a reviewer who may quote
brief passages in a magazine or newspaper or on radio or
television.

Canadian Cataloguing in Publication Data
Phleps, Hermann, 1877–1964
  The craft of log building
  Translation of: Holzbaukunst : der Blockbau.
  Bibliography: p. 326
  Includes index.
  ISBN 0-9691019-2-9 (bound). –
  ISBN 0-9691019-1-0 (pbk.)
  1. Building, Wooden.
  I. Title.
iv TH1101.P4713   694   C82-090096-6

Lee Valley Tools Ltd.
2680 Queensview Drive
Ottawa, Ontario K2B 8J9

Trade Distribution in North America by:
Firefly Books Ltd.
3520 Pharmacy Avenue
Scarborough, Ontario M1W 2T8

Design: Eiko Emori, MFA, MGDC, RCA

First printing 1982
Second printing 1983
Third printing 1986

Printed and bound in Canada

Contents

Preface   1
Introduction   2
What is Craftsmanship in Wood?   5
The Structure of Wood   31
The Circulation of the Sap and Girdling   35
Swelling and Shrinkage   36
Felling   39
Felling Time   44
Working Solid Timber   45
The Properties of Wood   48
Species of Wood Commonly Used in Building with Timber   49
Log Wall Construction   52
Cornerwork   60
Tieing in Partition Walls   68
Pegging and Dowelling   70
Added Bracing – Stub Walls and Vertical Tie-logs   74
Sill Construction   77
Roofs   85
Roofs of Sod or Turf   86
Thatched Roofing   90
Tamped Thatching   91
Sheaf-thatched Roofing   94
Loose-laid Thatch   97
Thatch-tiled Roofing   98
Wooden Roofing   99
Shingled Roofing   101
The Making of Shingles   102
The Loose-laid Shingle Roof   104
The Nailed Shingle Roof   110
Boarded Roofs   121
Roofs of Stone   123
Roof Framing   124
Open-ceiling Structures   124
Eaves Framing without Supporting Beams   155

Eaves Framing with Beam Support 157
Floor and Ceiling Construction 160
Doors and Doorways 164
Scandinavian Door Framing 165
Celtic and Celtic-Germanic Door Framing 179
Bavarian Door Framing 194
Special Types of Door Framing 215
Windows 227
Balconies, Walkways and Other Protruding Features 244
Gable Sheathing 264
Flared Log-end Treatment 269
Columns and Uprights from across Europe's Log Building Areas 280
Moulded Contouring 289
Interior Finish Work 301
A Selection of Log Structures from Scandinavia to the Southern Alps and
    Carpathians 303
Source References of Figures 323
Bibliography 326
Index to Figures 327

Publisher's Foreword

Books come to be published in curious ways. *The Craft of Log Building* came to me quite by chance, and like the pebble dropped in the mill pond, the ripples created by its coming are still widening.

David Perch, a long-time collector and an expert on Canadian edge tools, has been sharing odds and ends of minutiae in the tool field with me for many years. To one of our many meetings on some aspect of log building tool design, he brought a copy of Hermann Phleps' book, *Der Blockbau*. The quality of the illustrations and the intricacy of detail were immediately apparent. A tentative decision to translate and publish the work was quickly made.

Over the several years needed to prepare the translated text and handle the host of other problems posed by such an undertaking, the outlines of two parallel images gradually began to emerge.

On the one hand, as successive installments of the translated material became available, the realization began to grow that this book was quite as striking in substance as it had first been in appearance. Not least among the attractive impressions which began to form was the author's singular intimacy with his subject and his evident stature as a spokesman for the value of the old-time skills and attitudes which had created the exemplary logwork in the book.

Paralleling this development and resulting from the translator's extensive research efforts, an image of the man who created the book also began to take shape, causing us to begin seeing Hermann Phleps as something of a ''familiar stranger''. With *The Craft of Log Building* now in hand, the reader will be able to assess the author's message and approach in person.

To complement this, a brief note on the author and his work as they have become known to us is in order.

Hermann Phleps has been referred to as one of the old masters in the field of European wooden architecture, and even a cursory look at his career spanning nearly sixty years will support this view. Born in south-eastern Europe in Birthälm, Transylvania (now Biertan, Romania) in 1877, he pursued his advanced education in Vienna, Karlsruhe and Dresden, following which he began a teaching career at the *Technische Hochschule* in Danzig (formerly Germany) in 1907. His work at this school covered nearly forty years, during which time he not only lectured on the art and science of timberwork, but also organized a number of exhibitions on the use of colour in architecture, old Germanic building techniques, nd the craft of wrought-iron work. Being a practising architect as well, he also found time to build a number of structures in the Danzig area and in Hermannstadt in his native Transylvania. Following the upheavals of the Second World War, he was forced to give up his work in Danzig, with the consequent loss of much of his painstakingly gathered research material. In subsequent years, he resumed his life's work in West Germany.

Der Blockbau represents the first of the author's two major works, and appeared at roughly the mid point of Phleps' career which covered the years 1908 to 1964. The author was sixty-five at its time of publication, and already had behind him well over one hundred essays and articles on a wide variety of architecture-related topics, particularly building with wood. In addition, he had written a half-dozen books on architectural subjects and one on wrought-iron work. In the years following publication of *Der Blockbau*, four more of his books appeared, including one on timber-frame buildings in Germany (1951) and another on the stave churches of Norway (1958). His second *magnum opus* (to which reference is made in the present text) appeared, following his death, under the editorship of Ernst Mix. Entitled *Alemannische Holzbaukunst* (Franz Steiner Verlag, Wiesbaden), it is an equally thoroughgoing account of the distinctive timber-frame tradition of south-western Germany. Although unable to witness its publication in 1967, Hermann Phleps continued to work on it right up to his death in 1964 at the age of eighty-six.

If Hermann Phleps had known that his work would eventually be translated into another language he undoubtedly would have been concerned about the fidelity of such translation. It is difficult to imagine anyone who could have better reflected Hermann Phleps to the English-speaking world than Roger MacGregor, the translator of this work. Roger brought a sensitivity and a level of commitment to the work that is rare in any age. His ongoing concern for the quality of the work, both in content and form of presentation, was remarkable. Long after he had fulfilled his contractual commitments, he continued to provide invaluable information, advice and assistance in all aspects of the publishing effort. Most importantly, he became a friend.

In the time honoured manner of a prolegomenon of this sort, I would like to thank David Perch for bringing *Der Blockbau* to my attention, Lionel Koffler of Firefly Books for his sage advice on the many aspects of publishing, and Roger MacGregor for being an outstanding professional.

Leonard G. Lee
President
Lee Valley Tools Ltd.

Preface

First and foremost, this book is intended to foster a truly craftsmanlike attitude toward wood, and to help professional and layman alike better appreciate the exquisite beauty inherent in a pure form of architecture so appropriate to the essential nature of wood. Because building with wood must be viewed as the wellspring of architectural design, the benefits of properly appreciating this field can well extend beyond timber alone.

Another asset is that information of value to ethnologists quite naturally emerges when the various methods of log building and framing are looked at in terms of kindred features.

The author's interest in this branch of architecture was first awakened some 40 years ago in the course of lectures on the timber architecture of Germany, given by his eminent teacher, Karl Schäfer at the *Technische Hochschule* in Karlsruhe.

The work of preparing and organizing the material for this book has been greatly furthered by grants from the Free City of Danzig and from the German Research Association. Of those who aided the work of compiling information on individual buildings, etc., thanks are especially due to the staff personnel at the *Höhere Technische Lehranstalt* in Beuthen (Upper Silesia) and the outdoor museums in Stockholm, Oslo and Lillehammer, as well as to Prof. Moro of Villach, Austria and master carpenter Vinzenz Bachmann of Mettenham in Germany's Chiemgau region and to both Hermann Zickeli and Max Schön of Munich. Special thanks as well to Mr. Ernst Braisch and Martin Augustin for their help with the illustrations and drawings. As a prelude to the book itself, sincere thanks to all of the above.

Hermann Phleps

Introduction

This book is designed to urge both the architect and the professional carpenter to more fully appreciate and understand the essential nature and character of wood, the warmest and most alive of building materials. In so doing, it strives to both stir and guide the creative imagination of builders and designers. In addition, the book attempts to take up at a point in time when solid timber architecture was still untouched, or nearly so, by the damaging influence of stone architecture. In other words, it is a return to the school of the old-time craftsmen. The knowledge and experience amassed there down through the centuries, nay the millennia, have produced examples of the most outstanding artistry, from which we can inevitably derive benefit.

It is the author's hope that from the very outset, the illustrated material of the book will inspire the reader's interest for personal involvement in the creative process which is building with wood. However, to simply approach this task with only the training available to us even today would still be to fall short of the book's objective. Invariably, an individual's ability to build or design assuredly and naturally with timber will be directly proportional to the range of buildings and techniques which he personally examines to develop an understanding of what constitutes pure design in wood. Once the essence of the subject is grasped by way of this instructive approach, the individual is in an outstanding position, even vis-a-vis the challenges of the present.

The very nature of wooden architecture, wherein the exterior design most vividly reflects an evolution from within, gives it a certain timelessness. When properly executed, it invariably exudes warmth, appealing to us with a special kind of charm. When we stray, however, from the sound principles of naturalness and compatibility of design, no material shows it more woefully than this selfsame wood. The point is that we tend to feel a much greater affinity for wood than for stone. There was the Grand Master of the Teutonic Knights, for example, who had a wooden addition built onto his splendid residence at Marienburg castle in Prussia to provide homier living quarters. Then too there was Nietzsche, the great thinker, who longed to be able to live in a timber-built house.

It is features such as those touched upon here which also dictate that wooden or timber architecture be the starting point for any program of architectural studies. By following the process from the initial woodworking operations through to the completion of the finished structure, the aspiring architect has the opportunity to see in wood fundamental principles which will also stand him in good stead when designing or building with other materials as well.

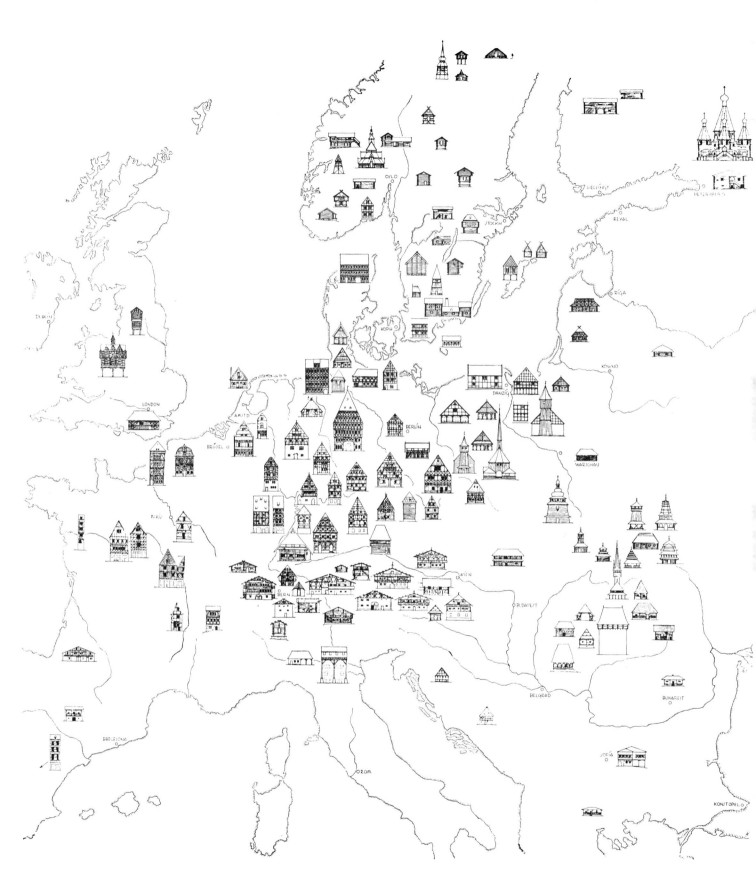

Fig 1
The geographical range of timber architecture in Europe.
Beginning in Scandinavia, horizontal log construction
forms a continuous chain, skirting timberframe and post-
and-beam methods to the east, and reaching down as far
as Switzerland and into the Balkans.

However, even the trained carpenter would do well to acquaint himself with the old-time joinery techniques, at least those formerly used by timbermen of his local area, so as to enhance his professional skill and knowledge to the utmost.

Because the selection, inspection and tending of the various tree species demand far greater care than is the case with other building materials, the importance of proper training and understanding in these areas cannot be overstressed. This is what places wood in a class by itself right from the outset in terms of that ''closeness to the earth'' so desirable in our building and design.

Compared to bygone days when the men who worked the land were still their own carpenters, joiners and wheelwrights, our knowledge of the distinctive attributes of the various species of wood, and hence our familiarity with them, is in sad decline. To illustrate this point, a folklorist by the name of Blau found a farmstead in the Bohemian Forest, worked by folk from Austria's Kärnten province, on which 27 different types of wood had been used in the building of the farmhouse and the making of household utensils and farm implements. Each had been specifically selected to take optimum advantage of its distinctive qualities. To this day, farm people in Kärnten still make use of at least 12 different species of wood.

Because present circumstances oblige us to economize to the utmost on our timber and lumber, it behooves us to make the worthiest possible use of our forest resources. This involves combining careful management and selection with the finest in professional craftsmanship and building practice.

This survey of the field of wooden architecture and building with timber covers two volumes. The first deals with horizontal log construction, which mirrors the nature and character of wood in the most manifold fashion. In addition, building with solid timber is most admirably suited to acquainting anyone interested in the field with the satisfaction and enjoyment afforded by this material, while also illustrating the integrity of approach necessary to working with it.

What Is Craftmanship in Wood?

"Expertise is a requisite for any form of endeavour, whether life itself, some creative activity, or anything else. Such expertise is only to be had by focussing your attention and concentrating your efforts".
– Johann Wolfgang von Goethe

The craftsman's emotional and sentimental attachment to his métier is most pleasingly and naturally expressed when his material is handled and worked in a manner becoming to its distinctive character. This is not to say that the outside observer need know or understand anything about the special qualities of certain materials or the skills involved in working them. Only the layman has this luxury, however, since it is one thing to simply respond as an observer to work by someone else, and quite another to be the actual creator.

To assure that his craft is learned properly, the aspiring professional must not only develop the skills of the trade, but simultaneously train his eye by studying existing

2

3

Figs 2 and 3
Black Forest shake and shingle maker at work. Bolts of wood are first split into smaller blocks with a broadaxe, then riven into shakes or shingles of the desired thickness using mallet and froe (**2**) on the shakemaker's bench (**3**). The elongate fibres of the wood come apart most easily in this direction, with the froe acting as a wedge.

examples of design, woodwork, building and the like. In this context, he must try to establish in his own mind why one particular shape, contour or design appeals to him, while another does not. This personal involvement will provide him with a wealth of knowledge and experience which will be a constant source of inspiration and enrichment in his own work. Furthermore, he must assess every interplay of form and line which catches his eye to determine whether or not it portrays an harmonious blending of functionality, craftsmanship, and the distinctive attributes of the material.

This will in fact be the approach underlying every chapter in this book dedicated to wood. To help the reader feel more readily at home with this concept, the book begins with a brief outline of what is intended by the term ''craftsmanship in wood''.

We may think of wood as being a sheaf of fibres having different properties in the longitudinal direction than crosswise (*cf.* p. 36). When split open along these fibres, it

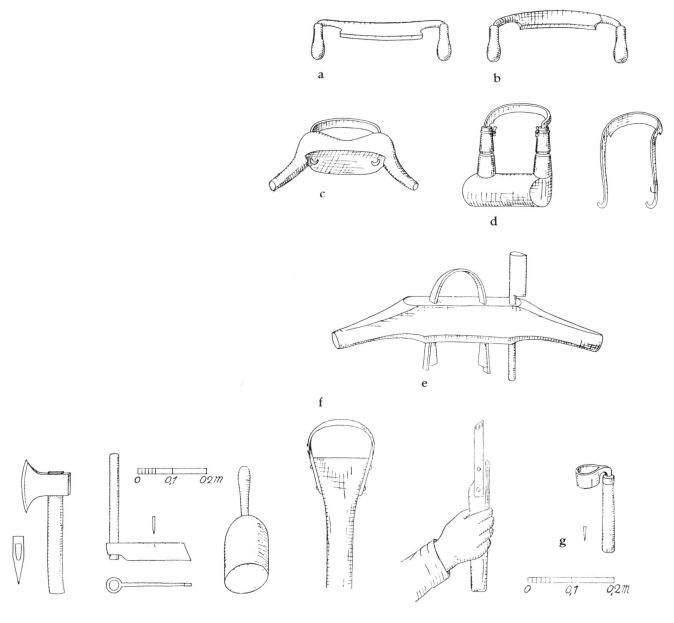

Fig 4
Splitting tools from the Black Forest, including hatchet, froe and mallet or club.

Fig 5
Straight drawknife (**a**), curved drawknife (**b**) and several related woodworking tools from Scandinavia (**c**, **d**, **e**, and **f**) and Switzerland (**g**).

offers less resistance than it does laterally. This process of lengthwise separation along the fibres is known as splitting. To this day, shingles and shakes are among the items still produced by splitting (Figs 2 and 3). These articles are the product of an age-old splitting technique which first involved riving bolts from larger lengths of tree trunk. This process leaves the fibres of the wood largely undamaged. Originally, wedges were used for this work. As techniques were improved and perfected, however, there evolved the various splitting tools for making shakes and shingles (Fig 4). Initially,

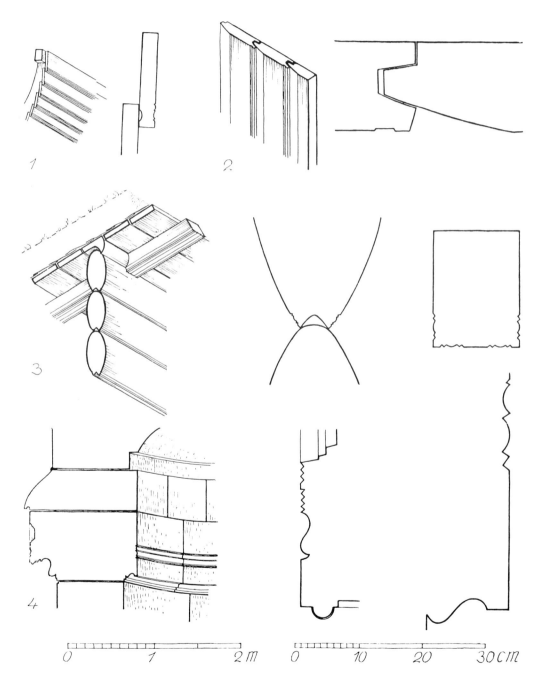

Fig 6
Grooved and moulded edgework beautifully suited to the inner structure of wood. Samples of woodwork from Scandinavia (dating from the Middle Ages) and a reproduction of same in stone from the period of the Germanic migrations. (**1**) from the Viking ship at Gokstad (9th century); (**2**) vertical planking on Scandinavian stave churches; (**3**) from a log granary in Austad, Setesdal; **4** from the exterior and interior cornices on the mausoleum of Theodoric in Ravenna, Italy (early 6th century).

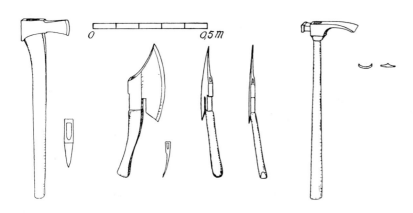

Fig 7
Carpenter's axe, broadaxes and adze.

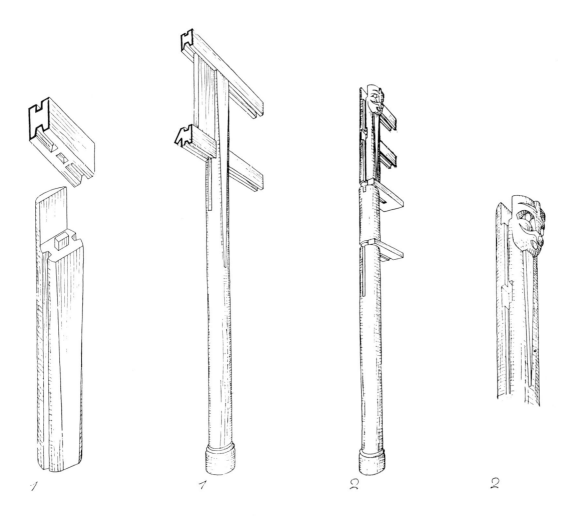

Fig 8
Wooden columns from the stave churches in: **1** Aardal;
and Gol **2** in Norway. A base has been fashioned from the
thicker butt end of the logs, and different techniques used
to fit the top end and the plate on the inward-facing side.
From a creative point of view, this represents the same
train of thought as that involved in Fig **9**, but on a higher
plane.

scrapers were used to smooth the surface of the shingles. From these there developed the drawknife, either with straight or curved blade (Fig 5). The marks which these tools left on the wood inspired woodworkers to use them for decorative work as well. To apply such decoration along the length of members, while keeping it straight and symmetrical, required the use of a guide or jig such as that shown in Fig 5. The edges of beams or planks offered the most obvious place for such ornamentation (Fig 6). Thus, even ancient Germanic architecture shows evidence of this decorative treatment; a practice which has retained its popularity in Scandinavia right up to the modern era.

Another method of lengthwise embellishment involved cutting the wood fibres on an angle with a broadaxe (Fig 7) or drawknife (Fig 5). While the previously mentioned technique was confined to surface decoration, we now find entire members and features being shaped and contoured to portray all manner of architectural expression.

Some of the finest and most elegant examples of this work are found on the columns and pillars of Scandinavian stave churches, where this type of tapering provided an organic transition from the log in the round to the squared plate member. The two pieces might be made to flow smoothly into one another, easily achieved by mortising the plate (Fig 8/1). Alternatively, an effort might be made to place special emphasis on the tops of the columns, in which case through-mortising provided the suitable fitting technique (Fig 8/2).

We find a somewhat similar trend on horizontal wall logs, although in this instance the decorative work has a specific function. As illustrated in Fig 9, this approach involved hewing the logs near the corners to provide a more stylish appearance. The hexagonal endwork shown in Fig 9/1 was done with a straight drawknife, while a curved drawknife was used to create the slightly fluted effect in Fig 9/2. Figs 10 and 11 indicate the wealth of design possibilities inherent in the drawknife. All of these examples are from the timber battlements of the Deutsch-Weisskirch citadel church in Transylvania. Fig 12 illustrates the consumate skill with which craftsmen used this technique to create even figured motifs. A related development is the distinctive

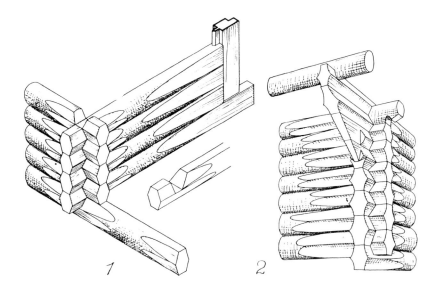

Fig 9
Beautiful hewn cornerwork on round logs, Swedish style. In addition to the log builder's axe, this work also involved use of the drawknife, either straight (1) or curved, as in 2. These two examples, both on granaries in

Sweden, clearly reveal how the interplay of cornering technique, the nature of wood, and the tools used has produced designs which vividly portray the unique qualities of the chosen material, and which are astonishing in their naturalness.

● 9

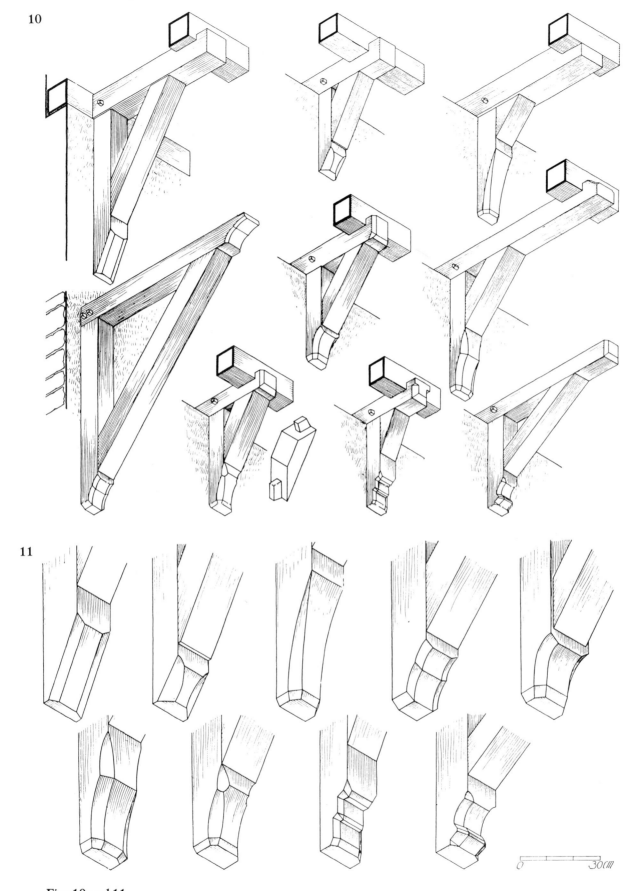

Figs 10 and 11
Decorative drawknife work on suspended braces from the
timber battlements of the Deutsch-Weisskirch citadel
church in Transylvania. The variety of decorative styles
possible using this technique is astonishing, as is the fact
that all are beautifully in keeping with the nature of wood.

klingeisen carving found on the doorposts of log buildings in Austria's Steiermark and Tirol provinces (Fig **13**).

To turn a round log into a timber squared on four sides, woodsmen originally used a technique known as hewing (Figs **14**, **15** and **16**). This too involved splitting, although in shorter sections. To facilitate the hewing operation, large notches were cut in the log with an axe at intervals of roughly 60 cm (Fig **14**), following which the excess material was removed, first with an axe (Fig **15**), then with a broadaxe (Fig **16**).

From this purely functional process, the creative imagination of the old-time craftsman gradually evolved artistic forms of expression (Fig **17**). Without complete mastery of their craft, however, artisans of the day could never have arrived at such unique designs. The items pictured in Fig **18**, including cantilevered endwork in the Upper Bavarian style and a bracket from a timberframe structure in Lower Saxony (Germany), provide striking evidence of how handcraftsmen skilled in drawknife work and living in different areas were able to develop similar designs independent of one another.

Being the most violent of tools in its impact on wood, the saw is more heedless in its operation than are the splitting tools mentioned thus far (Fig **19**). Despite this, the nature of wood is such that it responds well even to this type of working. It is interesting to note how, in certain instances, sawing had a functional application, while being purely decorative in others. To contrast the two, we shall first examine a utilitarian application, specifically the support props under certain European log granaries (Fig **20**). In their most ancient form, these props appeared under storehouses in the Valais of Switzerland, where slabs of stone were placed between these posts or legs and the building itself to keep out vermin (Fig **20/1**). The weight of the building is transmitted to the posts via the interlocking cornerwork. Over the years, there was a natural move toward tapering the posts at this point, with further refinements in the form of chamfering and fluting. The next two items from Norway and Sweden (Fig **20/2** and **20/3**) show the stone slab having been replaced by heavier sill logs made especially wide on the bottom.

Even here, however, there is still a sense of upward movement toward the point of support. In Fig **20/3**, where the prop both sits on and supports notched logs at their point of intersection, the sense of motion is in fact in two directions. In **20/4**, the protective slab has been incorporated into the wooden support post itself. In this piece of work, we now find evidence of the saw having been used in addition to the broadaxe

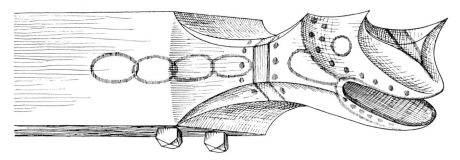

Fig 12
Drawknife carving, using both straight and curved shaves, on the end of a brace forming part of a timberframe. Coloured in red and black. From the Rupertiwinkel region, Berchtesgadener Land, Germany. Displayed at the Exhibition of Southern German Folk Art in Munich, 1937.

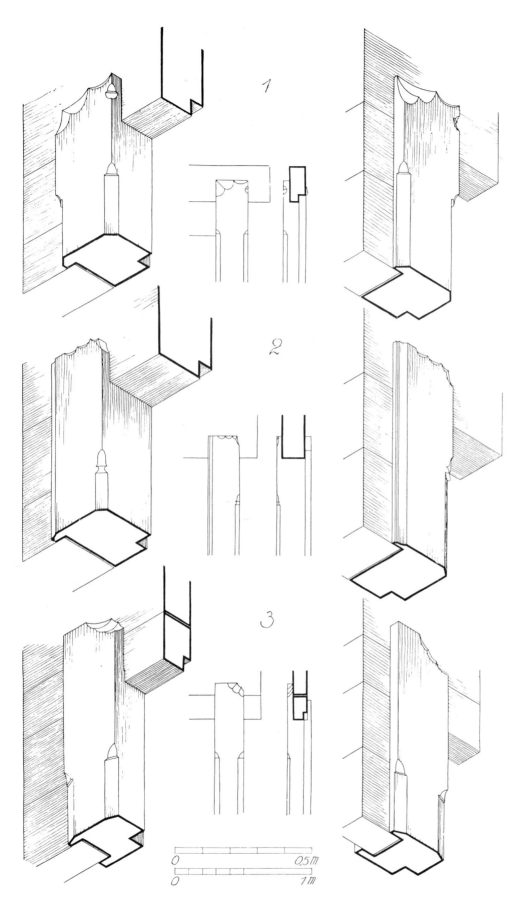

Fig 13
Decorative *klingeisen* carving on door framing from Schüttlehen-Ramsau near Schladming in Steiermark province, Austria (top, from 1598), from the Forstau region on the border between Salzburg and Steiermark provinces (middle, 1762) and from Zell in the Zillertal valley (bottom). One specialized use of the *klingeisen* was in curved dovetail work. This unique tool had a slightly upturned blade, marginally longer than the thickness of the logs.

Figs 14, 15 and 16

Axemen hewing timbers in the Chiemgau region. The logs were set up on trestles, following which chalk lines were "snapped" on them to mark the hewing line. Scoring cuts were then made to this chalk line approximately every 60 cm. The excess wood between the scoring cuts was first removed with an axe, then smoothed with a broadaxe. Once two sides had been hewn, the log was turned over and the process repeated. The above photos show this second stage in the operation. Notice the stance of the hewers with the log to their left.

14

15

16

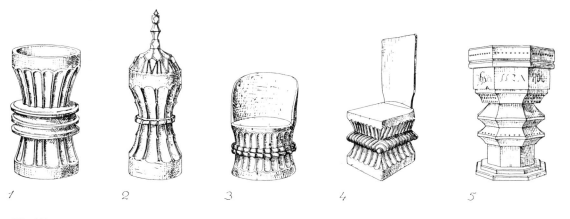

1   *2*   *3*   *4*   *5*

Fig 17

Baptismal fonts and seats carved from sections of tree trunk. In the smaller sense, the first inspiration for these forms came from the simple whittling of a stick of wood, while on a larger scale, their shapes represent a further evolution of hewing as shown in Figs **14**, **15** and **16**. While **17/1** to **17/4** from Norway are untainted wooden designs, **17/5** from Transylvania is reminiscent of architecture in stone, as it seems to have been set upon a separate base.

● 13

and drawknife. This applies to **20/5** as well, where the slotting technique used to tie the tapered prop into the cornerwork of the building is particularly interesting. All of these items clearly show how the hands which made them were guided by the nature of the material and the function it was to serve, combined with skilled craftsmanship and a genuine feel for the work.

The next items, a series of upreaching pillars (Fig **21**), offered greater scope for creativity than the previous ones. Despite this, we still find a similarity of approach. In **21/1**, the plate timbers are mortised into the upright, which has accordingly been left full-size at this point. In fact, special efforts were even made to emphasize this feature

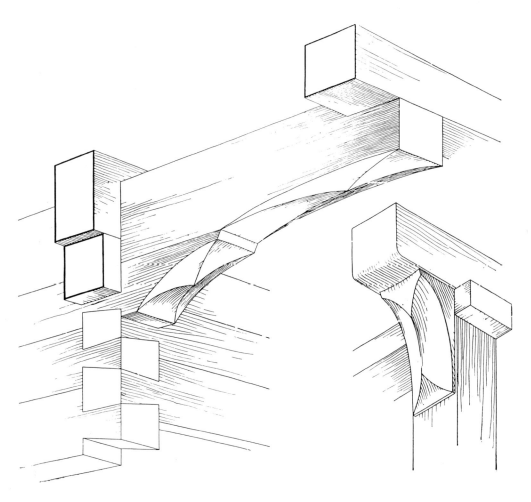

Fig 18
Skillful matching of wood's properties and the potential of the straight and curved drawknife to provide decorative touches to cantilevered log ends (Upper Bavaria) and a bracket from a timberframe structure in Lower Saxony (Germany).

Fig 19
Sawing involves the movement in one direction of a series of slender chisels (teeth), arranged one behind the other on a band (sawblade). Each of these chisels removes a thin shaving as it moves along. The greater the number of these teeth, the more rapid the sawing operation. To prevent the sawblade from binding in the wood, the teeth are alternately bent outward or offset, while the sawblade may be tapered toward its back.

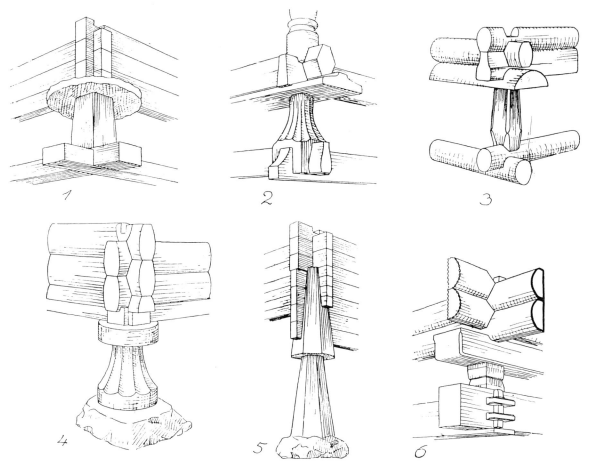

Fig 20
Granary props (supports, legs or posts), showing
workmanship with axe, broadaxe, adze and straight
drawknife (**1**, **3**, **5** and **6**), curved drawknife (**2** and **4**) and
saw (**4**, **5** and **6**). Item **1** is from Zermatt, Switzerland; **2**
from Vinje (Telemark), Norway; **3** from Aelvdalen,
Sweden; **4** from Sirdal, Norway; **5** from Längenfeld, Tirol
(Austria); and **6** from Waldhaus, near Bern, Switzerland.

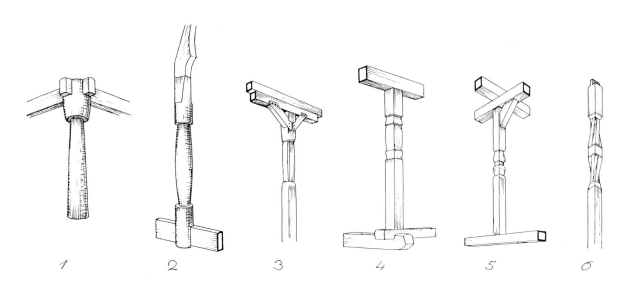

Fig 21
Columns fashioned with saw, axe and broadaxe in
addition to straight drawknife (**1** to **6**), firmer chisel and
skew chisel (**5** and **6**) and firmer gouge (**6**). Items **1**, **3**, **4**
and **5** are from Transylvania; **2** is from Borgund, Norway
and **6** is from the Chiemgau region of Upper Bavaria.

15

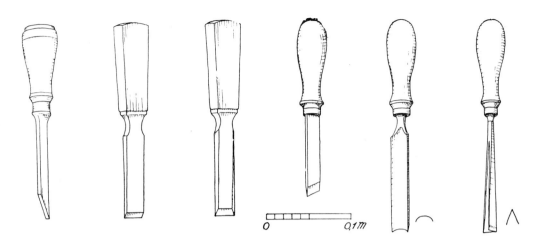

Fig 22
Chisels and gouges, bevelled on one side (English style) or
both sides (German style). **1** Mortise chisel, used for
working across the grain and chopping mortises. **2** and
3 Firmer chisels, used for removing wood and smoothing.
4 Skew chisel, used as a carving knife. **5** Firmer gouge,
used for cutting rounded grooves and hollowing.
6 V-gouge, for edgework.

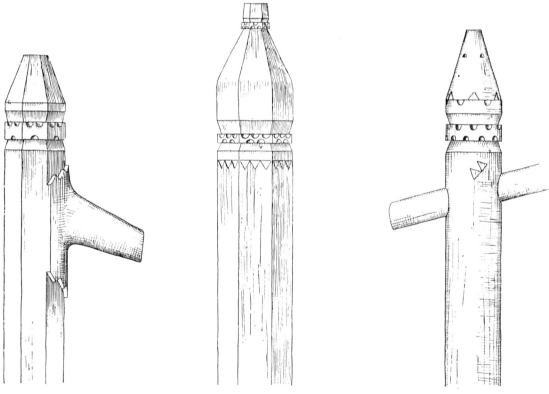

Fig 23
Decorative well-tops and spouts from Alpbach in Tirol
(Austria), 23 cm, 29 cm and 21 cm in width. These items
have been fashioned with broadaxe, drawknife, chisel,
gouge and handsaw. The only traces of the latter,
however, are found where a small collar has been left
around the tapered part of the upright. To soften the harsh
impression created by the sawcuts, a gouge was used to
pattern the edges. One interesting feature is the natural
limb formation which has been cut out and incorporated
into the design in **23/1**.

using saw and broadaxe to taper the post near the top. The second pillar shows this tapering and recessing on both ends. This produced a bulged appearance which was considered attractive as it conveyed a sense of strain. This fundamental concept is reiterated in the subsequent items, accompanied by a variety of more detailed modifications. In **21/4**, the saw cuts give the entire construction a distinctive look. In **21/3** and **21/5**, the marks left by the saw have been softened by rounding the edges with a chisel (Fig **22**). As with other tools, it was only natural that the traces left by each stroke of the chisel would inspire new design ideas. At times, this resulted in design-work which may at first glance appear convoluted, but which is actually startling in its simplicity, if we consider the woodworking operations from which it evolved (Fig **21/6**). In other instances, saw and gouge were used in concert to create singular designs such as those shown in Fig **23**.

However, it is the oval-hewn logwork and bulged-out doorposts of Norwegian log structures which provide the most eloquent evidence of the heights to which the natural inventiveness of the early craftsmen was able to soar (Fig **24**). In section, a

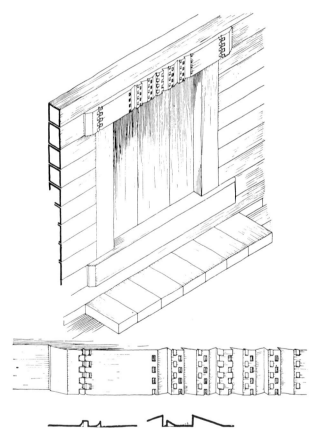

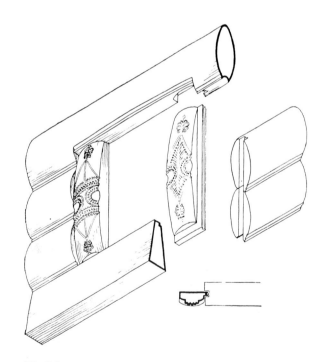

Fig 23a
Doorway of a barn in the Tuxertal valley of the Tirol (Austria) showing decorative trimwork on the lintel. The design is similar to that in Fig **23**, but a double repetition. Shaping the major contours involved sawing deep cuts into the lintel, followed by angled cuts beginning at the walls. Decorative patterns were then chiselled into the narrow strips between the bevelled sides. Again, these patterns consisted of angled and vertical cuts.

Fig 24
Loft doorway from Telemark (Norway). The logs have been given an oval contour, with the longer axis of the oval being vertical. This creates a sensation of strain in the vertical plane. Accordingly, the trimmers serving as doorposts also reflect this feeling in their bowed-out styling. The dynamic eloquence created by this exceptional feel for the work ranks with the crowning achievements in the language of wooden architecture. In the age of classical antiquity, this distinctive form was used on stonework as well. The lower edges of the logs have been decoratively grooved with a tool similar to the one shown in Fig **5e**.

round log shows the same dimensions from the centre in every direction, which is why it may be rolled. However, an oval-hewn log is of varying thickness in profile, with the greatest being along the lengthwise axis of the oval. This is what gives these logs their appearance of bulging muscles. It was only natural for builders to give the doorposts, set vertically to the run of the logs, this same breath of vitality, likewise resulting in a bulged-out look.

The few items presented thus far have given some idea of the nature of wood. Opposite in character, however, is stone. This fact is vividly illustrated by the manner in which the two materials occur in nature (Figs **25** and **26**). The most salient features of stone are its weight and a structure which offers uniform resistance in all directions (excepting the slatelike rocks). Because of this, it is inadmissible to try to transpose certain forms and designs from one of these materials to the other. Regrettably, this very thing did occur, even during the heyday of timber architecture, since stone was sometimes mistakenly regarded as more sophisticated than architecture in wood. The columns and pillars shown in Fig **27** reveal how even early contacts resulted in attempts to faithfully reproduce details of stone architecture in wood. Reworking the base of the Romanesque column, for example, posed no real difficulty, because of a tree's naturally greater thickness at the butt end (Fig **27/6**).

Even without taper in the log or timber, a desirable effect could still be obtained, as shown in Fig **27/4**. However, the shape of the capital, originally hewn from blocks of stone, gave builders in timber greater difficulties (Fig **27/1**, **27/2** and **27/3**). Unless they wished to begin adding pieces to increase the size of the column at the top, they were compelled to find some way of utilizing the natural size and shape of the tree. The

Fig 25
Woodsmen in the Black Forest, partially peeling newly felled fir trees. Even in this first stage of working the wood, we see evidence of the vitality of the material. Stretched out at full length, each trunk hints at motion. The manner in which the bark is removed bespeaks the care with which the inner structure must be treated.

Fig 26
The Burrer Quarry near Maulbronn in Württemberg, Germany. In themselves, the granular and uniform structure of the rock and the chunkiness of the block of stone being hoisted by the crane are enough to clearly show how completely different this material is from timber (*cf.* Fig **25**).

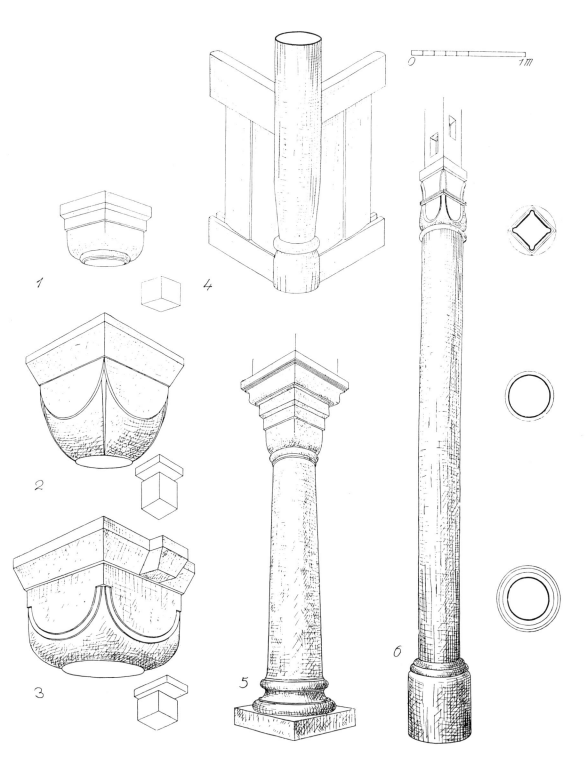

Fig 27

A comparative look at Romanesque columns in stone and wood, clearly showing how the capital form derived from a block of stone (**1**, **2**, **3**, **5**) was adapted to conform to the natural shape of a tree trunk (**6**). Notice also the redesigning of the base (**5**), where the thicker butt end made a greater section possible (**6**) and again when this option was absent (**4**). Items **1** and **5** are from the *Michaelskirche* church in Fulda (*c.* 820); **2** is from *St. Maria auf dem Kapitol* in Cologne (consecrated in 1065); **3** is from St. Aurelius in Hirsau (consecrated in 1071); **4** is from the stave church in Borgund (early Gothic addition to the structure built around 1150); **6** is from the stave church in Flaa, Hallingdal (13th century).

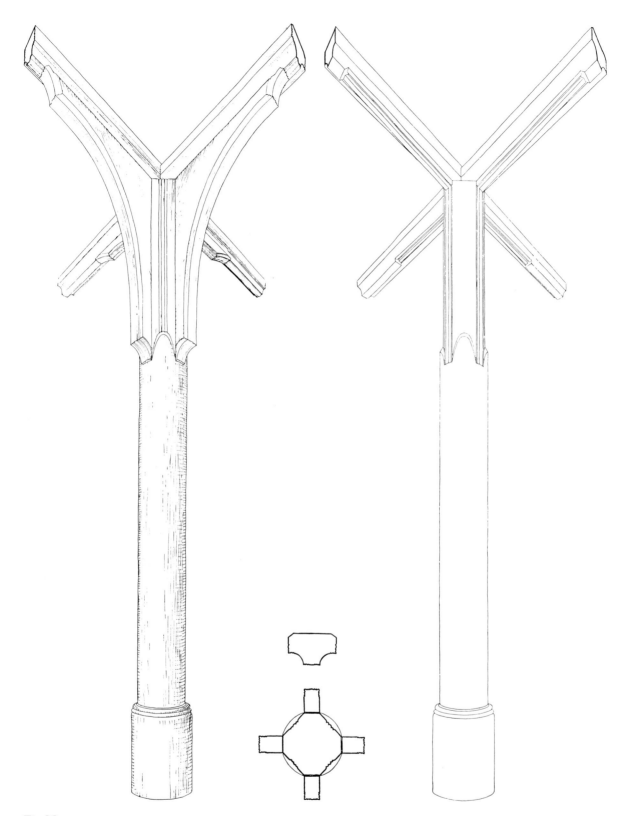

Fig 28
Centre column from the 13th century stave church at Nes,
Hallingdal (Norway), a classical example of pure design in
wood. Although the foot of the column is patterned after
the Romanesque-style stone base, it was not
objectionable, since the broadening of the column at this
point was obviously compatible with a tree being naturally
larger at the butt than at the top. In this situation, notice
the transition from rounded form to octagonal shape at
the point where the brackets begin.

column from the stave church in Flaa (Norway) shown in Fig **27/6** reveals how something new emerged from the limitations of timber.

As stone architecture grew and spread, it exerted a more and more pervasive influence on wooden architecture. A comparison of the columns in Figs **28** and **29** will show how far timber architecture had gone astray under the domination of architecture in stone. In Fig **28**, all of the work is in keeping with the character and the nature of wood, with the exception of the base, although even this feature has been skillfully redesigned. In Fig **29**, however, both the column and the beams show alien features which cannot belie the influence of stone. The column itself has not been fashioned as a unit in cylindrical form to reflect the original shape of the tree trunk, or at least given a squared profile such as that of a timber. Instead, it has been divided into a pedestal and a pillar mounted atop it. This approach is, however, perfectly consistent with the nature of stone. In addition, the contouring of the beams is too heavy and coarse. In

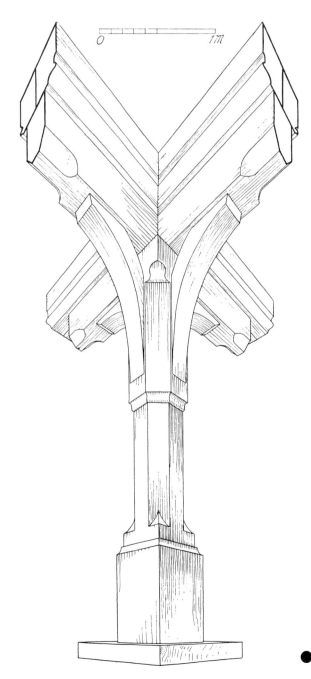

Fig 29
Wooden column from Ulm (Germany). The influence of stone architecture is visible in the plinth-like base, the manner in which the change from a square to an octagonal form is made, and by the markedly powerful contouring of the beams. Contrasting these features with the support brackets on the columns, which are made in purely wooden fashion, one might be misled to believe that he is looking at two different materials.

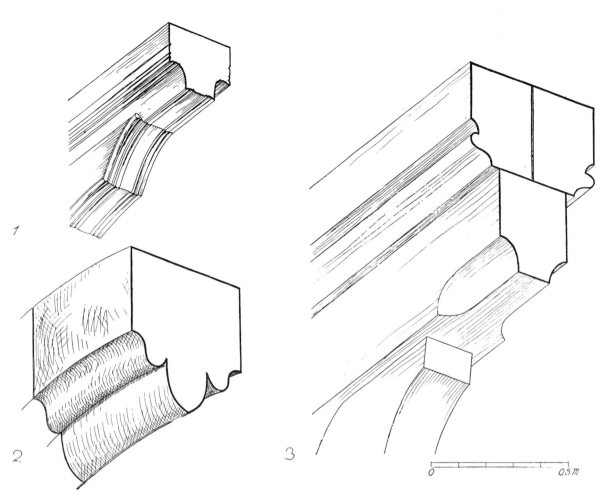

Fig 30
Sections of contoured members in wood and stone. Item
1, showing detail of the column from Nes (Fig **28**), reveals
decorative grooving beautifully in keeping with the inner
structure of wood, *i.e.*, its grain. Item **2**, part of a cross rib
from the *Waldrichskapelle* chapel in Murrhardt
(Württemberg) displays the distinctive features of stone.
In this case, the distinctly symmetrical form has been built

up from a number of pieces of stone, each of which has a
uniform structure in every plane. This and its great
strength in compression permit it to be shaped quite
differently and contoured more radically than wood. Item
3, a section of the beams shown in Fig **29**, shows wood
being subjugated to stone, as the shaping of the decorative
work is conspicuously close to the contours of stone ribs.

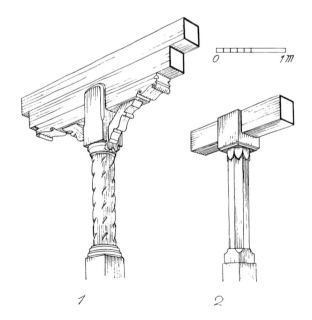

Fig 31
Although these wooden columns have been worked with
the customary tools such as axe, broadaxe, drawknife,
chisel and gouge, their shapes are not entirely in keeping
with the nature of wood. Rather, they are clearly copies of
columns in stone. Item **1** is from Laupen, **2** from Lech,
both in Vorarlberg (Austria).

appearance, they are reminiscent of the stone ribs in medieval vaulted construction, in their time considered among the greatest masterpieces of architecture. In Fig. 30 a closer look at this transformation is provided by detail from the two columns mentioned and a section of a stone rib.

One important groundrule of timber architecture is that shaping or contouring not efface the basic shape of individual members. In fact, it is delicately proportioned decorative features which give timberwork its singular air of refinement. The

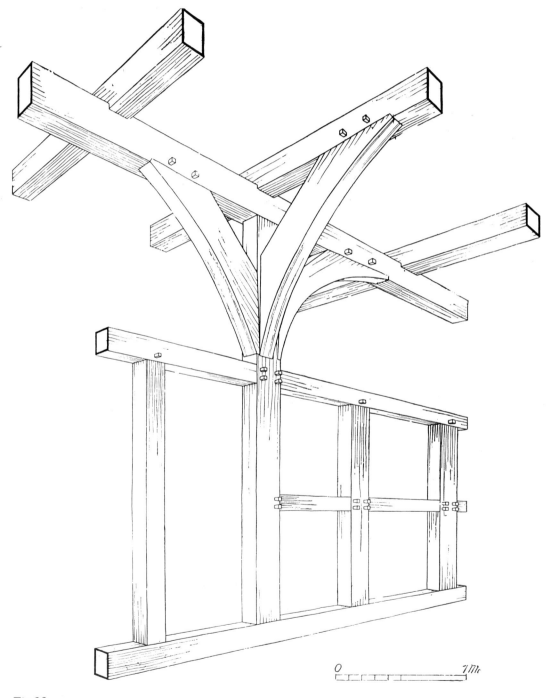

Fig 32
Timber framing from *Niedersachsen* (Lower Saxony).
Germany, now in Menden, Westphalia, showing how the
builder's exuberant feel for his craft is expressed in the
sense of exertion portrayed by the bowed-out styling of
the braces.

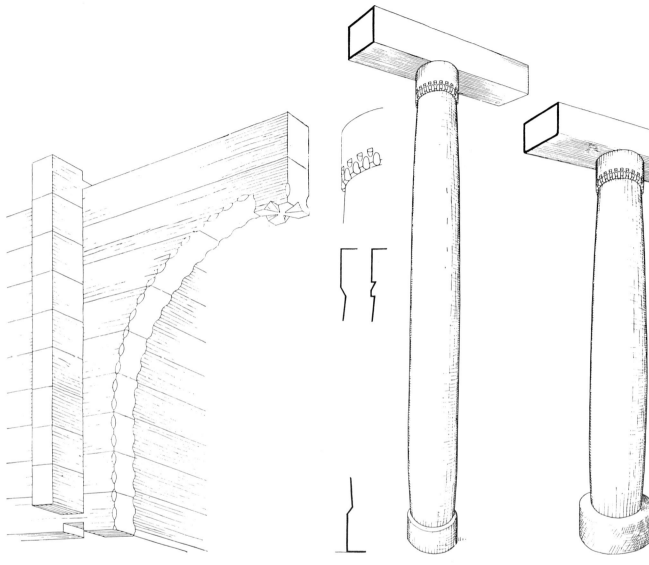

Fig 33
Flared endwork on a log house in Sarnen, Switzerland,
crowned with a fine piece of decorative carving in relief,
nicely in keeping with the solid log.

Fig 34
Wooden columns from the *Quellenkapelle* chapel of the
Wallfahrtkirchlein (Church of the Pilgrimage) in
Kleinkirchheim, Kärnten. As can be seen, the round logs
have been given a slightly swollen appearance by working
them with a drawknife. The natural round shape was
retained at the top, accentuating the knob crowning the
column. This same approach was used on the foot of the
left-hand column as well to fashion a base. In the right-
hand column, this feature is provided by a stone slab. It is
exceptionally instructive to see how clearly these two
items portray the differing nature of wood and stone as
building materials, each nonetheless expressing in its own
distinctive fashion a unified whole. Using these same
designs, had the base of the left-hand column been
fashioned of stone and that of the right-hand one of wood,
the result would have been an undesirably deceptive and
distorted impression (maximum diameter of column
shafts: *left*, 24.7 cm; *right*, 29 cm).

objections which were noted vis-a-vis the column in Fig **29** apply equally to those shown in Fig **31**. In the first item (Fig **31/1**), for example, the manner in which the support brackets meet the column is more in keeping with stonework than with wooden architecture. In Fig **31/2**, the capital is again reminiscent of a block of stone, and much too much wood has been removed for the sake of an alien form.

If these much too convoluted styles were placed beside the columns shown in Figs **28** and **34**, it would be evident how far their builders had strayed from what is appropriate to the nature and the character of wood. For the craftsman who is aware and attuned to his material, wood has its own way of showing what constitutes organic design. In the piece of timberframe work from *Niedersachsen* (Germany) shown in Fig **32**, for example, there is a beautiful vitality about the way in which the knee braces transmit the load from the joists to the posts of the wall, somewhat like compressed springs. A similar feature can also be found in the flared extension of the solid log wall shown in Fig **33**. Because this construction involved a completely different approach to resolving the structural forces at work, it was necessary to express the character of the horizontal logwork by at least accenting the underside of the log which topped off the flaring design.

The finest examples of this phenomenon are shown in two beautiful columns from Kleinkirchheim in Kärnten, Austria (Fig **34**). A stone base has been set under one of them, its shape conspicuously displaying the differing nature of this material. While this feature is missing from the other column, its lower end has been nicely designed

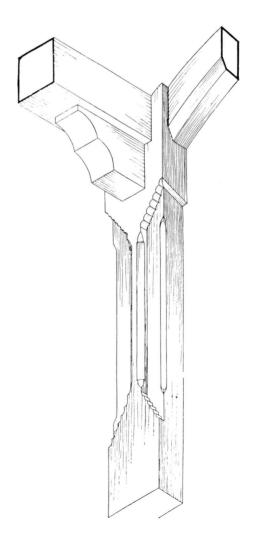

Fig 35
Wall pillar from the so-called Brixener Room of the *Volkskunstmuseum* (Museum of Folk Art) in Innsbruck, Austria (16th century). The arrangement, worked with regular chisel, skew chisel and gouge, is lacking the horizontal layers common to stone columns. The manner in which the raised central rib reaches upward as if from a root structure and then spreads out at the top like the branches of a tree, creates a sense of natural strength. The joist and saddle appear to be resting in the crotch of a tree. Notice also the shaping where the two outermost chamfers have been worked into the corner.

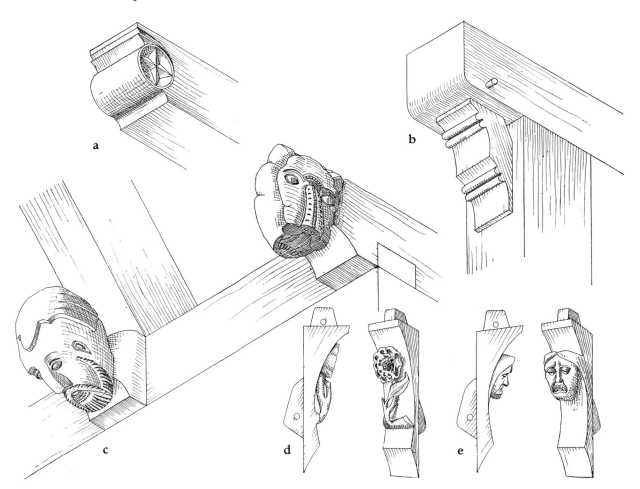

Fig 36
Beam ends and brackets, their decorative work beautifully
in keeping with the nature of wood and adhering to the
basic contours of the various members; **a** from a
timberframe house in Halberstadt, Germany (16th
century); **b** from a bell tower in Münster, Germany;
c from the church in Sparboen (Norway); **d** and **e** from a
half-timber house in Marburg, Germany (c. 1500).

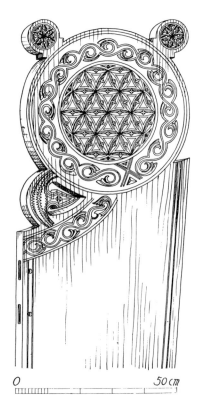

Fig 37
Section of a bedstead from Rauland in Norway. The large
circular feature and the two smaller ones have been
arranged and proportioned to reflect the original squared
contour of the plank. In cutting out the smaller rounds,
care has been taken to leave as much material as possible
to protect them against breakage.

0   50 cm

commensurate with the trunk of a tree by drawing it in slightly just above the base and by retaining the basic natural shape. Because wood has such a unique inner structure, the craftsman must make every effort to exploit this aspect in his building, whether the items involved be logs, beams, planks or boards. This is what gives timber-built structures that special ''natural wood'' mark.

The observer finds himself attracted not only by the pleasing interplay of shape and line in itself, but also by the sense that he is looking at wood. This is why it is so important that decorative work not conceal the sense of the basic lines of the original piece of material, even though there might well be potential for more imaginative contouring (Fig 35). The items grouped in Figs 36, 37 and 38 provide closer insight into this issue. Included in the designwork are figured motifs and geometric patterns.

The requisite that the original shape of the workpiece remain discernible, so richly documented in the aforegoing illustrations, applies equally to lathe-turned woodwork. Because pencil and paper came to be involved in the designing of items during the decline of the old skilled crafts, occasioned by the splitting of labour into those who designed on the one hand and those who worked with their hands on the other, this area of woodworking also witnessed some unfortunate trends, at times exceeding the bounds of acceptability. The Romanesque pew in Fig 39 shows in astonishing fashion both the richness of expression and the degree of refinement possible when the previously enunciated criteria are adhered to.

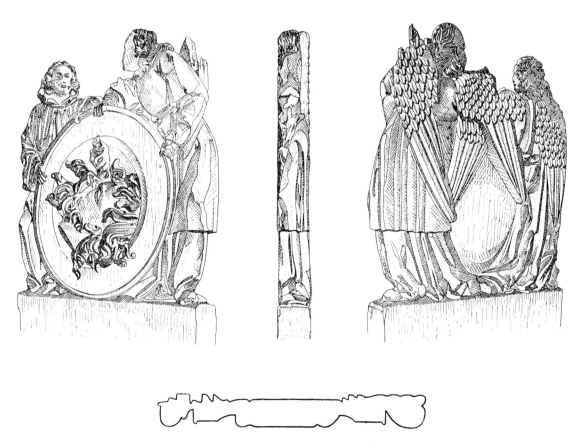

Fig 38
Portion from the end of a pew in the *Johanniskirche* (Church of St. John) in Danzig (Gdansk, Poland), 15th century. In this item, which far exceeds the purely ornamental, a master craftsman has created a piece of exceptional artistry, despite the confines of the thin piece of material. This retention of the basic form of the wooden plank gives the whole a distinctive appearance which helps highlight the nature of the wood. The sectional view shows the lengths to which the artist went in carving the figures.

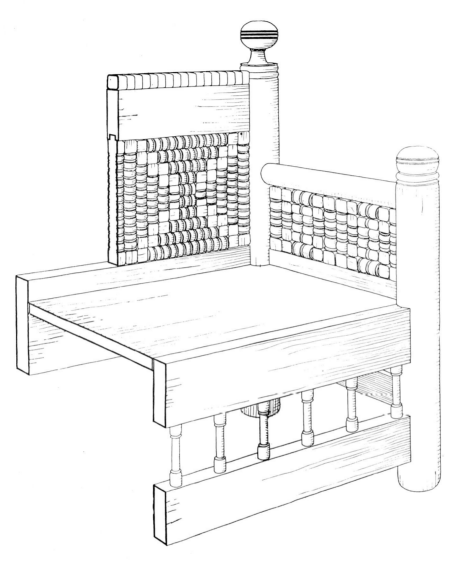

Fig 39
Portion of a Romanesque pew from the abbey church at
Alpirsbach (Württemberg, Germany). The wooden seat
and rails have been left plain, with ornamentation
confined to the turnings filling the back and side panels.
Closely following the rounded form of the arms and legs,
the turnings highlight the nature of the wood.

Fig 40
Section of a catch from a barn door in Niederneuching
from the year 1581. The original practice of chiselling out a
shallow groove to mark the position of the holes for the
pegs moved builders to think of deepening the groove,
thus creating a deep indentation and a distinctive piece of
handcraftsmanship beautifully suited to woodwork. This
design, striking in its naturalness and originality, was
native to the log construction of Upper Bavaria, where it
was also combined with more intricate decorative
designwork.

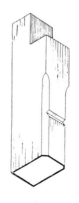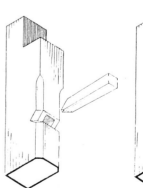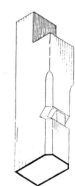

The use of the wooden peg in Fig **40** illustrates, in embryo as it were, the kind of imaginative workmanship possible even on fastenings. Used in the building of doors in Bavarian log construction, the peg sits in a chamfered indentation, forming a piece of ornamentation only conceivable in wood. The initial impetus for this feature came from the practice of chiselling a shallow indentation to mark the position of a pin or peg.

In the era of the highly skilled crafts, the professional carpenter's feeling of intimacy with his work stirred him to give an artistic touch even to places not normally visible or seen only with difficulty. In Europe, roof structures from the Middle Ages offer many outstanding examples of this phenomenon. What elegant and yet exuberant feeling is expressed in the portions of roof framing shown in Fig **41**, considering that all are from military structures! The timberwork on the right is from the sanctuary of the citadel church in Gross-Kopisch, while that on the left is from a tower of the citadel church at Birthälm, both in Transylvania. In the latter case, the beam ends, although hidden by

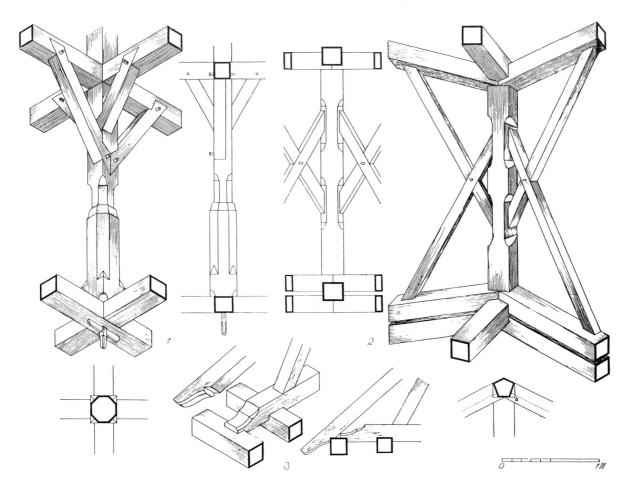

Fig 41
Timberwork from a tower of the citadel church at Birthälm (**1** and **3**) and the sanctuary of the church at Gross-Kopisch (**2**), both in Transylvania. In item **1**, the timber used for the centre post has been fashioned very artistically at its wider end into a beautiful design, which, despite its fineness of detail, still combines nicely with the halved braces to form a unified whole. The craftsman's enthusiasm for his work even produced decorative effects on parts of structures, such as beam ends (**3**), which would

be hidden by other members. Item **2** clearly shows how the contouring of the cornerpost was necessitated by the shape of the larger structure. To make accurate insetting of the cross-braces possible, the surface of the post was hewn so as to be square to the sides of the polygon, but only where the braces met the upright, thus avoiding unnecessary work. The hewn-out areas create a naturally pleasing design on the front face of the post, again making an effective whole.

the rafter tail-pieces, have not been cut off at an angle, as would be the most obvious method, but rather drawknife-carved instead, terminating in two downward swoops. However, the cornerpost from Gross-Kopisch also captures the imagination with its skillful shaping to conform with the polygon design of the structure.

On a concluding note, our look at organic design will include two items naturally shaped for a given practical application. In the forest, craftsmen would seek out trees which branched or forked appropriately or showed a desirable form from trunk to root structure, hence requiring only limited shaping with the tools (Fig 42).

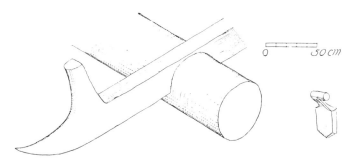

Fig 42
Natural crook-ended rafter from a sod-roofed log building in Sweden and a doorstop from Kärnten, Austria. Both provide striking evidence of how, with only limited application of his tools, the craftsman of years ago was able to create astonishingly expressive and alive designs from naturally occurring tree growths.

The Structure of Wood

Wood is a fabric composed of various kinds of plant cells. In the larger sense, the diversity of its structure can be seen even in the varying appearance of sections taken in different directions through a tree. In this context, we may distinguish three types of section, all at right angles to one another. The first is a cross section at right angles to the lengthwise axis of the trunk, while the second involves a longitudinal radial section, taken through a radius and the long axis of the trunk. The third type is a lengthwise tangential section, cut tangent to the growth rings and at right angles to the first two sections (Fig 43).

A cross sectional cut reveals the pith at the centre, surrounded by the woody mass making up the bulk of the trunk. Encasing the outermost layer of wood formed by the growth cycle is the cambium, a thin sheath of delicate cells responsible for the new growth of the tree. In turn, the cambium is enclosed by the inner bark or bast, and finally by the outer or cork bark. The successive envelopes of wood, which appear as so-called annual or growth rings, each consists of a porous, light-coloured structure surrounded by a darker and denser layer (Figs 44 and 45). The lighter portion, formed during the rapid growth of spring, is known as earlywood, while the denser part which grows more slowly is called latewood. The transition from one growth ring to another is more pronounced than that between earlywood and latewood. In hardwoods, other pores known as vessels are also visible. These are unique cells not found in softwoods. In addition, there are delicate rays or wood rays which run outward in a radial direction from the innermost growth ring. Further outward, these are also accompanied by secondary rays. In softwoods, they are so fine that they cannot be seen with the naked eye.

A longitudinal radial section shows the fabric of cells as a pattern running along the length of the trunk. On straight-grained wood, the growth rings appear in parallel layers, the vessels show up as hairline cracks, and the wood rays appear somewhat like bands. A tangential section shows the rays in cross section, while the cut through the growth rings produces wavy lines of varying thickness.

The cells which make up the wood vary in elongation, wall-thickness and position. Each is surrounded by a cell wall and contains only air, water and air, sap alone, or all three of these. Some cells may be tracheids, mostly arranged longitudinally and serving as arteries for the water rising from the roots to the branches and leaves, and for the nutrient salts and nitrogen which it contains. These arteries also carry the contents of the parenchyma to the buds as the sap rises. Secondly, there are sclerotic cells; narrow, elongated, thick-walled structures with confined cell cavities which serve to stiffen and strengthen the tree. Thirdly, wood contains parenchyma or storage cells, arranged lengthwise in the tree and at right angles to this axis, and containing for the nutrition of the other cells substances necessary for regulating metabolic activity and storage during the winter dormancy. The majority of these are located in the medullary rays.

The hardwoods, which are subject to markedly heavy evaporation compared to the softwoods, contain so-called vessels in addition to the tracheids. These form by intergrowing with the tracheids and provide tubes of varying length which assist the rising of the sap.

Wood fibres consist of a large number of cells intergrown side by side and in tandem. There are fine passageways in the walls of the cells, permitting exchange of substances from one cell to another. In softwoods, resin ducts are interspersed among the cells from place to place.

A microscopic view of a cross section through a pine tree (Fig 45) clearly shows the contrast between the earlywood with its wide cells and thin cell walls, and latewood with its noticeably narrow, thick-walled cells.

As they initially develop, cell walls are of cellulose, soon turning woody, however, with the depositing of various substances. Within the growth rings, the woody mass of the earlywood is open and porous, as opposed to that of the latewood which is harder and more solid. In the older portion of the tree, minerals, tannin, resins, gums and

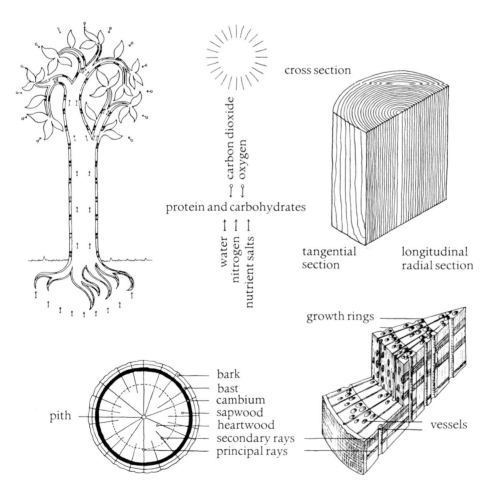

Fig 43
Schematic representation of the flow of sap within a tree under the influence of sunshine, as well as the anatomical structure of wood.

other preservative substances continue to be deposited, while lignification accompanied by drying increases. This inner part of the tree, no longer involved in growth, is called the heart or the heartwood, while the outer portion in which the movement of sap continues is referred to as the sapwood. When there is a conspicuous colour difference between the heartwood and the sapwood, we speak of a heartwood tree. Where this colour distinction is lacking, the tree is known as a sapwood tree. We speak of a tree having heartwood, ripewood and sapwood if there is a gradual transition in colour.

In the living tree, the walls of the cells are continually saturated with water. The varied substances found in cells include air and water and the resins, tannin, and wood gum referred to earlier, in addition to colouring matters, oils, fats, carbon dioxide, calcium and protein substances and starch; the latter two being the main constituents of the parenchyma cells.

In the soft deciduous species and the conifers, this starch is transformed into droplets of fat and oils in the winter, although it remains as starch in the hard deciduous species even during this cold season. On the basis of this characteristic, trees are classified as oily or starchy.

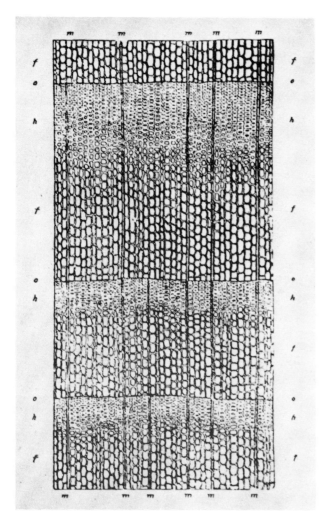

Fig 44
Cross section from the trunk of a fir. *o* to *o* indicates confines of the growth rings; *f* to *f* shows earlywood and *h* to *h* latewood; *m* to *m* shows medullary rays.

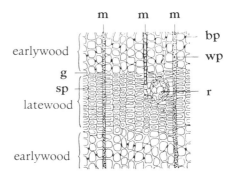

Fig 45
Cross section of a pine. **g:** growth ring border; **m:** medullary rays; **r:** resin duct including secreted resin droplets; **bp:** bordered pit; **wp:** simple or window-like pit; **sp:** split pit.

33

During the growth period, wood cells grow inward from the cambium, while bark cells grow outward, with new growth in the latter case proceeding more slowly than in the former. In addition, cells in the form of bark scales are pushed out from the bark. In northern climes, cellular growth inward from the cambium ceases in winter.

In most tree species, the inner cells begin to undergo a change at a certain age. The passage of water and the flow of the sap are choked off by increased hardening, resulting in a lifeless structure. However, this added heartwood increases the strength of the wood, and usually its durability as well.

The quality of wood is affected in large measure by climate and soil conditions. For example, timber from the high mountain valleys, with their harsher climate, is more durable and heavier with more compact growth rings than that from lower elevations.

The Circulation of the Sap and Girdling

The living tree obtains its nourishment in the following fashion. The root fibres draw in water, nitrogen and nutrient salts from the soil and force them through the tracheids of the sapwood right up to the tips of the leaves, where excess water evaporates (Fig 43). For their part, the leaves take carbon dioxide and oxygen from the air. Under the influence of sunlight, proteins and carbohydrates are formed, both nutrients essential for growth. These pass into the inner bark, transported by the tracheids of the bast and the sieve tubes, as well as into the parenchyma of the cambium and the medullary rays and on down into the root structure. If, sometime prior to felling, the flow of sap is interrupted by the removal of a strip of bark from around the tree just below the crown, nutrients can no longer be carried to the rays and the roots. The roots in turn can no longer be stimulated to absorb fresh water, nitrogen and nutrient salts. The nutrients produced in the leaves remain trapped in the crown, which continues to flourish for a time. Moisture rising from the soil carries the remains of cell sap and nutrient salts upward. The life processes of the tree begin to fail and the trunk begins to dry out below the ring of removed bark. Cut off from their supply of water, the leaves eventually wither and die. The well dried trunk is free of starch, shows no wind shake, and is resistant to insects and fungi.

Swelling and Shrinkage

One of the most important characteristics of wood affecting its handling and working is that it decreases in volume or shrinks when it gives off moisture and increases in volume or swells when moisture is absorbed. Swelling begins immediately once water is absorbed. Before wood can shrink, however, most of the water in the cells must first evaporate (which takes place at a moisture content of 20%), enabling the stretched cell walls to give off the water which they have absorbed. Wood is constantly striving to maintain a moisture content equal to that of the air. When this stage is reached, we speak of wood or lumber as being air dried. In this situation, its moisture content will be some 14–15%. If we compare this with newly felled timber having a moisture content of approximately 45%, and further bear in mind that the moisture content of the heartwood is roughly 15%, but that of the sapwood is about 50%, we have a striking picture of how volume can vary with evaporation. This points to the fact that one of the first considerations, even when a tree is being felled, is how to deal with these stresses and how to inhibit or prevent shake or checking.

In the transition from green wood to the bone-dry state, *i.e.*, the point at which it ceases to have any moisture content, the dimensions of wood change, as illustrated by the following percentages (from F. Kollmann, *Technologie des Holzes* [The Technology of Wood], 1936):

species	along the grain	radial to the growth rings	tangential to the growth rings	by volume
oak	0.4%	4.0%	7.8%	12.6%
elm	0.3	4.6	8.3	13.8
beech	0.3	8.8	11.8	17.6
fir	0.1	3.8	7.6	11.7
spruce	0.3	3.6	7.8	12.0
pine	0.1–0.4–0.6	2.6–4.0–5.1	6.1–7.7–9.8	11.0–12.4–15.0
larch	0.3	3.3	7.8	11.8

Fig **46** shows the swelling curve for pine, from the bone-dry state to a moisture content of 50%, while Figs **47** and **48** show the result of shrinkage on a cross section. This characteristic plays an important part in every aspect of building or working with wood, and for this reason will be mentioned often in conjunction with the various items illustrated and discussed in this book.

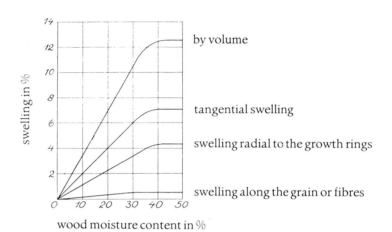

Fig 46
Swelling curve for pine.

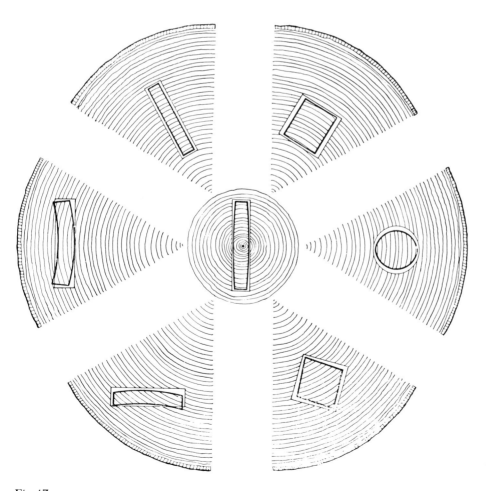

Fig 47
Distortion on a variety of sections due to shrinkage.

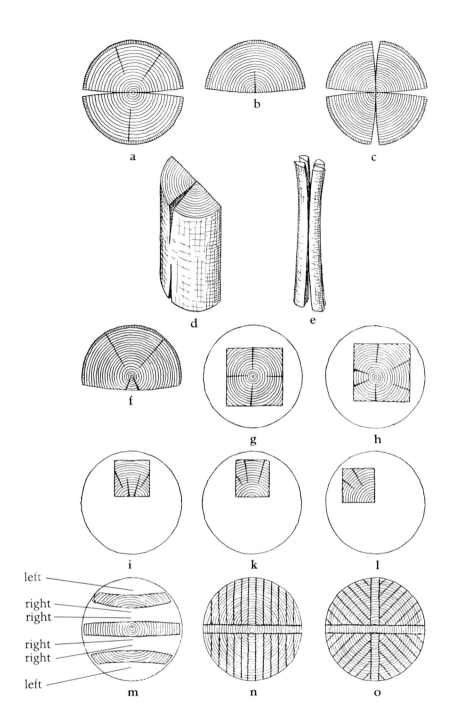

left
right
right
right
right
left

Fig 48
Showing checking on logs and squared timber caused by shrinkage, and warping on sawn lumber. **a** On an unpeeled round log cut in two, shrinkage, which increases toward the outer growth rings, is most evident on the cut surfaces, which take on an arched shape. In this case, heart shake readily occurs in the rounded portion.
b When the bark offers only slight resistance to severe shrinkage of the sapwood, a short heart shake opening to the pith may develop. **c** If a log is quartered, the wood yields to shrinking in large measure and, if left unpeeled, shake in the sapwood will be insignificant or eliminated completely. **d** Half-logs frequently show heart shake emanating from the ends, which dry out most rapidly.
e Being the younger wood, the sapwood contracts more severely than the heartwood, with the result that the quartered log spreads apart. **f** On a false half-log, which still contains the heart in the larger half, a number of short yet severe shakes develop on the heart side. By contrast, checking is minor on the rounded side. **g, h, i, k, l** In squared timber, whether hewn or sawn, checking depends upon the orientation of the growth rings as seen on the butt end. To most effectively guard against checking, logs are sawn at right angles to the growth rings, i.e., parallel to the wood rays. **m** If planks or boards are taken from a log with cuts parallel to a diameter, the dissimilar fashion in which growth rings shrink is highlighted by the fact that the portion passing through the heart takes on a curvature outward to the "right", while the other side bends toward the sapwood, i.e., inward to the "left", thus making a pronounced bow facing the heart. **n, o** Because of these characteristics just mentioned, boards are cut at right angles to the growth rings.

Felling

The bonds between the log builder and his material begin to form in the forest itself, even prior to felling, because quality is a factor of such importance. Quality is dependent upon such a variety of circumstances affecting growth that the utmost care must be taken to properly inspect the material. At one time, this was a matter of course. In 1435, for example, master builder Hans Gilgenburg went out personally into the forest to select the timber for the building of the *Marienkirche* church in Danzig. Today's builders simply order their lumber and timber already milled, without detailed knowledge of its place or origin.

We have already noted that the characteristics and the location of a site, as well as climatic factors, may govern the quality of wood. If a forest stand is open to the north, this favours strength and hardness. If exposed to westerly winds, however, trees in a stand may develop ring shake or heart shake (Fig 49).

Even when it is still standing, we can see whether a tree has grown straight or developed a twist, and whether its wood will be clear, *i.e.*, whether or not the limbs have been removed early enough to a height of at least 10 meters. To a degree, it is also possible at this stage to determine if a tree is healthy or touched by disease. Externally, hardy shoots, uniform leaves, and a smooth bark visible beneath the wrinkles of the outer bark are all signs of healthy growth. A time-honoured method of determining the quality of timber involves striking a portion of the trunk, from which the bark has been removed, on the south side. A healthy tree gives a clear ring. On felled trees, this test involves striking the butt end. If the blow produces a dull sound or no sound at the opposite end, this points to diseased areas, heart rot, heart shake or frost cracks.

There are two kinds of spiral twist, one of which is acceptable for building purposes, while the other may produce major distortions with potential for structural problems. If the twist runs counter to the sun (*i.e.*, right hand), the old-time dictum of the Bavarian carpenter was that this wood would retain its shape when felled. If it runs

Fig 49
Ring shake (left) and heart shake (right). The former develops from overly rapid drying and shrinking of the innermost core, while the latter results from non-uniform growth of the individual annual rings, which sees a more vigorous ring overgrowing a slower one, stunting its growth. This creates cavities, which may become complete rings if the tree is exposed to wind.

with the sun, however (*i.e.*, left hand), the bundles of fibres attempt to twist back during drying and in the dried state. This process, which may go on for years, is so powerful that it may force log walls out of plumb and loosen or even force apart roof framing.

To test for twist, the right hand is placed on the trunk of the tree, as shown in Fig **50**. If the twist runs toward the little finger, it is said to be right hand, and the wood considered usable. If, however, it runs toward the thumb, the twist is left hand, and the wood unusable.

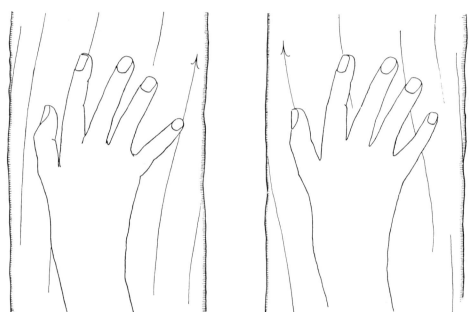

Fig 50
The traditional Bavarian carpenter's technique for determining spiral grain. If the spiral is in the direction of the little finger (left), it is right handed; if it follows the thumb (right), it is left handed. In the former case, the wood is usable, but should be rejected for building purposes in the latter instance.

51

52

53   54

55   56

Figs 51 to 56
Fellers at work in Germany's Black Forest. In Fig **51**, the
bark is removed just above ground-level to prevent the
saw from being damaged by dirt spattered on the trunk by
rainfall. In Fig **52**, the cut is begun with a cross-cut saw on
the side opposite the direction of fall. Fig **53** – to prevent
the saw blade from binding, chisels are driven into the
saw-cut to act as wedges. In Fig **54**, an axe is being used to
cut a notch into the side opposite the cut. Fig **55** – by
driving in the wedge-like chisels, the tree begins to sway.
In Fig **56**, the tree gives way toward the saw cut and falls.

When the tree is felled, it is cut off from the earth which has given it life to that point. This felling now brings it fully into the hands of those who will work it as a material. A felling crew consists of two men (Figs **51** to **56** and **57**). To begin with, a small amount of bark is removed from the stem just above the ground using an axe. This is to prevent the saw from being damaged by any particles of dirt spattered on the trunk by rainfall. The initial cut is then made with a cross-cut saw on the side away from the direction of fall, extending in roughly four fifths of the diameter of the trunk. To prevent the saw from binding, wedge-like chisels are driven into the cut once the saw blade has penetrated to its own width. Next, an axe is used to chop a notch into the opposite side of the trunk, extending almost to the saw cut. Finally, the chisels are driven further into the cut, forcing the tree to totter, then bringing it down. It is a moving experience to witness this once soaring giant come crashing to earth; the emotional impact doubtless a reflection of our inner feeling for this living gift of nature, which man may decide to drop in any specific direction he desires.

As soon as the tree is down, it is immediately limbed up to the crown. The crown itself is not sawn off until a short time later, because until its needles wither, it continues to draw from the trunk liquids which can otherwise cause problems. To aid further drying, while at the same time avoiding checking, the stem is partially peeled (Fig **25**), which involves removing individual pieces of bark with a hewing axe. If the wood dries too quickly, the sapwood will split, producing cracks and openings, in which harmful spores carried by the wind may settle.

If the bark is left on, however, this chokes the sapwood, producing chemical changes which make the stem particularly prone to attack by insects and fungal decay.

It seems a curse of sorts, that the moisture from the soil, which formerly nurtured the tree and gave it life, should suddenly become its enemy as soon as it is felled and cut off from its roots. From this moment onward, the tree is totally in the hands of its human custodians, who must now set it aside for careful seasoning once it has been partially peeled as previously described.

To prevent decay and rot, logs must not be left on the forest floor, especially during the warm season. As soon as they are felled, they must be placed on skids, hauled out of the woods as soon as possible, and stacked where they are protected from direct sunlight, exposure to wind from one direction, and, most importantly, from the wet.

If great care is taken to properly oversee the seasoning and drying process, this effort will be richly rewarded, as the wood will not only be more resistant to insect or fungal attack, but also be less prone to checking and cracking.

As a general rule, two years are considered necessary to fully air-dry logs. Timber which has been rafted (and hence leached) dries more quickly than do green logs.

Fig 57
Loading logs in Bavaria's Chiemgau region. The chain, which is secured to the wagon, is wrapped around a log, then hitched to the workhorse. As the horse moves forward, the log rolls up a pair of skids and onto the bed of the wagon.

Cracks and checks are created because certain cells dry more rapidly than others. The cells of the sapwood are larger than those of the heartwood, and the outer growth rings are thicker and more widely spaced than the inner ones. They take in water more rapidly than the heartwood, yet dry out more quickly. The changes in volume produced by this unbalanced drying process set up stresses, which in turn create cracks.

Of course, the bark does provide natural protection against these cracks, but because the wood may be damaged if the bark is left on after felling, this type of drying may only be used if the tree has previously been readied by girdling. As soon as the bark splits open, however, heart shake occurs, opening in wedge-shaped fashion outward from the centre. Evaporation is most marked on the ends of the logs, producing the first checks and cracks. These can be countered by painting the log ends, glueing on a paper covering, or by driving in clamps.

Fig 48 shows how checking caused by shrinkage occurs on round logs and squared timbers. Even on the stump in the woods, however, cracking may occur as a result of premature drying and shrinking of the innermost core. Emanating from the pith, these cracks mostly parallel the medullary rays, decreasing in size as they proceed outward (Fig 49).

At times, even non-uniform growth in the individual annual rings may result in splitting along these cracks, producing so-called ring-shake.

Felling Time

Even today, opinion varies as to how felling time affects the properties of wood. Popular belief favours winter over summer as the best time for felling, while written accounts as far back as Vitruvius (10 BC) express this view as well. One old-time adage held that:

If in Yuletide days you're felling,
Tenfold the lifespan of the dwelling,
By Fabian and Sebastian (January 20),
Sap is on the rise again

In Austria's Kärnten province, the farm-folk maintain that:

When the larch is cold and bare,
Timber felled is true and fair.

Such winter-felled timber, it is held, will not be prone to checking.

The rationale for this widespread belief in winter-time felling has always been that this is when the least amount of sap is in the tree. Curiously, however, December is the very time when the moisture content of the softwoods approaches the peak moisture figure reached in July. In light of this, it would seemingly be more accurate to say that timber should not be cut while the sap is "on the move".

Numerous folk beliefs attest to the importance which our forebearers attached to fixing the proper time for felling. In Upper Bavaria, for example, the German woodsmen still say that a tree which "suffers injury" during the *Darrstunde* or dry days will inevitably dry out, although the wood will have the finest properties possible for felled timber. In Austria's Kärnten province, the same is said of the period around *Medardus*, although this is not in reference to the calendar day of the same name. Perhaps the term "injury" is a now-obscured reference to girdling, while the "dry days" may mean the period when the sap is not flowing.

From as far back as the end of the 18th century, the view has been voiced that summer felling is the equal of winter logging, provided that the timber is properly handled and thoroughly seasoned once cut. It must be conceded, however, that a number of studies have shown winter-felled timber to dry more slowly than summer-cut wood, resulting in significantly less checking and other associated problems. Furthermore, lumber from unseasoned summer-cut timber has been shown to rot more rapidly than that felled in winter. The only advantages of winter felling, some suggested, related to the physical conditions on the ground at that time of year. Others even maintained that the leaching caused by rafting timber was no longer as important a factor as once considered, since the damaging spores of red rot had been found to attack leached timber as well.

Countering the limited laboratory tests of those who champion summer felling, however, stand the centuries-old structures of timber-built architecture as monuments to the reliability of wintertime felling. Whatever position one may take on this issue, both approaches share the common imperative that the timber be handled with the utmost care, thus putting it in a class above all other building materials.

Working Solid Timber

The first step from round log to squared timber is "rough hewing", a preliminary axework operation which can be carried out in the woods or at the work site. This operation leaves the naturally rounded contour, *i.e.*, the so-called wane-edge on the log here and there. Proper hewing, with the logs up on stands or trestles (Fig **15**) and chalk-lined, involves both the axe and the broadaxe, making for more smoothed squaring of the timber. From a creative standpoint, this is the most dynamic operation, as we feel in the physical hewing marks of the broadaxe the craftsman's art in the making.

Splitting with axe and wedges, at one time employed to make half-logs and planks from logs, is an age-old technique. Planks used to be riven from half-logs, with the result that no more than two planks could be had from a single stem. However much

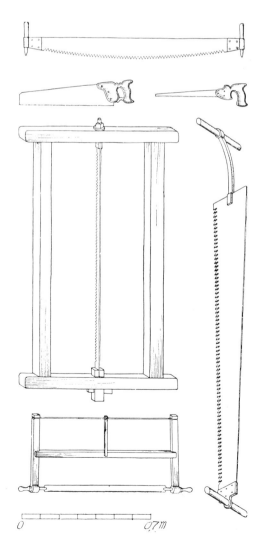

Fig 58
A collection of handsaws. Above, a cross-cut saw, operated tangential to the horizontal. The configuration of the teeth reflects the back-and-forth arm motion of the fellers, thus the curved shape of the blade. At right is an open pit saw, also known as a plank or ripping saw. This is also a two-man saw, but operated with an up-and-down motion. To gain maximum advantage from the sawyer's strength, the blade is widened toward the top end. Accordingly, the force parallelogram dictates that the saw follow a forward motion as it is pulled downward. Below the cross-cut saw are shown a carpenter's handsaw and a keyhole or fret saw, operated by one man. Because these saws cut with a downward motion from the handle, the blade must be strong, tapering toward the back to prevent binding. At centre is a frame saw with blade tightened in place, also a one-man saw. Below is a bowsaw, again operated by a single man. Tension on the blade can be adjusted by a stretcher cord and tightener.

0   *0.7m*

we might lament this practice as wasteful, it did have the advantage of keeping the woodworker in close touch with his material, helping the craftsmen of this era to create the most outstanding achievements in the field of wooden architecture. Such delightful and exuberant designs as those epitomized by the wooden architecture of Norway (*e.g.* Fig **24**) could never have been created without this deep empathy between craftsman and material.

Saws, either manually operated (Figs **58** and **59**) or mechanically powered, may be used to cut timber to any desired size and shape, making for efficient use of the resource. It was the saw, however, which we may refer to as the most heartless of tools, which initiated the loosening of the bonds between craftsmen and timber. It is telling to note that where the saw did not come into general use until relatively late, as was the case in Norway, the natural and distinctively wooden styles survived longer than in areas where the saw emerged earlier.

Our intimate feel for wood is lost most completely when we abandon the handsaw, which can be visually guided, for the automation of the power saw.

So it is that today, the creative imagination finds itself confronted with the timber and lumber offered by the commercial lumberyards. Only rarely, to express some romantic bent toward the out-of-doors and the natural world, do we turn to the natural round-log form whose shape best reflects the feel of the living tree. The only way out of this predicament is to consciously return to the rich design heritage of our ancestral timber-built architecture, which is free of these inhibitions. In this context, we only have to look at the delightful verve of the old Norwegian doorposts as they reach upward, yet bow inward toward the door header, to sense an initial intimation of the nature of wood. On the other hand, this brings home to us how much potential for creative expression we have lost.

Fig 59
Scene depicting logging operations, from the *Deutsches Museum* (German National Museum) in Munich. In the background, loggers are at work felling. At left centre, the hewing process is shown in three stages. At right, sawyers are shown ripping timbers with a plank saw, while at left, planks are being cut with a frame saw. At the far right, stacking to allow proper drying is shown.

We sense the unique makeup of wood even when the tree is being felled, and also during splitting, hewing, or even sawing by hand. Through experience, we become familiar with the way in which wood offers a completely different resistance when worked with the grain as opposed to across it. However, the more the worker relies on the tool to do the job for him, the more the bonds between the craftsman and his material begin to slacken. This process, which became apparent even with the introduction of the saw, has a more refined parallel in the replacement of the drawknife by the plane (Figs **60** and **61**). Every stroke of the drawknife gave new shape to the material; providing ever fresh impetus for innovation. With the plane, however, shaping is pre-determined, ruling out variation as the work progresses.

If we turn to actually building with wood, we encounter other properties. Longitudinally, for example, tensile strength is greater than compressive strength (by at least 20%), shearing strength is less than compressive strength (roughly $1/7$ to $1/10$, so that the sheer surface must be at least 7 to 10 times that of the corresponding bearing surface area). In addition, shearing strength across the grain is substantially greater than longitudinally.

When wooden members are in compression, the dissimilar strength of the growth rings becomes apparent. It may happen, for example, that growth rings in latewood come into contact with those of earlywood where two members abutt. To assure that compression is evenly distributed, a steel plate will be placed between the members in a case like this.

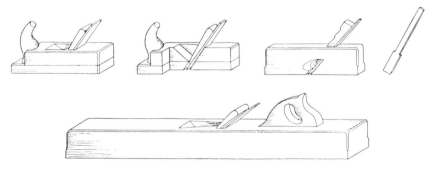

Fig 60
A variety of planes. The iron or blade sits in a slot in the body of the plane and is adjusted by a wedge. Above left, a jack plane; right, a rabbet plane. Shown below is a long plane.

Fig 61
Moulding planes. The cutting edge of the irons shows the profile which the plane was designed to cut. The sole is shaped to hug the profile as closely as possible. A ''fence'', adjustable by threaded spindles (at left), makes it possible to cut the profile at the proper distance from the edge and in a perfectly straight line.

The Properties of Wood

The length of time wood will last depends upon a number of factors. Outdoors, it will last longest in an air-dried environment. Underwater, its lifespan is unlimited, as long as no gases are present. The most harmful effects result from alternating wetting and drying, which make wood prone to fungal attack, particularly if it contains starch and protein or unlignified cells (sapwood).

To counter this type of problem, fungicidal preservatives have long been used to impregnate wood. However, the most effective defence is still, as it has always been, to deny moisture access in the first place through proper construction.

We shall return to the properties of wood and how to best utilize them when we look at the various aspects of building with solid timber, where we can relate them to concrete illustrations.

Suffice it to say, however, that a number of wood's properties make it particularly well-suited for home building. It is easy to work, and a poor conductor of heat, cold, sound and electricity, in addition to being dry when structures are properly built.

Species of Wood Commonly Used in Building with Timber

Hardwoods

Oak

Pedunculate oak grows in Europe, North Africa and the Far East on loose, fertile soil in open country, and in rich, loamy sandy soil. It grows to 160–200 years old, up to 40 meters in height and 2 meters in diameter. Its heartwood is yellow to reddish or grayish brown, lighter in the sapwood, with noticeably thick wide medullary rays. It is very durable and weather-resistant, although its sapwood is susceptible to rot fungus and attack by borers. In water, it turns black because of the tannic acid it contains.

The Sessile or Durmast oak grows to 60 meters in height. Its wood is yellowish and harder, but not as tough as that of Pedunculate oak.

Evidence shows that as far back as the early Middle Ages, oak was being used in the construction of homes and churches, and even today, it is still the most important native hardwood in structures built to last.

It is especially well suited for timberframe work. In log construction, oak logs may be found making up the sill course or, in plank form, as wall material on solid-timber walls.

Oak has long found extremely widespread use in the making of dowels and pegs. Because of its resistance to moisture, it is also suitable for window frames, although it must not be structurally joined with softwoods, because the two woods work to different degrees. Its toughness also makes it desirable for stair treads and interior strip flooring. No less important is the role of oak in furniture making.

Elm

There are numerous types of elm, which may be ranked in order of quality as follows: Smooth-leaved elm, Wych elm and European white elm. The elm grows in the temperate zone of the Northern Hemisphere and in the tropical mountains of Asia. It thrives in any firm, moderately moist soil and grows up to 30 meters in height. Its heartwood is reddish-brown, while the sapwood is a creamy or buff colour. Elm wood is heavy and hard, extremely tough, hard to split, resilient, and a match for oak in terms of utility. It does not warp readily, and is very durable, both when dry and when green. It is highly resistant to attack by worms and borers and dries slowly. Because it is not common, it is mainly used today for furniture and by carriage-makers and millwrights. At one time, it was also used in timber building, a case in point being the stave church at Urnaes in Norway, constructed near the end of the 11th century. Elm logs were also used occasionally in the first course of log buildings in the Valais, Switzerland.

The Semi-hardwoods

Larch

The Common larch grows in Europe, Siberia and North and South America, and thrives especially well on rocky, deep rich soil, growing to 45 meters. The longer it grows, the more valuable it becomes. Its quality varies with the soil and climate of the site. The wood, with a very narrow pith, is reddish-brown in the heartwood and creamy in the sapwood, and contains numerous resin ducts. It is coarse-grained, denser and stronger than other softwoods, and splits easily. It has excellent load-bearing properties and is classed between Pedunculate oak and pine in terms of quality. When exposed outdoors, sunshine makes it bleed resin, which at once forms a protective coating against the elements, much like a dark varnish. This coating also helps ward off attack from worms and borers.

When first used on a building project, larch timbers are nice and white, but even after two or three years they take on a darkish coloration ''as if blackened by smoke'', to quote a Swiss chronicler around 1548. Larch is highly resistant to alternate wetting and drying, and has long been widely used in building and construction. In wooden architecture, it provides the finest material for log construction, in addition to use for shingles, window frames and interior panelling. Regrettably, it is no longer used in anything approaching the quantities of former years, due to scarcity of supply.

Because it is tougher than other softwoods, it is more expensive to mill. In Kärnten province, for example, the charge used to be five and a half to six Austrian shillings per cubic meter for larch and four and a half shillings for spruce. In Hofgastein, in neighbouring Salzburg province, the figure was ten to eleven shillings per cubic meter for larch, as opposed to eight to nine shillings for spruce.

Softwoods

Spruce

Known as European spruce in southern Germany and Baltic whitewood in the Baltic provinces. The spruce is found throughout Europe and, with pine, is the softwood most widely used for building and construction in Germany. It thrives best in rich, rocky, humus soil and in a moist climate. It also grows, however, in more severe and northerly locales, where it then provides the finest timber and lumber. Tapering sharply, the trunk may reach 50 meters and the tree may grow to 100–200 years old, with a diameter up to 1.3 meters. Heartwood and sapwood show the same light reddish and cream coloration (sapwood trees). When properly handled, it will provide durable wood, although less weather-resistant than larch and pine because of its low resin content. It will rot readily if repeatedly exposed to wetting and drying. It is more easily crosscut than ripped, which is often accompanied by binding of the sawblade. Before it is cut, the stem must have properly matured in order to produce durable building material. Because of its numerous resin or pitch pockets, spruce is less suitable for boards than is fir. In the field of timber architecture, it has long been a favourite material for log building. In addition, it is also used for making both laid-on and nailed shingles in the absence of larch or pine. Inside, it is used for ceiling beams or joists, roof framing and floors, as well as for furniture.

Fir

The fir grows in Europe, Asia and North America. In Germany, it is found in large dense tracts in the Black Forest and in the uplands of Swabia. Reaching 60 meters in height, its stem is less tapered than the spruce. It may grow to 450 years of age. The wood is reddish or creamy in colour and, like spruce, is the same colour in both heartwood and sapwood (sapwood tree). The growth rings are very prominent. The wood is soft, low in resin, light and easy to bend and split. The wood from a tree grown in a mountain area is better than that from a moist soft soil. In terms of durability, it places far behind the resinous spruce, being best suited for furniture and interior work. When used for furniture, one drawback is that it grays with age.

Pine

The Scots pine grows in the northern temperate zone from Spain to eastern Siberia and from northern Italy to Lapland. It thrives on any soil, but does best on deep humus-rich sandy soil, reaching 40 meters in height and up to 1 meter in diameter. It may grow to 300 years old. When mature, its heartwood has a weather-resistant quality similar to that of oak and larch. Immature trees have an overly high sapwood content. When newly felled, both heartwood and sapwood are yellowish to reddish-white in colour. As it dries, however, the heartwood turns a brownish-red. It has numerous large resin ducts and pronounced annual rings. Pine is soft, coarse and tolerant to drying and wetting. It is used in every area of timber architecture, though particularly well suited for log construction, window frames and a variety of interior applications. Weymouth pine is somewhat darker in colour than the Scots pine, though its properties are similar.

Swiss Stone Pine

This species grows in the Alps and the Carpathians, reaching 15 meters in height. Its heartwood is reddish brown, while the sapwood is a creamy colour. It is extremely light, soft and easily split. Because of its pleasing colour and fine knotty grain, along with its attractive resinous aroma, it is still widely used in the Alps for interior panelling and wainscotting.

Log Wall Construction

Log walls are made of logs or planks laid one on top of the other in courses, and derive their structural strength primarily from fitting and interlocking at the corners (Figs **62**, **63** and **64**). The most primitive form of fitting was a rounded notching on one side, as shown in Fig **62**. This technique has been traced back to the late Bronze Age, as evidenced by the pole-log structures of Persanzigsee Lake and the island redoubt of Buchau in the Federsee Moor of southern Swabia, excavated by Hans Reinerth. In both instances, notches were cut into the upper surface of the logs at the corners; this being the simplest way of laying them up.

Logwork walls gradually evolved from the simple timbers on the ground, on which rested the roof of the crude shelter hut. As time went on, men ventured to add another round of logs to this sill course, thus forming an upright wall in the process. In contrast to timber-frame walls, which began imbedded in the ground to shore up the earth embankment around the crude shelter hut, log walls were born out in the open air.

Because of the tapering shape in which trees grow, it was necessary when building with logs in the round to alternate the tops and butts with each course, in order to keep the walls level (Figs **67** and **68**). Builders retained this technique when they began using hewn logs. Moreover, it was inherent in the nature of round notching that the courses of logs were offset by half the thickness of a log. The alternating notching at the

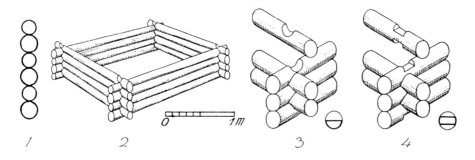

1 *2* *3* *4*

Fig 62
Construction of a natural round-log wall. Because the logs are smaller in diameter at their tops than at the butt (**1**), they must be reversed in each course in order to keep the wall level (**2**). The interlocking corners provide the main structural support for the log walls. The earliest form of cornering was simple round notching (**3**), followed later by lock notching (**4**).

corners locked each course of logs in place. To produce a level wall using this building technique required straight logs, particularly when left unhewn. Best suited in this regard are the softwoods, although hardwoods such as oak and elm were also used in log building, either hewn or split.

At times, oak timbers would even be reduced to plank dimensions for building walls. The old logwork walls of hewn or sawn timber varied in thickness from 12 cm to 15 cm, although today's factory-produced versions are as little as 7 cm in thickness, this being the least dimension which will still meet insulation standards (Fig 69). In section, these planks measured 25 cm to 30 cm in width, occasionally reaching as much as 40 cm, or even 50 cm, at the butt end.

In selecting the species of timber for building, its response to moisture has long been an important consideration. Accordingly, the timber selected for the sill course would be the most durable species available in a given area. In Switzerland, for example, where spruce was the wood generally in use, larch would be obtained for the sill logs, and where this most durable of softwoods made up the regular logwork, elm would sometimes be used for the bottom course. In eastern Transylvania, sturdy logs of oak would frequently make up the first round, topped by log walls of fir.

Fig 63
Yard enclosure, showing the fence logs braced by stepped cross-walls of stub logs, from the *Älvroshof* grouping in the museum at Skansen, Stockholm. The stub-logs are keyed into the fence logs.

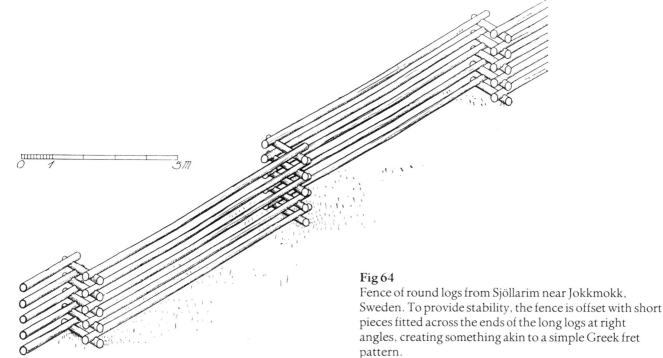

0   1   5 m

Fig 64
Fence of round logs from Sjöllarim near Jokkmokk, Sweden. To provide stability, the fence is offset with short pieces fitted across the ends of the long logs at right angles, creating something akin to a simple Greek fret pattern.

● 53

In terms of durability, the species still in use for log building may be ranked as follows. First and foremost comes oak, followed by larch, pine, spruce and fir. It is important that the logs selected for building be as uniform as possible in thickness, and that none contains left-hand twist. Where sawn timbers are used, it is also extremely important that they be cut properly from the logs, so as to prevent checking due to shrinkage (Figs **71**, **72**, **73** and **74**). If sawn from full logs, the heart must be in the

65

66

67

Figs 65, 66 and 67
Hay barns and cattle shed from Steiermark and Kärnten provinces in Austria. Fig 65 is from the village of Turracher Höhe, Fig 66 from Gmünd and Fig 67 from Ebene Reichenau. The three structures show how it is possible to imagine the evolution of the log wall as it gradually rose in height from the crude shelter which was nothing more than a roof overhead.

68

Fig 68
Hay barn from Radenthein, Kärnten, of natural round logs. The logs are secured by round notching at the corners and by dowelling, which is doubled near the door and window openings.

Fig 69 (opposite)
Sectional view of various types of logwork. Items **1** and **3**, which show the natural round-log contour, are not restricted to any particular area, while **2** and **7** are found in Sweden and Russia. The V-grooving on the bottom of the logs shown in **4** and **8** is typical of Norway. In the idiom of the same country is the oval technique shown in **5** and **9**, and in a modern variation in **10**. Item **6** shows an older design and **22**, a more recent one from Switzerland, while

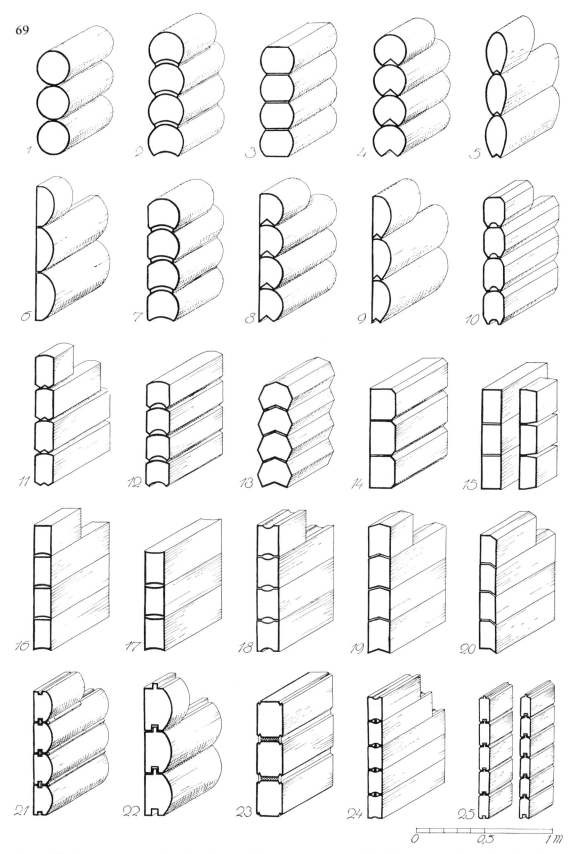

11 and 12 show hewn and chamfered logwork from Sweden. Items 14 and 20 are from Germany, Austria and Switzerland; 23 is from Silesia and the *Riesengebirge* mountains; 13 is from France; 24 and 25 are modern factory-produced designs. Because wood has a tendency to work, timber should be hewn or cut so that the heart is as close to the centre of the log as possible. For half-logs, it should end up in the outward-facing side. Figs 48 and 49 show the effects of checking. Old-time craftsmen were so skilled in their handling of timber that even hewn half-logs with one side touching the pith would not show major signs of checking. To counter the problem of warping, which affects the more recent styles 24 and 25, the planks were kept narrower (approximately 17 cm, including the tongue). The various shapes of the lengthwise grooving resulted from efforts to achieve a tight fit.

centre of the timber; if milled from half-logs, the saw-cut must pass through the centre of the heart, with this surface of the timber being placed so as to face outward when used on a building (Fig **70**).

As building traditions and practices advanced, parallelled by equally advancing craftsmanship, log walls witnessed a wealth of varied stylings, both in the shaping of the actual logs and in the fitting and joinery techniques used.

Looked at in cross-section, we can see two trends (Fig **69**). One of these, the most ancient and most in harmony with the nature and character of wood, is based on the original form of the log in the round. It may include the natural full-log shape (Fig **69/1** to **69/4**) or involve a number of half-log styles produced by splitting with axe and wedge (Fig **69/6**, **69/9**, **69/21** and **69/22**). In some areas, the round form gave way to an oval, a move which moderated checking and showed great creative feel, while producing the most powerful depiction of strain in the vertical axis parallel to the wall surface (Fig **69/5**). The logwork shown in Fig **71** bears witness to the vitality and naturalness of this mode of expression. It is an outstanding illustration of how skilled craftsmanship, combined with genuine feel for the nature of the material and its use, can produce brilliant achievement in the artistic field as well.

The second trend is based on the hewn-log form, involving a shift from the round to a rectangular section (Fig **69/14** to **69/20** and **69/23**), ideally with the pith centered in

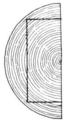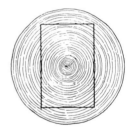

Fig 70
Showing the best way of cutting timbers from full and half-logs to most effectively prevent checking. When cut from half-logs, the side containing the heart should be placed facing outward when used for building.

Fig 71
Showing portion of a granary from Telemark (Norway), with logwork of oval-hewn full logs having the heart in the centre of each log. One log, the third from the top, has had left-hand twist, and shrinkage has produced such stress that the check has turned into a deep split. It is possible, however, that this split developed in the course of dismantling the building and transporting it to Skansen in Stockholm. Upper and lower logwork is tight fitting, although the fit of the twisted and checked log above the sill is not so admirable.

this rectangle (Fig **70**). Also encountered, however, are log walls of split and hewn half-logs (Fig **73**). Combination styles also exist, with round or oval logwork hewn to provide a flush surface on one side (Fig **69/7** and **69/19**). Some designs even featured walls hewn flat both inside and out (Fig **69/11** and **69/12**). Occasionally, the flush surface will be brightened by chamfering to coincide with wane edge on the timber (Fig **69/10** and **69/14**) or by full hewing to give a more angular profile (Fig **69/13**). As far as the rectangular form was concerned, sawing eventually replaced hewing as the means of shaping, either manually by open pit sawing or mechanically at a sawmill.

A wall of square-hewn logs lacks the expressiveness of the round log form. The individual log is lost among its neighbours, often being difficult to pick out as a separate identity within the wall, even with close inspection (Fig **73**).

At times, uneven shrinkage combined with uneven stress and strain may jeopardize the snug fit of the logwork. To counter this problem, builders resorted to a number of alternative solutions. In some instances, they tried to achieve the tightest possible fit between the logs by flush fitting (Fig **69/3**, **69/14** and **69/15**), concave grooving (Fig **69/2** and **69/7**), or even a V-shaped channel (Fig **69/13**, **69/14** and **69/20**). Another approach was to "chink" a building by driving oakum into the joints. Years ago, the practice in Kärnten was to groove out the logwork at the joints, then fill these with moss and plaster (Fig **69/15**). Today, log builders in this region and in

Fig 72
Detail of a log granary from Waldhaus, Canton of Bern, of notched and fitted split-log construction. The shrinkage checks which can be seen on the logs indicate spiral or straight growth in the original tree.

Fig 73
Portion of a log house from Arzbach, near Lenggries in Upper Bavaria, with dovetailed corners. The logs have been split and hewn from half-logs. The wood has been carefully seasoned prior to building, and this coupled with the expert workmanship, has produced a structure almost free of checking and so tight-fitting that the joints between the logs are barely discernible. The protruding log shows the heart centered in the timber.

neighbouring Salzburg province cut this groove on the inside. Once the seams are chinked, the walls are plastered or covered with panelling. The fitting technique first mentioned involved applying chinking material before setting the logs in place, then letting the logwork settle on the seams to seal them. This means that the logs no longer sit flush upon one another, either inside or outside, instead touching in a ridge or spine on one or both sides. In some styles, the underside of a log is grooved out and fitted to match the convex surface of the log below it (Figs **69/4**, **69/5**, **69/8** to **69/12** and **75**). In other cases, the underside of the log is hollowed out, then seated on the flattened upper portion of the log beneath, as in Fig **69/16**. Alternatively, the logs may be hollowed both top and bottom (Fig **69/17** and **69/18**). Because the point of contact between the logs is near the sapwood, or in fact actually in it, the logwork presses together snugly here. While this is desirable, it necessarily means that the building will gradually settle, a situation which we will discuss in the next chapter.

The gaps between the logs were often filled with moss or oakum, and in Norway, even with a woollen material stained red or blue. A more recent style (Fig **69/24**), a variation of **69/18**, utilizes tarred hemp rope between the logs. In the Alpine regions of Austria, log builders currently chink their seams simply by laying down two rows of hemp rope between the flat, level surfaces of the logs.

Another approach was to try a tongue and groove system (Fig **69/22** and **69/25**) or even an inset spline between the logs, as in Fig **69/21**, which involved grooving the logs top and bottom. To maintain as tight a seam as possible, the ends of these splines must not sit at right angles to the run of the logwork, *i.e.*, to the surface of the walls, but rather at an angle. In both of these methods, the seal can be improved by inserting tarred hemp rope into the groove. Once the angle between the wall surface and the seat of the logs drops below 90°, exterior walls exposed to rain are subject to swelling, causing unwanted working in the logs, possibly forcing them out of plumb. Fig **69/19**

Fig 74
Twisted log ends on a house from Zillerthal near Hirschberg in Silesia. This structure was built roughly a century ago as part of a small community laid out around a number of courtyards. To quickly provide housing for refugees from the Zillertal valley in Tirol, the usual seasoning time for the timber was cut short. As a consequence, the centre-cut logs twisted in shrinking, producing the distortion in the photograph. This was also the reason for the checking and splitting in the log ends.

and **69/20** are prone to this kind of problem. In the latter case, this drawback is further exacerbated by the fact that the weight of the building does not bear down on this outside problem-area.

To prevent moisture from entering the joints, some modern-day techniques use a bevelled edge or a sloped surface between the logs (Fig **69/25**). Regrettably, these neither promote rapid runoff of driving rain nor prevent water from seeping into the joints, to say nothing of enhancing the attractiveness of the whole.

A unique method of chinking log buildings in the *Riesengebirge* and *Isergebirge* mountain areas involved use of a mud and chaff mixture (Fig **69/23**). To provide a foothold for this mud mortar, space was left between the logs. To further secure the chinking where it was exposed to the elements, grooves were also run along the outer edges of the log joints. One modern technique (Fig **69/21**) utilizes nailed-on strips of wood to help seal the joints, with the nails alternately angled downward and upward into the logs.

To shed driving rain and reduce the tendency of the wood to absorb water, the surface of the logs must be smooth, with no sign of saw marks. Unless the builder has been able to use one of the older methods of broadaxe hewing or drawknife smoothing, a plane must be used for finishing.

While wall surfaces must be properly smoothed, even greater care must be taken in the actual fitting of the logs. Here again, the plane plays an important part, along with both straight and curved drawknives. In Salzburg province, the plane used for hollow-grooving the logs was known as a *Fugenholzer*, operated by two men. Final smoothing would then be done with a long jointer, which might reach as much as 1.5 meters in length.

Cornerwork

Cornering techniques may include round notching, a wide variety of lapped and locked styles, simple and compound dovetailing and numerous lock-and-step variations. Cornerwork has witnessed substantial evolutionary changes, vividly illustrating the ways in which builders sought to overcome the various problems which may occur in this area. As noted earlier, round notching with the log-ends extending beyond the joint is the oldest of the techniques (Figs **62**, **68** and **75/1**).

In an effort to achieve a tight-fitting joint at the corners, builders departed from the original rounded contour and began trying a variety of alternative approaches. Fig **75/8** shows logs in the round having retained their natural shape beyond the corner. Other approaches, however, involved skilled axework treatment of the logs at the corners, which facilitated scribing and notching and inspired craftsmen to make of the joint a distinctively decorative motif (Fig **75/2** to **75/6**). The tools used in this work were broadaxe, drawknife and chisel.

Round notching eventually gave rise to lock notching (Fig **62/4**), with logs being fitted both top and bottom. As techniques evolved, the craftsman's love of innovation even led to the adoption of a lock-and-step system (Fig **78**). An additional method involved intricate fitting of both upper and lower surfaces in locking fashion, a system used not only on round logs, but on half-round, oval-profile and squared logs as well. Fig **75/9** to **75/15** show this technique applied to rounded or partially rounded logs, clearly reflecting the wonderfully instinctive feel for their medium which led the old-time builders to such innovations. The square-hewn examples shown in Fig **76/16** to **76/23** point to a similar approach. Here, where hand-hewing has given way to the primacy of the saw, the configuration of the joint is now a series of straight cuts.

One potential problem with simple interlocking corners on squared logs as in Fig **76/16**, **76/17**, **76/18** and **76/23** is that the log-ends are prone to twisting as the wood shrinks (Figs **74**, **79** and **80**), possibly resulting in loosening of the joints in this area where the impact of the wind is most severe. To meet this difficulty, numerous variations on the locking shoulder were incorporated into the joint (Fig **76/19** to **76/22**). This type of configuration was unnecessary in round log construction, since the natural interlocking of the logs at the corners provided a tight fit, not unlike that of a locking shoulder. To further reinforce the corner, the log-ends might also be secured by wooden pegs (Fig **76/21** and **76/22**). A unique notching approach from Sweden is shown in Fig **76/29**. In this joint, which was subject to the buoyant force of water, an attempt was made to further strengthen the round notching by the addition of corner posts, which are "gripped", as it were, by slots cut in the logs.

Fig 75
Round and lock notching used in cornering. Item **1** goes back to the late Bronze Age, and is in use even today on lesser structures in log-building areas of many different countries. Items **2**, **4**, **5**, **6** and **9** are from Sweden. Note the imagination and skill of the axemen in the detail of the log ends. While these reveal a trend to the picturesque, the Norwegian evolution in timber-built architecture was to strive for refinement of the joint itself, as illustrated by **10**

to **13** and **15**. The type of end treatment so cherished by the Swedes would have appeared fussy on the often oval-hewn Norwegian logwork, with its air of rippling muscles. Item **3**, from the Lithuanian-Belorussian border region, shows the cultural link with Scandinavia. In **7** and **14** from Switzerland, the austere design bespeaks a close kinship with square-hewn walls, despite the rounded exteriors of the logs.

76

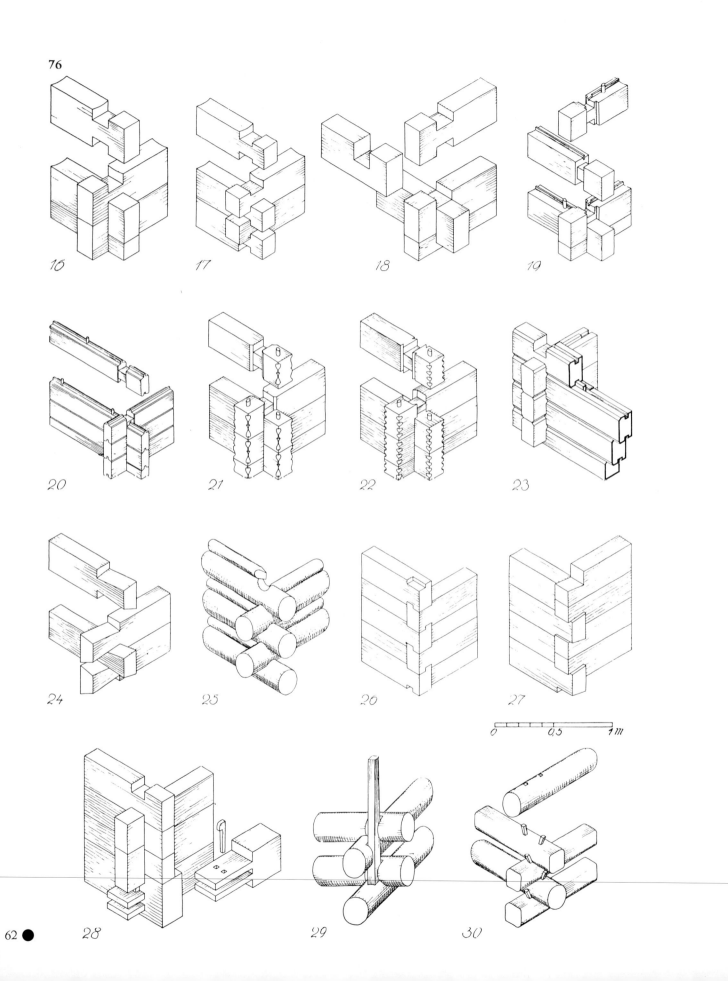

16   17   18   19

20   21   22   23

24   25   20   27

0   0,5   1 m

28   29   30

In the course of time, the extended cornerwork which accompanied round and lock notching lost its absolute domination of the scene with the emergence of lapped and dovetailed corners (Fig 77). These appeared in emulation of the smooth walls of solid masonry construction, and in some localities as a means of facilitating the application of exterior shingling.

When the mating surfaces of a timber joint are horizontal (Fig 77/31 and 77/32), pegging is needed to prevent the logs from shifting outward. Precise fitting of these pegs can be difficult, and there is the added problem that they are prone to shearing. To overcome this drawback, builders devised the technique of dovetailing (Figs 79, 80, 77/33 and 77/34). In the Vorarlberg of Austria, dovetails are known as kestrel-tails because of the resemblance in shape to the tail of a sparrow hawk. This type of keying relies solely on the sloped seating surfaces of the notch to prevent outward movement. As illustrated in Fig 81, a template was used to mark or scribe the individual dovetails.

Fig 76 (left)
Lapped, locking and dovetailed cornering. Item **16** shows the type of locked lap commonly found in the countries touched by the Alps. Because of the notching, the logwork compresses more at the joint than in the log-ends with their flattened contact surfaces. To compensate for this, the latter must include some allowance for settling. In **17** from Vorarlberg, this problem was avoided by leaving a generous space between the log-ends. If the recessed seat is extended right to the ends of the logs, this difficulty was avoided. Item **18** shows a unique cornering technique found in wooden churches in Silesia. Here the timbers in one course are top-notched only, while those in the other are notched top and bottom. Items **19** and **20** are modern-day approaches, incorporating a recessed shoulder to secure the joint against twisting and to shut out drafts. A somewhat similar method was being used on buildings in Switzerland many years ago, as shown in **21** and **22**. A more recent technique, illustrated in **23**, included a groove and spline arrangement to help secure the joint. Should the portion of the logs left after notching (which forms the bearing surface) become so small that compressive forces produce greater deformation here than in the log-ends, some space must be left between the ends to allow for settling. Items **24** and **27** show dovetailing extending beyond the corners. This picturesque motif is particularly encountered where the ethnic composition of the population shows a Slavic touch. Items **25** from the Alpine regions of Austria and **26** from Bohemia show two highly interesting techniques, one employing alternating courses of round-notched logs interspersed with smaller poles; the other featuring hewn timbers at two different levels keyed at the corners with a lock-and-step arrangement. The former is an original innovation; the second an enhancement of the same concept. The double mortise and tenon in the first course of timbers shown in **28** is from Switzerland, and is an added feature borrowed from another building culture, the Alemannic. Items **29** from Sweden and **30** from Salzburg owe their singular designs to their physical application. The former was used in the water, while the latter was designed to permit maximum space between the courses.

Fig 77 (overleaf)
Lapped and dovetailed cornering incorporating various locking techniques. The simple lapping shown in **31** makes it possible to keep the logs at the same level in every course. Like the double lapped corner in **32**, this method requires pegging to prevent outward movement. This type of keying and the dovetailing which followed it are confined to hewn-log construction. Where dovetailing was used on round logs, as in **33** from the Lithuanian-Belorussian border region, the logs had to at least be hewn at the corners. Item **34** shows a more recent example of dovetailing. In the next four techniques covering **35** to **38**, a lock and step sealing arrangement has been incorporated into the dovetailing to reduce drafts, as the corners can readily loosen due to uneven settling within the walls and the dovetail-work. It is interesting to notice how builders in different areas arrived at similar design solutions. Item **35** is from the *Danziger Werder*, **36** is from Switzerland, **37** from Sweden and **38** from Norway. Item **39** shows a more recent lock-and-step from an old timber-built church in the northern Carpathians, while **41** and **44** are from the Austrian Alps. It is not uncommon for cornerwork featuring notching of the dovetail surfaces to include two or more such notches, making for a kind of lock-and-step system. A unique, but now highly convoluted design is shown in **45** from Lake Tegernsee in *Oberbayern* (Upper Bavaria), in which a system of beads and coves has produced a miniaturized version of lock-and-step notching.

77

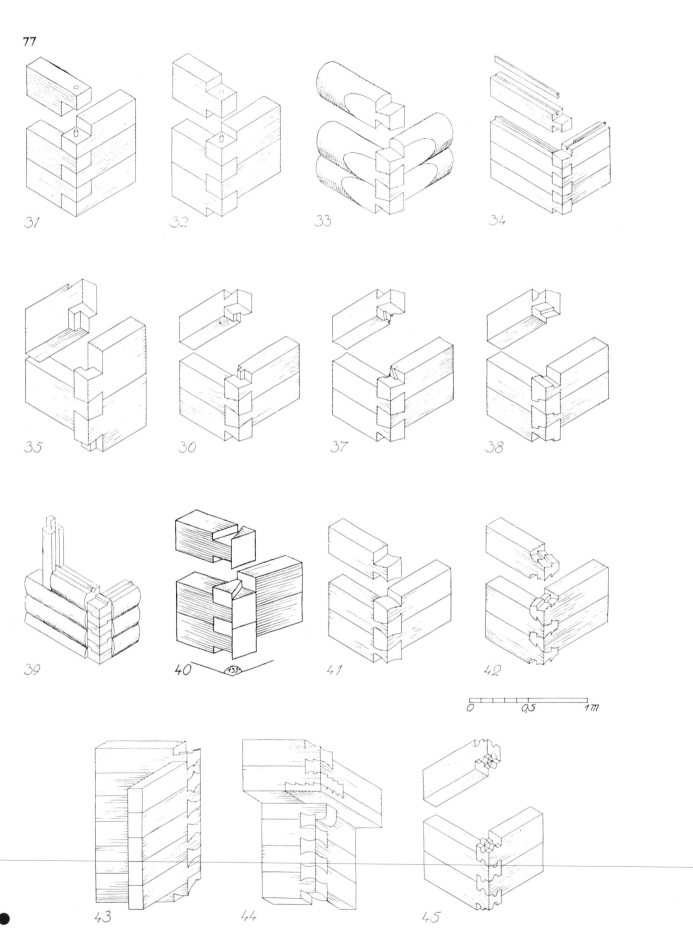

31

32

33

34

35

30

37

38

39

40

41

42

0   0,5   1 m

43

44

45

However, this joint also proved susceptible to uneven shrinking. To counter this problem, and to provide an even more airtight fit, further refinements were added. Special efforts were made to increase the tightness of the corner by sealing and locking the dovetails (Fig **77/35** to **77/37**) or by a lock-and-step arrangement (Fig **77/38**). Combined with lapped corners, the locking key featured in this approach simultaneously produced a substitute for wooden pegging (Fig **76/26**).

The pleasure and at the same time the pride which the old-time craftsmen took in their work even produced joints with curved mating surfaces such as the curved dovetail, both with and without added lock notching of the individual dovetails; the former shown in Figs **82** and **83** as well as Fig **77/42** to **77/44**, and the latter in Fig **77/41**. This type of cornerwork, which evidences a high degree of technical skill, was performed with a curved, knife-like tool known as a *klingeisen* (Fig **84**). The labour-intensive nature of this type of work may be gauged from the fact that in Kärnten, for example, it took four men an entire day to complete two courses of a grain storage shed measuring five meters square. Apart from this technique, which we may well call the "craftsman's pride", other joints showed an attempt to simplify the work by making each single dovetail cover a pair of logs (Fig **76/27**).

By contrast, yet another method of cornering featured protruding dovetail ends, reflecting a decorative inclination (Fig **76/24**).

In enumerating the various methods of cornering, mention must also be made of the practice of applying corner-boards over the flush endwork (Fig **85**). These were designed to keep out drafts, while protecting the ends of the logs from moisture. Because of the movement of the wood, corner-boards must not be nailed on until the logwork has come to rest, *i.e.*, until the walls have settled.

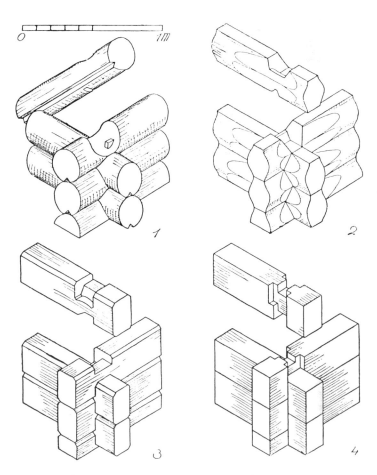

Fig 78
Cornerwork utilizing lock-and-step notching with a locking key. **1** Baltic countries and Russia; **2** Härjedalen, Sweden (17th century); **3** Dalecarlia (*c.* 1800); **4** southern Sweden.

79 **80**

Figs 79 and 80
Flat and curved dovetail corners from Niederneuching (1581) and Erding (*c.* 1600), Upper Bavaria. The timbers in Fig **79** are cut from the heart of the log. In addition to this type, Fig **80** also includes half-logs, one side of which

touches the pith. Both examples show how the working of the timbers can adversely affect the cornerwork, in addition to potential dangers created by changes within the structure as a whole.

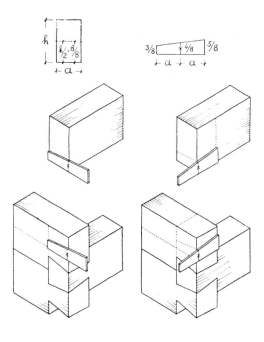

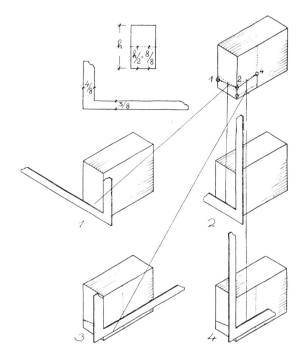

Fig 81
Scribing dovetails with a special template or square. At left, a wooden template sized in specific proportion to the sectional dimensions of the timbers has been made up, as shown in the drawing. First, the position of the lowermost cut on the dovetail is marked on the end of the log, starting from the bottom edge. Next, the side of the log is marked.

The upper cut is laid out in similar fashion from a centre line.

The special square also used for this work has two arms of unequal width. Again, the widths of these arms are in specific proportion to the sectional dimensions of the logs or timbers. The drawing shows the sequence of the scribing process in numerical order.

Figs 82 and 83
Curved dovetail cornerwork from Kärnten province,
Austria.

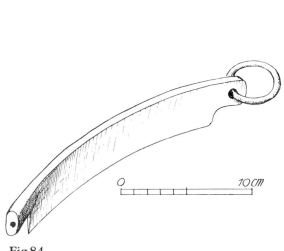

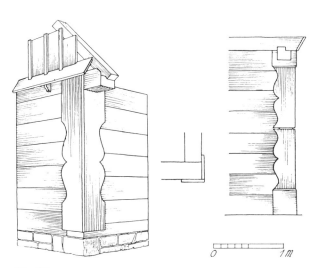

Fig 84
Klingeisen

Fig 85
Cornerboards covering endwork on log houses from the
district of Mohrungen (Oberland), East Prussia. These
protect the cornerwork against wind and water, while
providing a decorative touch.

Tieing in Partition Walls

The same fitting techniques used in the exterior walls were also applied to tieing in the partition walls. These included lock notching with protruding log ends, plain style (Fig **86/1**) or with an inset shoulder (Fig **86/2**), or use of flush dovetailing (Fig **86/3**). In Switzerland, a favourite practice was to alternate the lock notching with an inset dovetail in a rhythmical pattern, then decoratively embellish the projecting log ends (Fig **86/4**).

When the log ends were cut flush instead of protruding, the ends of the partition logs created highly effective ornamentation in themselves, set as they were in the horizontal logwork. Here, the ingenuity of the log-building carpenter scaled new heights of creativity, producing the most dramatic work ever realized by wooden architecture in terms of intricate joinery (Figs **86/5** to **86/9** and **87**). The patterned keying might depict hand tools, occupations, family initials, year of construction, the inevitable heart or, most dignified symbol of all, the place of worship (Fig **86/5**). In Kärnten, even the bottom course of logs was included in this interplay of form (Fig **86/6**).

As a rule, this intricate keying is so designed that each log may easily be set vertically into place (Fig **86/5** to **86/9**). As always, however, when ornamentation is overemphasized to the detriment of sound construction, a good thing was taken too far in this instance as well, when builders even began sliding the partition logs in horizontally (Fig **86/6**). In fact, when even this was not possible, woodworkers would sometimes chisel out patterns and inlay an appropriately shaped piece.

When logs are laid up one atop the other with a hollowed or scooped-out surface between them, meaning that they actually touch only in a long ridge or spine, compression causes greater settling in the walls themselves than in the keyed joints. Because of this, space must be left in this latter area to allow for subsequent settling.

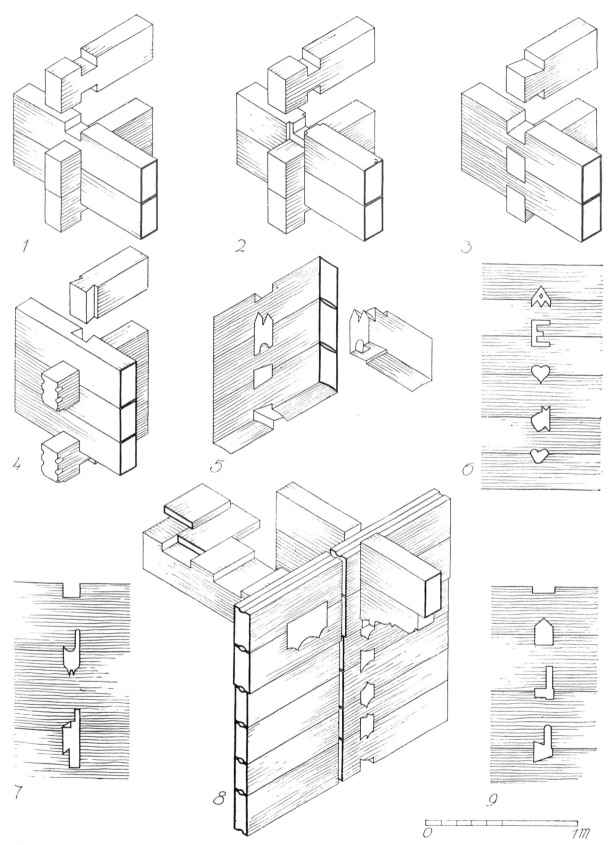

Fig 86

Partition walls keyed into exterior walls by lock notching, dovetailing and inset dovetailing. The same techniques are used here as for cornerwork. Here too, a snug fit is important, and at times, space for settling may have to be left. Item **1** shows common lock notching; **2** depicts the addition of an inset shoulder to the notching, while **3** shows a dovetailed joint. In **4**, from Switzerland, lock notching alternates in rhythmic succession with inset dovetailing. Items **5, 6, 7** and **9** from Upper Bavaria and **8** from Kärnten attest to the craftsman's earlier ambition and aspiration, combined with an endearing love for his work. Not content to simply create a sound joint, builders utilized the end faces of the partition logs to produce intricate and striking ornamentation, which stood out sharply against the horizontal logwork. In **6** and **7**, the decorative effect has been overdone, creating an affected appearance.

● 69

Pegging and Dowelling

By itself, the keying and fitting at the corners and at the intersection of partition walls is inadequate to securely hold the walls in alignment. Even here, the working of the wood may cause the logs to move in or out of the wall, producing undesirable structural deformities. To prevent this, wooden dowels or pegs 3 cm in diameter and 16 cm long were driven down through the logwork an average of 1.5 meters apart, with the dowels staggered every other course by half this spacing (Figs **88** and **89**). These dowels must be so shaped in cross-section and so oriented in the logwork as to eliminate cross-grain stress from the outset.

In the Bohemian Forest region, log builders used wooden pins in place of dowels; these being driven down through a log into the one below in a chiselled-out or bored hole (Fig **90**).

Fig. 87
Partition wall tied into the main logwork by intricate keying, from Arzbach in Upper Bavaria. The alternately protruding log ends, combined with the builder's obvious pleasure and pride in his craft, provided the stimulus for this exuberant touch. The design is such that the logs of both the exterior and the partition walls could be set vertically in place.

As a rule, oak was used for making these dowels or pins. Also used at times were small spruce saplings (Oberösterreich province, Austria), ash wood (Bohemian Forest), larch (Salzburg province, Austria) and cherry (Canton Valais, Switzerland), all of which would be slightly sharpened on the ends. Originally, dowel holes were chiselled out, but nowadays they are drilled or bored (Fig **91**).

In a variation of this in-wall reinforcement, a similar though much more rugged mechanism was used, in which a length of plank or stout board was mortised right into the wall to hold three courses of logs together (Fig **92/1**). At times, this vertical reinforcement would even extend the full height of the wall, as shown in Fig **92/2**. In the Masuria region of East Prussia, pebbles were used instead of pegs, these digging into the logwork as it settled.

At openings in the walls to accommodate doors, windows and the like, the dowelling extends close to the opening, frequently being doubled for added strength. Projecting endwork may also benefit from dowelling or pegging, since it helps prevent the log ends from twisting, while strengthening the joint as a whole (Fig **93**).

Fig 88
Doubled dowelling beside a listing door post on a hay barn from Hofgastein, Salzburg province. The deteriorated condition of the logwork clearly reveals the method of pegging.

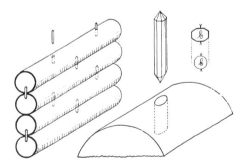

Fig 89
Pegging a log wall. To prevent the individual logs from shifting out of position, the courses of logs are dowelled or pegged together, using pegs about 3 cm in diameter and 16 cm in length, spaced a maximum of 1.5 meters apart and offset from one course to the next. To prevent the creation of stress across the grain, the pegs are shaped so as to be oblong in section *b*, with the shorter axis of the oblong matching the diameter of the dowel hole and oriented to sit at right angles to the wall line.

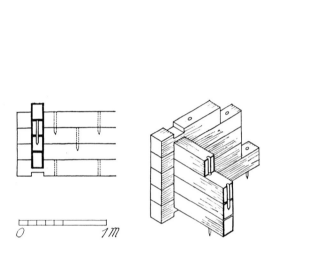

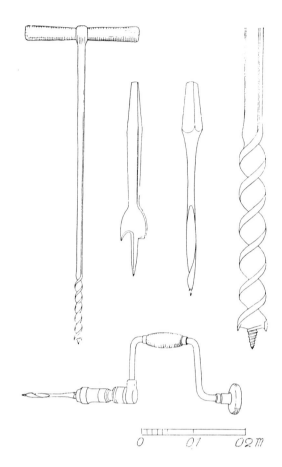

Fig 90
Method of pinning log walls used in the Bohemian Forest region. To prevent the log walls from shifting out of alignment, offset holes were drilled every second course, extending into the log below. Wooden pins were then driven home into these holes.

Fig 91
Boring tools. Above from right to left are a common auger bit, gimlet bit, center bit and hand auger. Below, hand brace and bit.

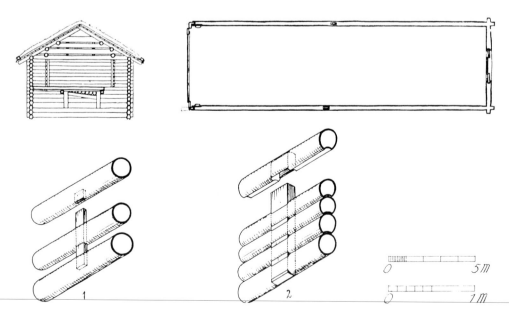

Fig 92
Walls reinforced by heavy splines mortised into the logwork. From barns in Norway and Sweden.

The most highly evolved item of timberwork incorporated in log walls is the vertical trimmer post, found in a broad array of configurations around doors and windows (Fig 94). The Scandinavian style is to set this trimmer into a slot mortised into the log ends (Fig 94/1). In the Alpine regions of southern Germany, the log ends, either plain or tenoned are set into a matching slot grooved out of the trimmer (Fig 94/4 to 94/6). In the whole area stretching from Kärnten northward to Bavaria, the log ends are simply butted flush and pegged or pinned in place (Fig 94/7 to 94/9). We shall look at this feature in detail when we come to discuss door and window framing.

Should irregularities in alignment occur as the walls are going up, a few blows from a heavy maul against a plank placed on the logwork will help correct this problem.

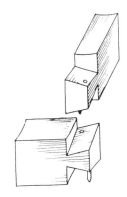

Fig 93
Technique for pinning dovetails used by log building craftsmen in Austria's Salzburg province. The wooden pins are offset, angled inward on one dovetail, then outward on the next. This system was used because there is greater settling of the logwork within the walls than at the notched joints, meaning that room for settling had to be allowed for in the latter. However, this resulted in a loose-fitting joint which did not become secure and tight until settling was complete.

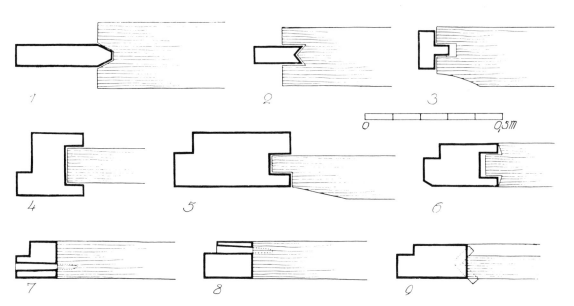

Fig 94
Methods of fitting log walls and door posts. Items 1 to 3 from Scandinavia show the door posts set into a slot grooved out of the ends of the wall logs. In its most original form, this groove was full thickness (1 and 2). When the upright was roughly the same thickness as the wall, a tongue and groove approach was used (3). Techniques similar to this latter one are still encountered here and there on hay barns and cabins in the Grisons region of Switzerland, inns from the Tirol, and in the remains of early habitations found on Oder-Alter Island, near Oppeln, dating from the 11th to 12th century. The mated V and W grooving shown in 2, which produced a very snug fit, is also typical of Scandinavian log building. The techniques shown in 4 to 6 (from Upper Bavaria and Switzerland) reveal the opposite approach, in which the log was mortised full thickness into the door post (4) or tenoned into a matching groove, creating what was essentially a vertical tongue. This method is the one which we can trace furthest historically, since it appeared as far back as the late Bronze Age in the log structures of Buchau, the island redoubt of Lake Federsee (1100–800 BC). Craftsmen in Austria's Kärnten province took a totally different tack (7 to 9), butting the logwork flush against the door posts, then securing it with wooden pins or pegs.

Added Bracing
– Stub Walls and Vertical Tie-logs

An average building log is something like 6 meters in length. Beyond this, two logs must be joined butt-to-butt (Fig **96**). In Scandinavia, where large-size timber was used, a favourite practice was to do this butt joining where partition walls were keyed into the outer walls. The six meter log is commonplace, being secured by the methods already discussed. Longer work, however, calls for some new approaches. One obvious option is to key short interlocking cross walls into the main walls (Fig **95**). Inside, these may also be tenoned into a vertical post for further support. Another system involves clamping the walls between two vertical tie-logs (Figs **95** and **97**), held top and bottom by slotted or peg-like cross members, themselves secured by wedges. These may also

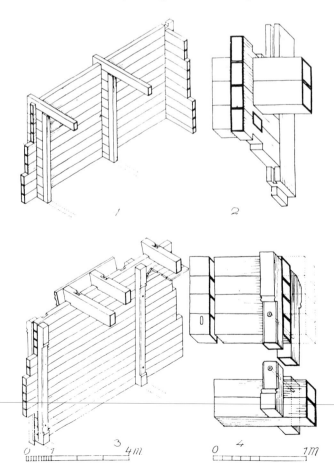

Fig 95
Two systems for reinforcing log walls. The first (**1** and **2**) uses keyed-in cross walls with mortised uprights, while the second (**3** and **4**) involves pairs of through-bolted retaining timbers. The former technique is from Switzerland and the latter from East Prussia. Because of shrinkage in the wood, the mortised uprights in **1** and the bolt holes in **3** must include allowance for settling.

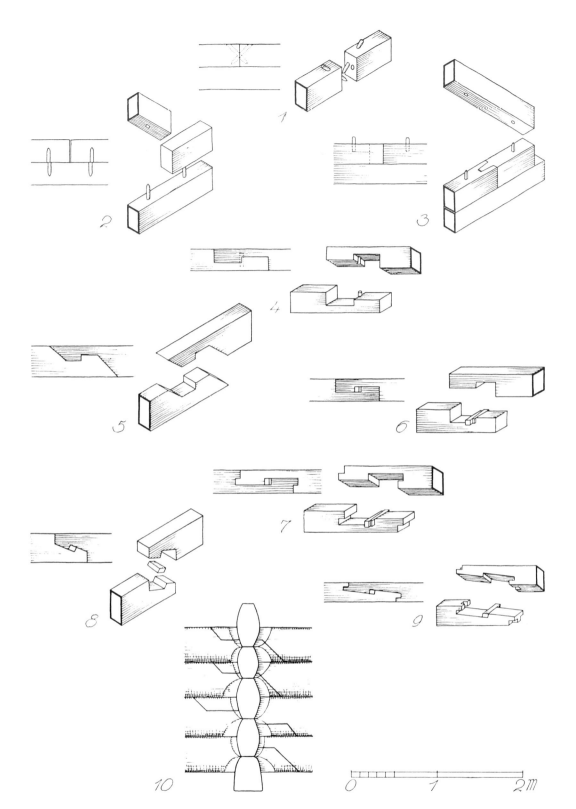

Fig 96
Butted and lapped timber joints. **1** age-old butted and
skew-pegged joint from Salzburg; **2** pegged technique,
with the slightly offset holes increasing the tightness of the
butt joint; **3** mortise and tenon combined with pegging,
from East Prussia; **4** pegged tabled scarf; **5** tabled scarf
minus peg, from Norway; **6** tabled scarf with double
wedge; **7** tabled scarf with mortise and double wedge;
8 splayed and tabled scarf with key, from Salzburg;
9 splayed double tenoned scarf including key from
Switzerland; **10** scarf-jointed timber keyed into logwork
at right angles, from Norway.

afford welcome reinforcement for gable-end walls, when the logwork here is neither interlocking nor dovetailed. Conceptually, this technique is derived from fence making, even finding application at times for interior use (Fig 98). In East Prussia, timber-built churches have the vertical ties bolted together instead of being secured by wooden cross-members (Fig 95). In this case, the bolt holes through the log walls have to be cut or drilled as a slot to permit settling.

To counter the severe wind pressure created by storms high up in mountain areas, builders would sometimes run steel reinforcing rod up through the walls. Imbedded in concrete in the foundation, these provide an effective anchoring system.

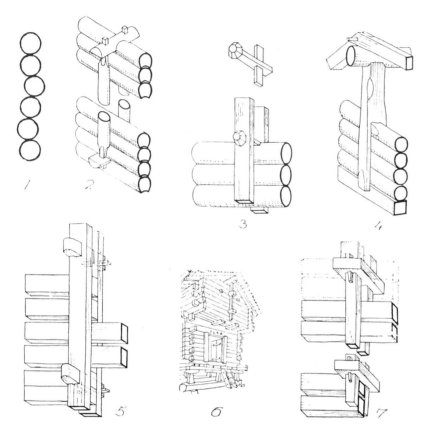

Fig 97
Vertical tie-log systems for reinforcing log walls. Because logs work in the walls, the notching at the corners is by itself insufficient to prevent the logs from shifting out of alignment (1). To both resolve this problem and distribute stress at a given point on a log over the whole height of the wall, European craftsmen resorted to numerous variations of the vertical tie-log system. Item 2, from the border region between Lithuania and Belorussia, shows a very old technique. The others, all from Switzerland, reflect a more effective system, because tension, and hence the strength of the bracing, is maintained by wedges.

Fig 98
Wooden stall enclosure in a livestock shed, from Setesdal in Norway. This feature expresses the same concept as that shown in Fig 97, although this would be earlier in evolutionary terms. In this instance, the ties are horizontal, holding the upright boards of the stall by being wired together.

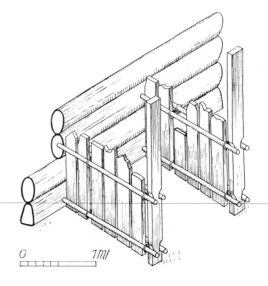

Sill Construction

As already indicated, log walls evolved from a single course of logs laid directly on the ground. In apparent deference to this early stage of development, log buildings continued to be erected right over the bare earth or on a tamped-earth floor, even after the adoption of proper foundations as such (Fig **99/1**). However, incentive for new arrangements was provided by the fact that, as a foundation, the earth varies widely in load bearing capacity and ground moisture. For one thing, builders began spreading the weight of the structures over a broader area by using larger diameter logs in the bottom course (Fig **99/2** and **99/3**). Floor joist systems of hewn or unhewn timber also came into use. A kindred structure, dating from the latter part of the Bronze Age, can be found in the island redoubt of Buchau, consisting of horizontal log joists resting on three pairs of sill logs, atop which the log walls were raised (Fig **103**).

In an effort to prevent moisture from seeping into the sill logs, early builders began placing stone under the most important parts of the wall structure, that is to say, under the interlocking corners (Fig **99/3**). In the course of time, this form of underpinning then evolved into a laid stone foundation, which afforded continuous full-length support for the sill course (Fig **99/2**). In certain types of log granaries, the stones formerly under the corners gave way to upright posts (Fig **99/6** to **99/9**) which themselves stood on slabs of stone (Fig **99/8** and **99/9**) or a sill course, either with or without a foundation (Fig **99/6** and **99/7**).

The original form of the floor as a levelled piece of earth endured for some time, as evidenced by the fact that when flooring as such did appear, it at first remained a separate entity from the wall structure (Fig **99/2** and **99/3**). When the organic connection between floor and wall did materialize, it took on a wide array of forms. When the flooring was laid directly over the earth, the floor boards were butted against the inside of the wall (Fig **99/4** and **99/5**). When the floor was elevated, similar techniques were used (Fig **99/6** and **99/7**), as well as methods which saw the flooring material extended outward beneath the lowermost course of logs and the exterior walls (Fig **99/8** and **99/9**). Only rarely was the flooring ever tied into the area where the weight of the walls is transmitted to the ground (Fig **100/3**). Eventually, contact with stone structures led builders to adopt the proper masonry foundation as the best support for log walls and floors. In the next series of illustrations, we shall examine the factors requisite to quality design in sill and foundation.

The greatest hazard posed to this part of a structure is moisture. Ground moisture may easily be repelled by a layer of asphalt roofing felt (Figs **101/7**, **101/8** and **102/2**).

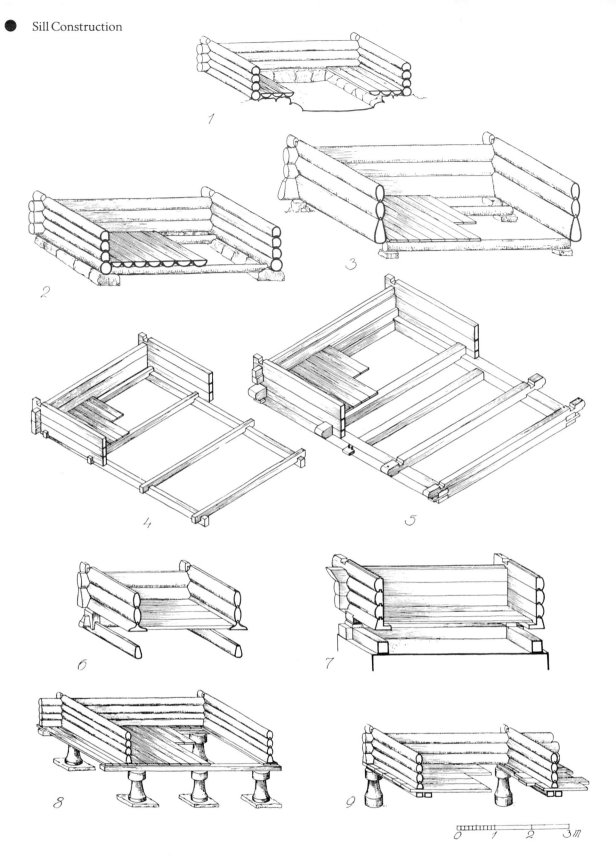

Fig 99

An array of sill and floor structures. **1** from an *eldhus* or separate cookhouse from Älfdalen, Dalarna; **2** from a *rökstugbadstugan* or smoke sauna from Rörkullen; **3** a *loft* from Haugen, Aaraksb, Sandnes, Setesdal; **4** a *stuga* or cabin from Hårsten, Möje, Uppland; **5** a granary from Lauperswyl; **6** a *loft* from Sondre Totakoygarden; **7** a granary from Schnottwyl; **8** a *bur* or storehouse from Håvardstad, Åseral.

In **1**, the bare earth is still being used for sitting and sleeping. In **2** and **3**, the floor has been added over joists, but still separate from the wall logs. In **4**, the lowermost logs have been notched out and set upon two lengthwise sill logs. In **5**, the sill logs have given way to a unique timber frame structure, in which the floor joists and the first course of the log walls are likewise keyed to form a tightly interlocked whole. In **6** and **7**, the buildings have been further elevated on corner posts, either fitted over or mortised into a sill course, with the floor seated on a ledge provided by the heavier first logs. In **8** and **9**, we finally have a platform created by the special sill system and the flooring, on top of which the logwork rests.

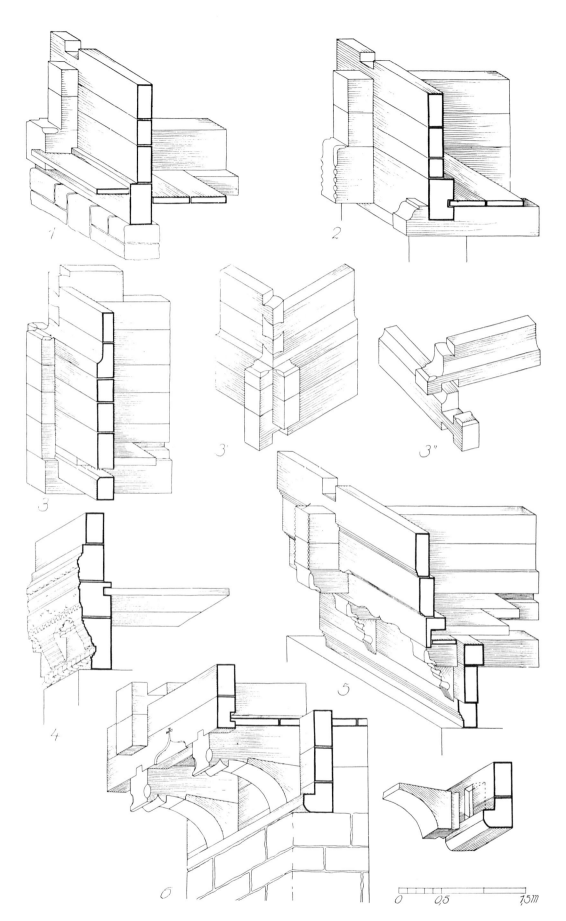

Fig 100
Detail of sills, joist systems and floors: **1** and **2** from farm houses in Keusche in Feistritz (Kärnten) and Interlaken (Switzerland); **3** from a granary from Radenthein (Kärnten) and Swiss farm houses; **4** from La Forclaz; **5** from Wittigen; **6** from Silenen.

The variety of alternative approaches to a particular aspect of building, expressed here both in the interplay between floor and wall on the inside, and in the formal structures of the exterior, provides some insight into the versatility of timber-built architecture.

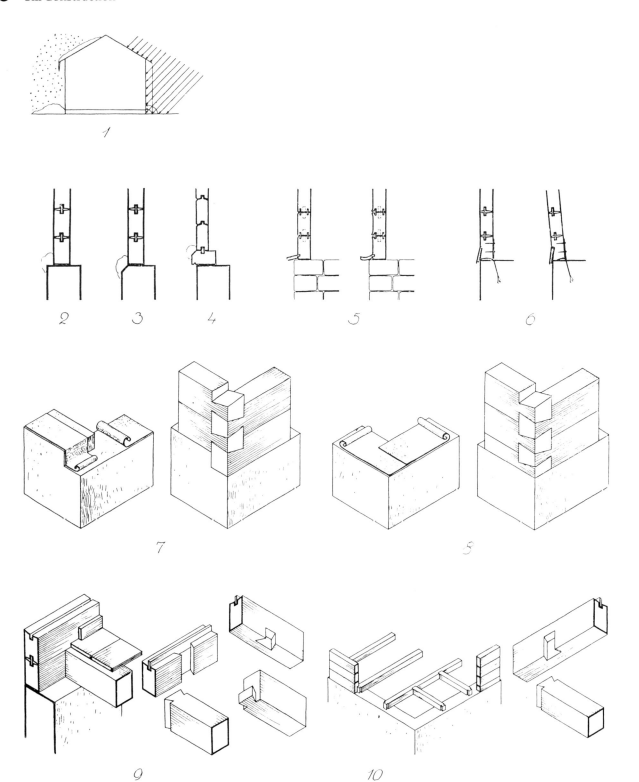

Fig 101

Sill design. Because of the danger posed by moisture from
without (**1**), structures must be designed to easily shed
rain and snow. Items **2** and **4** are faulty, as they allow snow
and rainwater to accumulate, thus permitting seepage of
moisture into the joints. Styles **5** and **6**, while somewhat
more intricate, are not rugged enough to withstand the
impact of weathering. Protection against ground moisture
may be provided by a vapour barrier of roofing felt on the
foundation. The more effective and easiest solution is to
set the sill course on a foundation which is at the same
level all around (**8**). To lock the walls firmly in place, the
floor joists may be dovetailed into the sills, as in **9** and **10**.

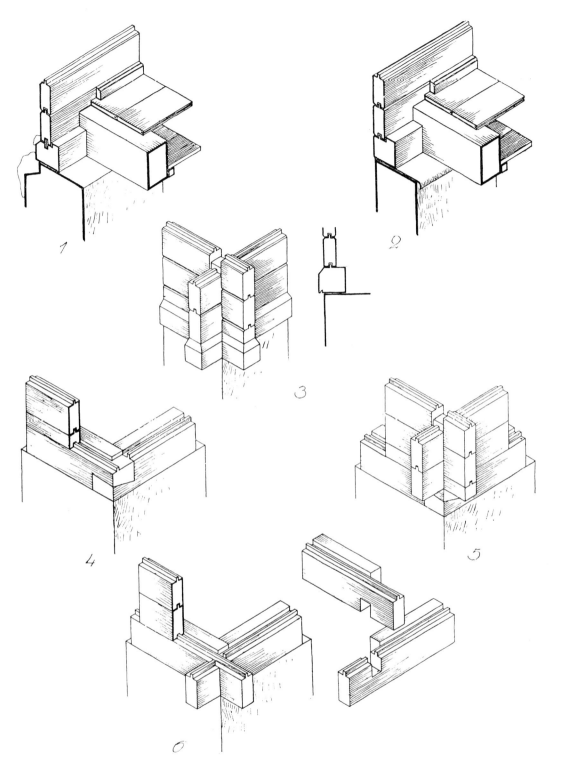

Fig 102
Sill and floor joinery. Styles **1** and **3** are fine in terms of
their interior layout, but poor as far as the exterior design
is concerned, because the protruding sill or protruding sill
and foundation provides too great an opportunity for
snow and rain to collect. Items **2**, **4**, **5** and **6** represent
proper design.

Fig 103
Solid timber floor deck of a log building from the island
redoubt of Buchau (1100–800 BC), in the marshland of
Lake Federsee.

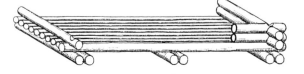

Provision must of course also be made to keep out driving rain, spattered water, and snow (Fig **101/1**). A broad overhanging roof was used years ago to provide some protection in this regard, but it alone is not enough. The sill itself must be raised a sufficient height above the ground, and designed to assure rapid runoff during a downpour. On the basis of these considerations, Fig **101/2** and **101/3**, which show the solid foundation projecting beyond the wall line, cannot be considered satisfactory, nor can Fig **101/4** or Fig **102/1** and **102/3**, where the sill overhangs the foundation. These latter styles tend to catch rain and snow; on the one hand facilitating the entry of moisture between the lowest logs, while also promoting wetting of the sill and/or logwork. The most desirable approach is to lay the sill flush with the foundation wall (Fig **101/8**) or even to extend it as much as 1 cm beyond the foundation (Fig **102/2**). Nor do the types of wooden drip-shield shown in Fig **101/5** and **101/6** assure proper protection. They not only catch snow and rain, but are also prone to deterioration due to weathering, a factor which at times may even jeopardize the structural integrity of the building (Fig **101/6**).

The greater the stability given the sill logs, the greater will be the stability of the structure as a whole. Because of this, we must devote special attention to this portion of the wall. The old-time craftsmen, for example, not only used thicker logs for the sill course, but also took special care to select certain species for their durability. It was customary, as we have already seen, to use the finest species available, such as larch, oak or elm, for this ''bottom round''.

If the sill is to be a heavier and thicker log than the rest of the logwork, the extra material should always be on the inside. This makes it much easier to securely tie the floor joists into the log walls; something clearly illustrated by comparing Fig **101/9** and **101/10** with Fig **102/2** and **102/4**.

To assure that the vapour barrier material lies flat with no kinks, the bottoms of the sill logs must be on the same level throughout (Fig **101/8**). Depending upon the sizes

Fig 104
Lower logwork protruding in plinth-like fashion on a granary from Radenthein, Kärnten (Austria). The projecting cornerwork reinforces the theme of outward spread set by the logwork itself, lending a distinctive air to this portion of the ground storey (cf Fig 100/3).

of the logs available to the builder, a log of average diameter will be keyed into one half again as large or one smaller by half (Fig **101/8**). Alternatively, the logs in the first round may all be of the same size, with the half-log offset not starting until the second course (Fig **102/4** to **102/6**).

To anchor the sill firmly in place and prevent any lateral movement, the most effective approach is to tie it into the floor joist system with dovetail notching (Figs **101/9**, **101/10** and **102/2**). This will assure that even at the lowermost horizontal structure, the log building is already an interlocked unified whole. This concept was

105

106

Figs 105 and 106
Log dwelling from Naters, near Brig (Switzerland). The floor joists, extended to carry the log wall, are braced by sturdy brackets keyed into a solid timber sill several logs high.

presaged by the ancient logwork of the island redoubt of Buchau, in that the floor of logs in the round was extended beyond the walls, which were then raised on it (Fig 103).

Man's urge to elevate the expression of form above the bare essentials and enrich it with ornamentation sought outlet even at the sill level. The most immediate potential for visually accentuating and highlighting this first course of logwork was afforded by a stout sill log extending beyond the face of the wall, as shown in Fig **100/1**. Further possibilities lay in extending the log ends and the floor joists at this point (Fig **100/2**), with these perhaps made to emulate paws seeking a foothold on the masonry foundation. However picturesque this motif might appear, it is unfortunately too prone to weathering to be considered a desirable model. In Kärnten province, a number of timber-built granaries feature the bottom four courses or so combined with protruding endwork to form a plinth-like base extending beyond the wall line above (Figs **100/3** and **104**).

Should the log wall rest upon a solid foundation above eye level where its lower surface is highly visible, the sill and even the ends of the joists, when present, were sometimes beautifully embellished. Such decorative work was not confined to the sill logs alone, but took in the logwork above it as well (Fig **100/4**). If the floor joists and the storey above them both projected beyond the face of the sill logwork, carved-in brackets also accompanied the decorative embellishment on the main sill and on the logwork at floor level. Combined with the exemplary treatment of the joist ends, this beautiful craftsmanship is a delight to the eye in its vigor and exuberance (Figs **100/5**, **105** and **106**).

The quest for new forms of expression even produced sillwork which reflected the motif of the joist-end in a frieze-like portrayal of carved brackets (Fig **100/4**).

We shall have more to say on the subject of actual floor coverings when we discuss floor and ceiling structures.

Roofs

The design of the roof superstructure and the properties of the materials used to cover it go hand in hand; a relationship most saliently expressed in the pitch of the roof. Because of this association, the nature of roof systems can best be appreciated by starting with a survey of the various types of roof coverings. From an evolutionary viewpoint, the pole roof with the slender rafters touching one another is the earliest form; the poles themselves actually creating a kind of roof covering, needing only some form of caulking or chinking.

Fig 107
Laplander's huts from Sweden. Items **1, 2** and **3** show winter versions. In **1** and **2**, the sod covering is laid to follow the slope of the roof, while in **3** the chunks of turf are shown placed horizontally, at the same time securing a covering of birch bark. In this instance, the saplings forming the roof are tightly spaced in keeping with the nature of a roof covering. By contrast, those of the summer shelter are placed further apart (**4** and **5**). This light construction was made possible by stretching reindeer hides over it as a roof skin.

Roofs of Sod or Turf

One of the earliest roof forms is found on the domed huts of the Laplanders. Even today, these crude shelters, composed solely of a roof structure overhead, exist in both a winter version (Fig **107/1** to **107/3**) and a summer style (Fig **107/4** and **107/5**). The former is a low, rounded hut of tightly spaced saplings bent over an interior frame resembling a sawhorse. The gaps between the saplings are closed by chunks of sod, either laid flat over the poles or stacked horizontally, somewhat in stonework fashion. Further protection is afforded by a covering of birch bark between the saplings and the sod (Fig **107/3**). The summer dwelling is simply a tent-like affair; its frame covered by reindeer hides. Because these are light, tough and waterproof, the saplings may be spaced further apart and the framework left more open than in the winter hut.

In evolutionary terms, there is a close relationship between the tent skin and the bark covering of the winter hut. While the steeply sloping roof provides the most favourable structure for the former, the fact is that the latter is a more delicate covering. This being the case, the sod serves to hold it in place and to protect it. On a steep roof, however, the sod is itself not durable enough to stand the impact of the elements, being forced apart and crumbled by rain, wind and frost. This could be accepted, however, for the brief period of the winter months for which these nomadic structures had to last.

For permanent structures, however, some more effective retaining system had to be arrived at. This was achieved by lowering the slope of the roof to the point where rainfall would easily run off, yet the sod roofing would still remain intact despite the impact of climatic conditions. This approach meant that only the edges of the sod roof had to be protected at the eaves and gables. Figs **108** and **109** show a number of alternatives designed to meet this situation.

Fig 108 (opposite)
Norwegian sod roofs. Item **1** is the earliest form, with the roof covering carried by a system of rafters side by side, to which is added a covering of birch bark several layers thick, topped by a layer of sod. These roofs require a gentle pitch to prevent the sod from sliding. Item **2** shows the second evolutionary stage, with the load bearing structure of alternating pole rafters and riven planks (from Kvern, Setesdal). Items **3** and **4** represent the third stage, involving a more open support system incorporating either rafter (**3**) or purlin framing (**4**), sheathed over to

108

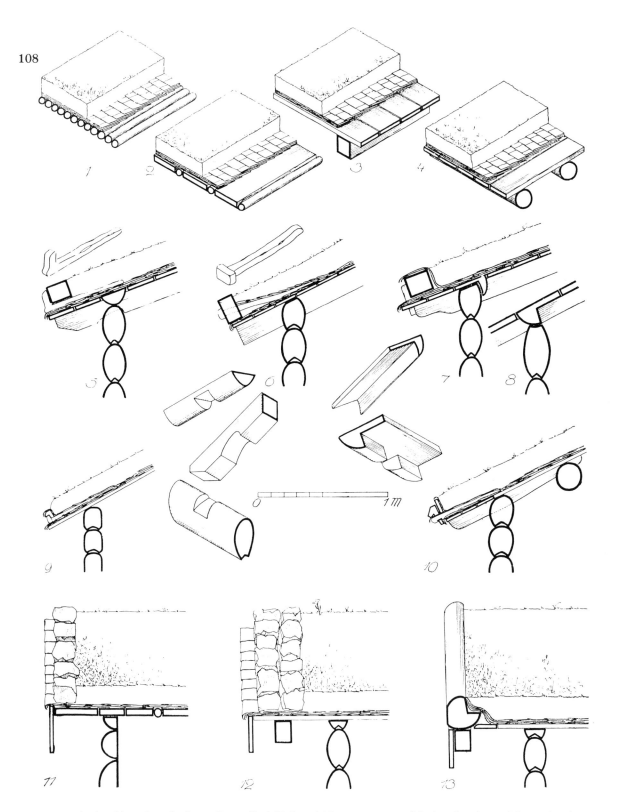

create the load bearing platform. Items **5**, **6**, **7**, **9** and **10** show a number of techniques for retaining the sod at the eaves. In **5**, from Setesdal, the timber at the eaves is secured by crooked wooden pegs weighed down by the sod. Item **6**, from Numedalen, uses the same system, except with huge wooden pins, while **7** from Gudbrandsdalen is secured by wedges driven into the roof decking. In **9** and **10**, likewise from Gudbrandsdalen, a round log has been used at the eaves instead of a squared timber, and secured by pegs made from a single piece of wood in the case of **9**, and from two pieces in the latter

case. Notice also that a drip cap has been incorporated into the eaves log system in **9**.

To provide a snug fit between log walls and roof decking, the wall is topped either by a half-log (**5**) or a log especially shaped to make the transition from wall to roof (**7** and **8**). On the gable end of the roof, the sod is held in place either by one or two rows of stone (**11** from Setesdal and **12** from Vest Agder). Alternatively, a shaped log might be used, as in item **13** from Numedalen.

At the eaves, the sod was held and protected by a squared retaining log (Figs **108/5** to **108/7**, **109/A** and **109/B**), known in Old Norse as the *torfvölr*, and in Swedish as the *mullås*, or by a round log serving this same function (Fig **108/9** and **108/10**). These were secured in place either by crooked wooden stops, known in Norwegian as *krokraptr* (Figs **108/5** and **109/A**), oversize wooden pegs (Fig **108/6**), wedges (Figs **108/7** and **109/B**) or wedged pegs, as illustrated in Fig **108/10**. Stops and pegs pass under the birch bark covering, thus being protected by it as well. On the gable-edge, chunks of stone in either a single or double row were laid directly on top of the birch bark to hold it in place (Fig **108/11** and **108/12**). Another method was to place a partially scooped-out log along the gable-edge to retain the sod (Fig **108/13**). The barge board, called the *windki* by the Norwegians and representing the most recent addition to the structure in evolutionary terms, was nailed either to the rafters (Fig **108/13**) or to the ends of the Ås or purlins (Fig **108/11**), depending upon the type of roof construction involved.

In the course of time, the superstructure over which the birch bark was laid changed from one of tightly spaced poles to one of roofing boards or planks obtained by splitting (Fig **108/1** and **108/2**). As the roof poles grew further and further apart, the rafter system was born, now demanding a special form of sheathing boards (known as *trod*)

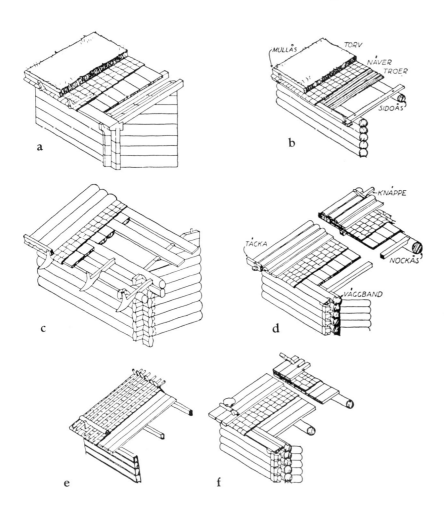

Fig 109
Sodded and boarded roof construction from Sweden. **A** and **B**: sod roofs. **C** and **D**: slab and plank roofing over board decking. **E** and **F**: boarded roofs with bark secured by saddle poles or saddle boards (*nockås*, ridge pole; *sidoås*, purlin; *näver*, birch bark; *väggband*, plate).

running parallel to the eaves (Fig **108/3**). By contrast, the sheathing of the purlin roof (Fig **108/4**), which is most closely related to **108/1** and **108/2**, is laid at right angles to the eaves.

However, this poses a number of special problems for construction of the roof overhang at the eaves (Fig **108/9** and **108/10**). This area can easily become too weak to support the combined weight of the eaves, the roof load and snow without suffering damage. To meet this exigency, builders would sometimes resort to the addition of auxiliary rafters, which extended up from the eaves as far as the first purlin (Fig **108/10**). Birch bark too was used to give protection to eaves timbers (Fig **108/7**), eaves logs (Fig **108/9** and **108/10**), barge boards (Fig **108/11** and **108/12**) and retaining logs at the gable edge (Fig **108/13**). This is a most vivid illustration of how knowledgeable our forebears were about how to protect various parts of a structure against moisture.

Sod roofing not only provides a protective mantle for the covering of bark, but is at the same time an effective shield against the cold of winter and the heat of summer. A benign addition to the sod roof is the carpet of greenery which grows atop it, seeded by the wind and affording a picture of delightful charm (Fig **110**).

Not only must a roof provide proper protection, however, it must be firmly tied into the log walls. A wide variety of techniques evolved to meet this issue. In Norway, the rafters were fitted into the logwork in such a fashion that the sheathing boards were in contact with the logs. One other approach was to top the wall with a specially hewn log (a *naamtrod* in Norwegian) which by its shaping fit into the roof boarding in a variety of ways (Fig **108/5** to **108/10**). In Sweden, the popular method is to have the roof boarding flush against the plate log (Fig **109/A**) or to fit it into a slot grooved out of a heavier roofing board run at right angles along the eaves (Fig **109/B**).

Fig 110
Beautiful sod roofed guesthouse, part of the *Hjeltarhof*
farmstead from Gudbrandsdalen, built in 1565 and now in
Sandvig's outdoor museum in Lillehammer, Norway.

Particularly today, when we feel ourselves so tied to the notion of wood as a product of the sawmills, it is extremely instructive for us to see how innovative and ingenious the old-time craftsmen showed themselves to be in fashioning these beautiful plate and roof members out of full-size timber.

Thatched Roofing

Compared to roofs of sod, thatched roofs include a greater variety of techniques for applying the roofing material and securing it in place. Thatch may be tamped down, tied on in the form of sheaves or thatch tiles, or loose-laid. Accordingly, we may classify thatched roofs as tamped, sheaf-thatched, thatch-tiled or loose laid.

Tamped Thatching

Tamped-roof thatching is among the oldest forms of roofing known, used in centuries past by the North, East and West Germanic peoples. It involves the application of straw thatch to a framing structure resembling an upturned harrow; an impression created by the sharpened ends of branches sticking up from pole rafters, or a system of wooden pegs. Once laid in place on the roof, the thatch is packed down firmly underfoot (Figs **111**, **112** and **113**). This means that the roof framing must be particularly sturdy. Today, the roof of tamped thatch survives only among the North Germanic inhabitants of Gotland and its neighbouring islands, as well as in Zeeland and among the East Germanic people of the Transylvanian *Erzgebirge* and their western foothills.

Because the stalks of the thatch lie horizontal in this form of roofing, the slope must be very steep to keep out water. To provide protection against the wind, special arrangements are needed at the ridge. These may include a single log above the peak (Fig **113/3**) or poles on either side of the ridge (Figs **111/2** and **112**) to weigh down the thatch, held by scissor-poles astride the peak in the former case or vertical saddle poles in the latter. Since only the butts of the straw thatch show in this type of roofing, it gives the impression of a velvety texture. To assure that the stalks of thatch bind together well, they must not be too short. This tamped thatching is thicker than the sheaf-thatched roof, measuring 50 cm in thickness as opposed to 30 cm for the latter.

Fig 111
Tamped-thatch roofing (**1** to **4**) and thatching, loose-laid style (**5**). **1** Sweden; **2** Gotland; **3** and **4** *Erzgebirge* mountains of Transylvania; **5** Coastal Uppland, Sweden. In tamped construction, the straw or eel grass is laid horizontally, then packed into place by foot. Originally, the stubs of the branches were left on pole rafters to secure the thatch to the framing (**1** and **2**). A more recent structure in evolutionary terms uses spaced roofing boards and wooden pegs in place of the cut-off branches (**3** and **4**). To assure that this type of roof will shed the rain, a steep pitch is mandatory. On a loose-laid roof, the stalks of thatch lie parallel to the roof (**5**), kept in place by bearer poles and a gentle incline.

112

Figs 112 to 114
Tamped-thatch roofs from Gotland, Sweden (Fig **112**)
and the Transylvanian *Erzgebirge* (Fig **113**). Fig **114** shows
a sheaf-thatched style from the low-lying country of the
Erdinger Moos in Upper Bavaria. Although the weathered
condition of the structures does enable us to appreciate
the methods of construction, it also reveals the frailty of
these forms of roofing.

113

114

Sheaf-thatched Roofing

As the name implies, sheaf thatching involves tieing straw or reed in bundles 9 to 12 cm thick to roofing slats spaced 30 cm apart for straw and 40 cm for reed, using thin sticks known as sways (Figs **114**, **115** and **116**). Each successive layer of sheaves overlaps the previous one, extending roughly 24 cm below the sways of the preceding course, with the result that the roof is always three layers thick in section. This technique is suitable for light roof framing.

In days gone by, willow twigs were used to tie the sheaves in place. In case of fire, however, these burn through too quickly, permitting the burning thatch to slide off the roof and pile up in a fiery mass against the side walls. For this reason, galvanized wire is a better material for tying the thatch. If wire-tied, the thatch will burn out on the roof.

The thatcher applies his roofing material from a simple roof scaffolding system, consisting of a log 4 to 6 meters in length, suspended by ropes from the ridge, which also allow the scaffold to be raised or lowered (Fig **116**). At the ridge, a number of techniques have been tried to secure the roofing in place; one such involving special sheaves, either tied down with sways or nailed on (Fig **115**). Saddle poles might also be used over the thatch, at times even expanding to form a system of saddle-boarding astride the peak (Fig **115/7**).

The pitch of a sheaf-thatched roof must not be less than 45°. The life of one of these roofs depends upon the roof-slope and the orientation of the building, being 15 years at a minimum. The sunny side of a roof pitched at 60° to 70° may last from sixty to seventy years, and thirty to forty years on the shady side. Should moss grow up, it will absorb moisture, thus extending the life of the roof.

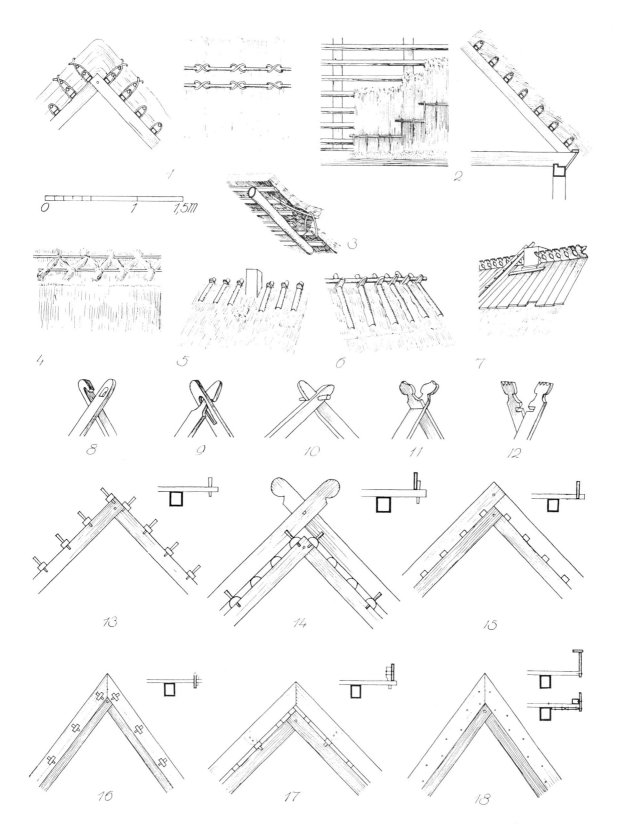

Fig 115

Sheaf-thatched roofs. Items **1** and **2** show sways used to fasten the sheaves of straw or reed. Item **3** is a roof eyebrow from Switzerland. Items **4** to **12** are retaining structures at the ridge from East Prussia, involving special *Strohpuppen* or ''straw dolls'' (**4**) and saddle poles (**5** and **6**) or saddle boards (**7** to **12**). Examples **13** to **18** show, in order, wooden pegs used to retain the thatch at the gable-edge (**13**) and barge boards, sitting astride the roofing boards (**14** and **17**). These barge boards might also be notched and fitted (**15**), tenoned and wedged (**16**) or nailed on with the addition of wooden nailer strips (**18**). The technique in **17** is overly contrived.

Fig 116
Painted scene showing thatching with water reed on a farm house in East Prussia. The thatcher stands on a log scaffold, held by two ropes tied to the ridge. This scaffold may also be suspended from iron hooks hung over the laths or roofing slats. The reed or hand-threshed straw is laid in sheaves, using a board guide to keep them level, so that the tips of the stalks are toward the ridge, while the lower ends are withdrawn slightly as the roof goes up. This produces uniform lapping of the thatch, while providing greater protection against rain. Each layer is tied to the laths using sways and galvanized wire; this lashing then covered by the following layer. The thatcher will do a section of roof at a time, its size depending on the length of his scaffold.

Loose-laid Thatch

A unique method of roofing patterned after that of the sod roof evolved in Sweden, where the straw is sometimes loose-laid over laths or spaced roofing slats, then weighed down with stout bearer poles (Fig **111/5**). Laid as it is on a low-pitched structure, this type of roofing is vastly inferior to the two previous types as far as dryness is concerned. Because of this, loose-laid thatching is only suitable for lesser structures.

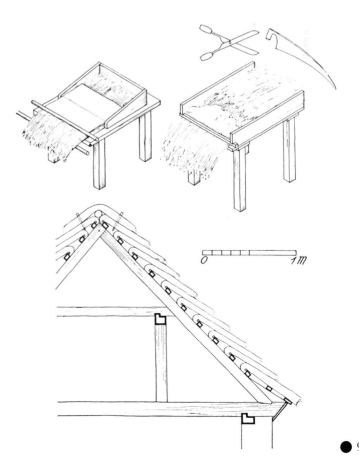

Fig 117
Thatch-tiled roofing. Shown above are the special tables for making thatch tiles. These may be as much as 70 cm wide and up to a meter in length. Gilly states that a layer of straw 8 cm is laid out on the table, with the tips facing the open end at left. A coating of fatty clay is then applied, following which the loose ends are wrapped around a sway known as a *Schindelstock*. The turned-over end is then given another coating of clay. Fauth talks about the first layer of straw being 5 cm thick, with the tips overhanging the table by 40–50 cm, followed by another heavy layer, but this time with the tips overhanging the opposite end of the table. The sway or *Schindelstock* is then pressed into the notches in the end of the table, and a coating of clay, 1–1.5 cm thick, applied. Next, the overhanging straw is folded back over the sway, pressed down into the clay coating and covered with another 1–1.5 cm of clay; this final coating being worked in with a spade. The ends of the straw sticking out over the table are then trimmed off with shears or a scythe. The thatch tiles are placed on the roof with the clay-coated side down, and tied to the roof laths with galvanized wire; the sway of one tile being pushed into the tile preceding it. This type of roof requires the same pitch as the sheaf-thatched style.

Thatch-tiled Roofing

In an effort to reduce the danger of fire, builders in some areas went over to a system of mixing clay with their straw, in addition to coating the underside of the thatch with this same material. Using this method, the straw was made into thatch tiles 6 to 8 cm thick on a specially designed table (Fig **117**). The process involved folding a narrow mat of straw, approximately 40 to 50 cm in length, back over a roofing stick or sway, following which clay was applied, first as a binder, then as a surface coating. To make the clay adhere better, a sharpened stick would be used to work the clay in among the stalks.

These tiles of thatch were applied in triple thickness over lath spaced roughly 40 cm apart by sticking one end of the sway into the adjacent tile and tying the other end to the lath with galvanized wire.

This type of roofing is usually 18 to 24 cm thick, and, like the sheaf-thatched roof, must be pitched at not less than 45°. At the eaves, specially made tiles 15 to 18 cm in thickness were used, while the ridge was formed by rolls of straw, likewise mixed with clay, soaked, then folded over the peak and pegged down.

118

119

Figs 118 and 119
Swedish log buildings with wooden roofs. At left is a stable and at right an upland dairyherd's cookhouse from Jämtland, now in Skansen. The roofs are of two layers of split planks, separated by a covering of birch bark. To hold the upper layer of slabs in place, a bearer pole is laid across each side of the roof and weighed down by stone. These poles are connected in yoke-like fashion by cross-ties to form a single frame, which fits like a clamp around the roof and gable ends.

Wooden Roofing

Compelled as men were in ancient times by the realities of the countryside about them, it is obvious that very early on in the evolution of the roof they also sought to make use of the materials afforded by the woods and forests alone. We may count among the earliest stages in this development a roof consisting of a double layer of half-round riven slabs, the top row covering the gaps between the slabs of the first, with the flattened surfaces face-to-face. To prevent leaking caused by working of the wood, this design was refined by interposing a covering of birch bark, as on a sod roof (Figs **118** and **119**).

In the course of subsequent development, the lower layer of slabs gave way to a sheathing of planks, while the upper layer either retained its form or likewise adopted the plank design (Fig **120/1** to **120/4**). The top slabs or planks are either hung from the ridge by interlocking them with those on the other side of the roof (Fig **120/1**) or held by retaining boards at the eaves (Figs **120/2**, **121** and **122**). These eaves boards were secured by stout crooked wooden stops, simultaneously crooked rafters, extending in one style beneath the sheathing up to the first purlin; in another, running all the way to the ridge as an integral part of the roof planking. Both permit a steep pitch to the roof. However, if a builder wished to protect the roof against wind by weighing down the outer roof covering with stone, a special system had to be used to prevent it from sliding off, once the roof was pitched at more than 30°. This system might be supported from the eaves (Fig **120/4**) or utilize a yoke arrangement strapped to the sides of the roof and the gables (Figs **118** and **119**).

In terms of durability, this type of roofing suffers from the never-ending cycle of moisture and dryness brought about by the elements. The very first signs of this, even while the wood itself is still sound, take the form of physical deformation caused by non-uniform shrinkage. The outer slabs, for example, will no longer lie flat on the birch bark underlayment. One other problem in this instance is that, even from the outset, the slabs do not fit together well enough side-by-side to keep out rainfall and moisture. Doubtless, these drawbacks were among the factors which led housebuilders of long ago to use wood in the form of small panels, laid in courses as with birch bark. Thus evolved the shingled roof.

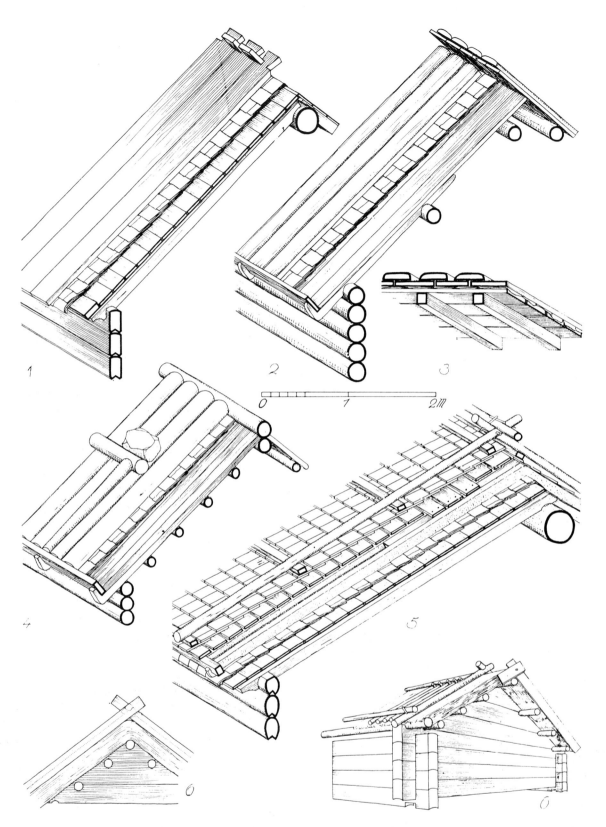

Fig 120
Roofing techniques from Sweden (1 to 4) and Norway.
1 Boarded roof with birch bark between decking and
outer roofing, from Bollnäs. The outer boards are
interlocked and sit astride the peak in saddle-like fashion.
2 Planked roof from Skarptäkt (Dalarna). Here, the
planks rest on an eaves board restrained by crooked stops.
3 Overlapping planked and boarded style from Mora.
4 Timber roof from Värmland in the manner of the old-

style *lubbendach* roof of Courland (Kurland, Latvia). In
this technique, the roofing is also held in place by a log
framework weighted with stone. **5** Sod and shingle roof
from Grösli, Norway. Vertical furring has been set into the
sod underlay to take horizontal strapping or battens. On
top of this are loose-laid shingles, held by bearer laths and
saddle poles. **6** Roofing of straw thatch, secured by saddle
poles and horizontal bearers.

Shingled Roofing

A shingled roof is one covered with thin slabs of wood, obtained by riving or splitting. These may be 8 to 25 cm wide and from 25 to 100 cm in length. This type of roof has been used by the Germanic peoples since ancient times, with recorded references going back as far as the first century AD. In an account dating from this period, Plinius describes the roofing of buildings west of the Rhine as including both *arundo* (water reed) and *skindula* (shingles).

Shingles must have been known to the Visigoths as well, as borne out by mention of a roof covered with *skalja* or shingles in the translation of the Bible by Bishop Wulfila from the middle of the fourth century (Old Norse *skilja* – to split or cleave; Gothic *skildus*, meaning simply board). References then began occurring with greater frequency in the Carolingian era and during the Middle Ages.

121

122

Figs 121 and 122
Sturdy retaining planks at the eaves on Swedish wooden roofs, from the outdoor museum at Skansen. It is interesting to note the remarkable degree to which the protective properties of birch bark have been exploited.

The Making of Shingles

Shingles are made from numerous woods which vary widely as to ease of splitting. These may be categorized as species which split easily and well, such as spruce, pine, larch and fir and those which split moderately well, including beech, oak, alder and ash. Foremost among commonly used varieties in terms of durability are shingles of oak, with an estimated life of 100 years; followed by larch shingles at 70 to 80 years, pine at about 40 years and finally fir at roughly 25 years. These figures envisage turning the shingles over after anywhere from twelve to forty years. One interesting point is that shingled roofs last longer at higher elevations.

In order to resist the impact of the weather, shingles must shed water along the grain, meaning that the physical structure of the fibres must not be damaged. This can only be achieved by splitting (Fig **123**). If shingles are sawn, the fibres are torn apart, thus tending to absorb water and hasten the deterioration of the wood. Furthermore, a protective coating forms on the surface of split shakes and shingles due to the depositing of residues, both during and after drying. This not only resists the weather, but is even said to have fire-retardant qualities.

The first consideration in shingle making is selecting the wood. This must be slow-growth timber with straight grain or some right-hand twist and as free from knots as possible. It must not be too young; the diameter of the particular trunk not to be less than twice the width of the shingles, which is to say, roughly 16 to 20 cm. Favoured because of their durability are heartwood and lightwood. At times, shingles are even smoked to prolong their service life. To this day in fact, shingles can still be seen stacked for smoking atop the chimneys of huts and cabins in the Alpine meadow regions.

Shingles are laid in overlapping courses in such a manner that the spaces between them are covered a number of times. To keep the shingles in place, two main systems are used. They may be held down by a weight which bears upon several rows or courses, or nailed in place singly to a suitable roof decking. Accordingly, we classify shingle roofs as either loose-laid or nailed.

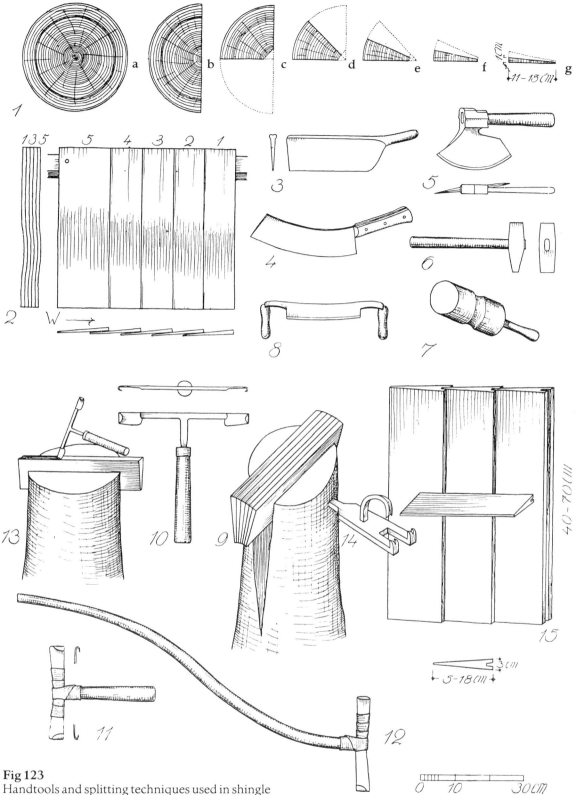

Fig 123

Handtools and splitting techniques used in shingle making (*cf.* also Figs **2** and **3**). Item **1** shows the method commonly used in the Black Forest for splitting shakes or shingles from rounds of wood (**a**) sawn from the trunk in the desired shingle length. First, bolts (**b** and **c**) are cut from the rounds by splitting while still green, since the wood splits most easily in this state. When adequately dried, these are split further, each successive cut again splitting the bolt in two until the desired thickness is reached, this being 6–10 mm on the average (**d**, **e**, **f** and **g**). In Kärnten, larch set aside for shingle making is allowed to season with the bark on, as this is said to make it split better. Item **2**: To achieve a good fit when the shingles are being laid, it is best to place them on the roof in the order they were split from the bolt. This enables them to nestle together in the most natural fashion, despite the irregularities inevitable when wood is split. Items **3** and **4** are froe knives or splitting knives, **5** is a broadaxe, **6** a hammer, **7** a wooden club. Item **8** is a straight-bladed drawknife, while **9** is the shingle-maker's block. **10, 11** and **12** are grooving tools for cutting left or right. Item **13** shows a groove being cut on the right side, and **14** shows a block hook for holding the shingles while shaving them with a drawknife. Item **15**: grooved-edge shingles.

The Loose-laid Shingle Roof

Using this technique, the shingles or shakes are laid so as to be laterally offset from those of the preceding course by half a shingle width, with the butts at a certain weather exposure, so that in section the roof is always at least two layers thick (Fig 124). Weather exposure between the courses is dependent upon the length of the shingles and the number of plies. For a three-ply roof of shingles 80 cm long, exposure should be about 20 cm. At times, roofs of loose-laid shingles may be as much as six-ply, i.e., six layers thick.

These un-nailed shingles may be laid on spaced roofing boards or battens (Fig 124 Items 1, 3, 5, 6, 8, 10 and 11) or over a sheathing of slabs (Fig 124/12) or boards (Fig 124 Items 2, 4, 9, 14 and 15). They are then held in place by chunks of stone; the weight transmitted downward by special poles, either round or split. These bearer poles, as they are called, may run parallel to the eaves, in which case they are closely spaced above every second roof batten (Fig 124/8 and 124/9). Alternatively, they may be placed diagonally (Fig 124/14). In both cases, the weight bears down on the shingles. Roofs of this type must be gently sloping to prevent the stones from rolling off; a pitch of 18° to 25° being recommended. One old-time formula was that the height of the ridge be one-sixth of the width of the gable. This would represent a pitch of 18.5°. To prevent rounded bearer poles from rolling, the practice in Austria's Salzburg province is to drive in long wooden pegs. Angled as they are toward the eaves, these tend to nestle against the roof (Fig 126). To secure bearer poles or hold-down laths, wooden pins are used, driven only into half-logs at the gable-edge (Fig 124/9) or completely through the shingles into the rafters (Fig 124/2). Naturally-crooked pegs inserted between the shingles are also encountered on occasion (Fig 124/5).

Fig 124 (opposite)
Loose-laid and weighted shingle roofs from: 1 Vorarlberg, Austria; 2 Switzerland; 3 Vorarlberg; 4 to 7 Switzerland; 8 Upper Bavaria; 9 Switzerland; 10 Salzburg; 11 Switzerland; 12 Allgäu; 13 and 14 Upper Bavaria and 15 Switzerland.
The shingles, laid three to six ply, rest on roofing laths or battens (1, 3, 5, 6, 8, 10, 11 and 13) or sheathing boards (2, 4, 7, 9, 12, 14, 15). Holding them in place are chunks of stone; their weight transmitted by bearer poles. These may be horizontal or diagonal (14). To prevent the stone from sliding off, the roof must have a flat pitch of 18°–29°. This notwithstanding, further retaining techniques were also used at times, including wooden pins driven through the shingles to hold the bearers (2, 6 and 10) or crooked pegs to perform the same function (5).
When the bearers were round, wooden pins were driven in to keep them from rolling. Not infrequently, the gable-edge is also used to help hold the roofing in place, particularly by tenoning bearer pole and roof batten through the verge board and wedging them together (8). In another style, the bearer poles are held by pins driven

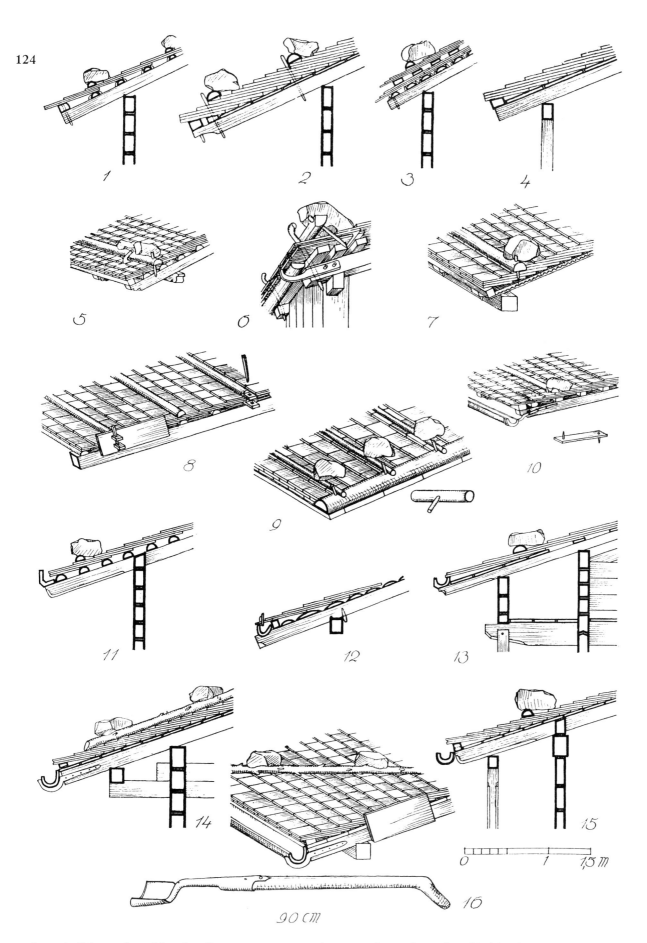

1
2
3
4
5
6
7
8
9
10
11
12
13
14
15
16

90 cm

0   1   1,5 m

into a half-log at the gable-edge. Gutters or eavestroughs of wood, made from a half-log using a slick-like gouge (16) are either mounted at roof level (11 to 13) or hung from the eaves (10, 14 and 15). To provide the proper slope for the doubled or tripled eaves course of shingles, a special

batten has to be added for the starter course. In Vorarlberg, there even exist double roofs of loose-laid and weighted shingles (3), involving a three-ply first layer, upon which battens have been laid and a second three-ply layer added on top.

125

126

Figs 125 and 126
Loose-laid and weighted shingle roofs from Hofgastein,
Salzburg province, Austria. On the hay shed shown in Fig
126, wooden pins have been driven in to stop the bearer
poles from rolling. On the right gable-edge, wooden pins
have likewise been used to protect the roofing with verge
or barge boards.

Fig 127
Another stone-weighted roof from Hofgastein, clearly
showing how the uppermost courses of shingles are
weighted at the ridge.

One technique used in Salzburg in this regard was to insert into the roofing special shingles having two projecting nails; one hooked over the batten or strapping, the other holding the bearer pole in place (Fig **124/10**). The bearer poles are also used to help secure the shingles at the gable-edge. In the most simple approach, wooden pins driven through the poles hold the shingles securely in place at the gable-edge (Figs **124/5** to **124/7**, **125** and **126**). Where verge boards or barge boards are used, every second bearer and the corresponding roofing batten are sometimes tenoned through it and wedged from the outside (Fig **124/8**).

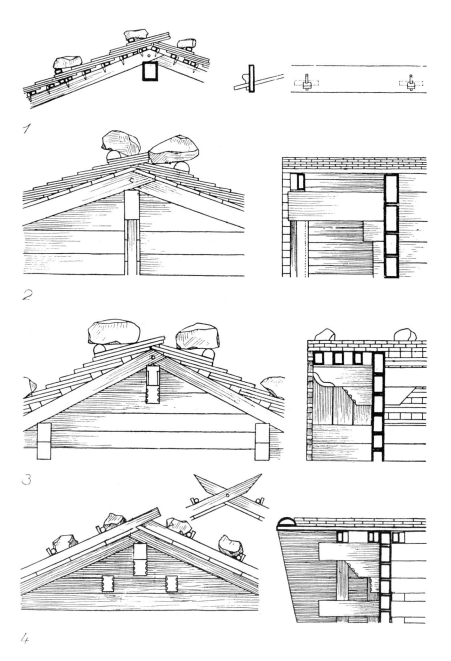

Fig 128
Securing loose-laid shingle roofs against rain and wind. To prevent water from entering the juncture of the two sides of the roof, the shingling on the weather side is thrust over the ridge. The bearer poles and the stones which weigh them down extend right up the roof to this point. Usually, the overhanging roofing protects sheathing against the wind (**2** and **4** from Switzerland), although in this connection, builders occasionally went so far as to use tightly spaced rafters to create a protective shield (**3**). In **4**, a half-log atop the sheathing serves the function of a verge board.

In Sweden and Norway, the horizontal laths are weighted by vertical hold-downs (Fig **129**), or conversely, the vertical hold-down poles are closely spaced and held down by bearer poles (Fig **130**).

The roof is most vulnerable to the weather at the ridge (Fig **127**). To counter this problem, the shingling is extended beyond the peak on the weather side, covering the point at which the two sides of the roof meet. Because the force of the system of weights is exerted downward, bearer poles weighted with stone are laid across each of the two uppermost courses of shingles which come together here (Fig **128**).

At the eaves, wooden gutters or eavestroughs made from half-logs were either mounted up on the rafters (Fig **124/11** to **124/13**) or hung below the eaves on the rafter ends with wooden or iron brackets (Fig **124/10**, **124/14** and **124/15**).

So that water running off would not disrupt traffic in front of a building, gutters were extended well beyond the end walls. However, because of ill-conceived building codes

129

130

Figs 129 and 130
Roof styles from Norway and Sweden weighted with bearer poles. Fig **129** shows a log house from Grösli (Numedal), Norway, from the year 1633. The building is roofed with sod, covered in turn by loose-laid shingles held in place by saddle poles and horizontal hold-downs (*cf*. Fig **120**). Fig **130**: shed in a Lapp camp, Skansen (Sweden). Here, saddle poles have been laid directly atop a covering of birch bark to hold it in place.

which called for storm sewers in town and country alike, gutters have almost entirely vanished from the scene. To assure proper runoff from the eavestroughs, the system had to be laid out correctly with proper drop in the gutters all around.

One advantage of loose-laid shingles is the ease with which the roofing can be renewed. Once the shingles begin to age, it is a simple matter to withdraw them and turn them over, thus exposing the heretofore protected side. This obviates the need to put on new shingles, making it possible, for example, to extend the life of a larch shingle roof to 80 to 100 years, as it otherwise requires replacement after at least forty years.

A drawback inherent in the gently sloping roof is that during the winter months, the snow frequently melts on the sunny side, yet stays on the unexposed side. As a consequence, the roof weathers more rapidly on the sunny side, and the shingles have to be changed more often than on the other side.

As far as roof rafters are concerned, their size and spacing depends upon the span between the supports and the thickness of the roof sheathing.

One further attractive feature of the weighted and loose-laid shingle roof is that it not only repels water and moisture, but also provides excellent insulation against heat and cold. Also, because this type of construction rules out roof valleys, a laid-shingle roof exerts a major influence on the configuration of a building.

Fig 131
Portion of a mill from Ebene Reichenau, Kärnten, in which both roof shingles and sheathing boards are fastened with wooden pegs.

The Nailed Shingle Roof

By nailing the shingles or shakes to a system of battens or roof sheathing, the builder gives himself at once greater freedom and design potential than is possible with the stone-weighted roof of loose-laid shingles. He may now go, for example, from the gently sloping to the steeply pitched roof, which allows rapid runoff of rainfall. Moreover, valleys hips and dormers may be added, and both roof framing and sheathing become lighter.

In the beginning, shingles were fastened with wooden pegs (Fig **131**). As early as the Carolingian period, however, roofs were being fastened with iron nails. Nailed shingles may simply be laid side by side (Fig **132/4** to **132/11**), overlapped laterally (Fig **132/1**), or grooved and fitted (Fig **132/2** and **132/3**). This latter technique, in which the shingles are tapered to one side with a groove cut into the thicker side, shows us the earliest form of the tongue-and-groove, which first appeared in the making of chests and the joinery of wall panelling and wainscoting, later being adopted by shinglers. The groove is cut with a special grooving tool known as a *nuteisen*, shown in Fig **123/10** to **123/13** and Fig **133**.

Since the groove in this type of shingles makes for a tighter sealed fit, some nailing can be dispensed with. While regular shingles must be nailed individually, nailing is only required on every fifth shingle if they are grooved.

Nailed shingles may be applied in a variety of ways. They may be slightly lapped laterally, as shown in Fig **132/1**, or laid side by side (Figs **132/8**, **132/9**, **135** to **138**, **139**, **142** and **143**). Courses may also consist of double layers of shingles, laid side by side and offset laterally from one another by half a shingle's width (Figs **132/4**, **132/5**, **132/10**, **132/11**, **134**, **144** and **145**). One other option is to lay each shingle so that its tapered side fits into the groove cut out of the thicker side of the shingle next to it (Figs **132/2**, **132/3**, **146**, and **147** to **153**).

Fig 132 (opposite)
Nailed shingle roofs from: **1** the Black Forest (ungrooved); **2** Silesia (ungrooved); **3** two-layer roof, Oberharz region (groove-fitted); **4** Salzburg (ungrooved); **5** to **7** Croatia; **8** Norway; **9** Croatia; **10** Salzburg and **11** Croatia.

Originally, shingles were fastened to the roof boards or battens with wooden pegs, later replaced by iron nails. If ungrooved, each shingle is nailed individually. If grooved, only the first course is fully nailed; after this, nailing is only required on roughly every fifth shingle. This type of

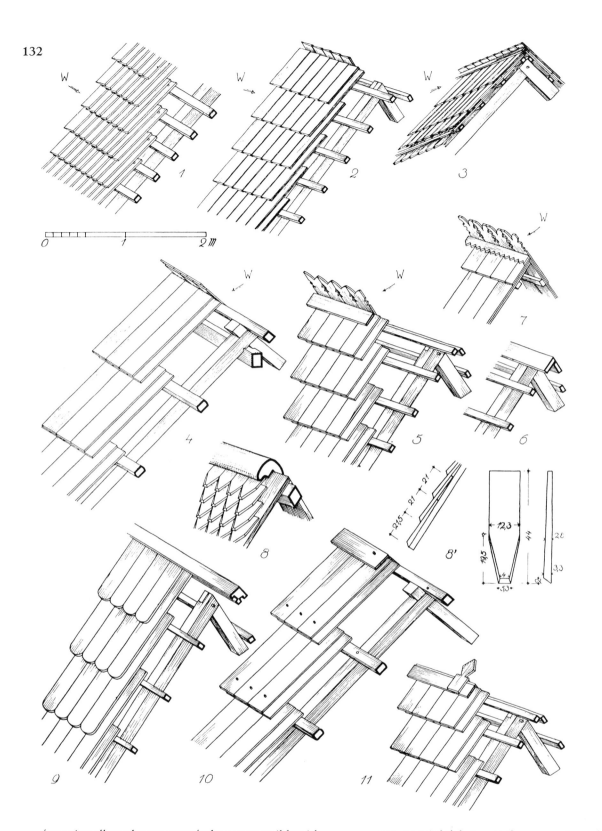

fastening allowed steeper roofs than are possible with weighted loose-laid shingles (common pitch: 45°), thus permitting more rapid runoff. In addition, roof framing and sheathing become lighter and more open than on the latter type. Ungrooved shingles are either straight-split (4, 5, 7, 9, 10 and 11) or tapered, either to one end (8) or one side (1), which allows them to lie flat against the roof. There are two types of overlap; lateral and vertical. One method of lateral overlap involves double layers of shingles, one covering the other fully and offset from it horizontally (4, 5, 10 and 11). Vertically, a given weather

exposure is left between the courses in such a manner that, in section, from two to five rows overlap. At the ridge, the shingles on the weather side may be extended over the peak (4), with a ridge board sometimes set up against this overhang on the other side of the roof for added protection (5, 7). In Norway (8) and Croatia (9) (where this design was carried by the Ostrogoths), the peak may be capped by a contoured or grooved-out ridge member. The practice of capping the ridge with two boards (10 and 11) is not advisable, since they tend to warp excessively, resulting in leakage.

● 111

Fig 133
Silesian shingle maker cutting the groove in a shingle. A number of shingles are clamped together, wide edge up, in the shingle maker's bench. Using a two-edged grooving tool known as a *nuteisen* or *nippel* (cf. Fig **123/10** to **123/13**), the craftsman grooves each shingle, first to the right, then to the left.

Fig 134
Farmhouse in Ebene Reichenau (Kärnten), shingled in two different nailed styles. On the older roof, at left, the shingles are laid side by side in single courses offset from one another (cf. Fig **132/8** and **132/9**). The only exception is the eaves course, which is doubled. The newer roofing, at right, shows double layers of shingles in each course. On the other hand, the courses overlap only slightly (cf. Fig **132/4**, **132/5**, **132/10** and **132/11**). On the more recent roof, the individual rows are three times as wide and offset twice as much as on the older roof, giving it a more rugged appearance.

To provide added protection against the elements, the courses of shingles were at times overlapped to such an extent that a vertical section shows as many as five layers.

At the hips, the courses of shingles may be continued right on over this feature (Figs **143**, **146**, **147**, **148**, **149** and **153**). In order to fit properly, the shingles actually at the hip and those adjacent to them must be narrowed at the top; the taper being more pronounced, the flatter the pitch. Furthermore, the weather exposure must not be too great, or to put it another way, the shingles must not be too long. In instances where they are long, the hips are covered with special shingles, overlapping in pairs (Figs **150**, **151**, **152** and **154**), or capped with boards, as seen in Fig **134**.

Valleys are treated in similar fashion, with the rows of shingles run on over them, provided that the shingles are not excessively long or the slope too flat (Figs **142**, **150** and **153**).

Nailed shingling allows the gable edge of the roof to be cut back at an angle (Figs **155** and **156**), or the addition of a design accent in the form of a sweeping eaves line, as in Fig **157**.

135

Figs 135 to 138

The stave church at Borgund, Norway, dating from the middle of the twelfth century. Fig **135** shows a view from the south-west. Fig **136** is a portion of the church from the south. Fig **137**, part of the west facade. Fig **138**, west portal.

With the exception of the lower gallery or *sval*, the entire structure is covered with shingles, nailed to board sheathing (*cf.* Fig **132/8**). At the peak, the shingles are covered by cockscomb ridgework or *bust*, decorated with patterned cut-outs and dragon's heads, the latter added during renovations in 1738. The hips are covered with boards as well, although of lighter construction, not unlike an inverted eavestrough. Where sloping roof surfaces intersect, the shingles meet a slightly dished-out wooden valley. The barge boards are shingled in unique fashion, with the shingles alternately overlapped at right angles; one row on the gable edge of the roof, and the other on the verge board.

136

137

138

139

140

141

Figs 139 to 141
Nailed-shingle roofs from Salzburg province, Austria. In Fig **139**, the rows of shingles have been carried over onto the gable board, with the roof shingles covering the edges of the gable-board shingles. In Fig **140**, where the entire gable has been shingled, the roof shingles are laid on a gable-board or barge-board set out from the wall. The third item (Fig **141**) is akin to the first, except that both shingles and gable-board have been scalloped to form decorative trimwork, which looks frivolous and affected.

142

Fig 142
Shingled tent-like structures in a Swedish military camp. The rows of shingles encircling the conical roofs rise over the very flat valleys of the dormers in a gently arching curve. Even the peaks have been neatly shingled.

143

144

145

Fig 143
Bell tower from Stasjö in eastern Jämtland (Sweden), built by Pal Person, a farmer, in 1778–1779. On the octagonal cupola, the rows of fish-scale shingles are run on over the hips, requiring special fitting of the individual shingles at this point.

Figs 144 and 145
Nailed-shingle roof on a shed in Turrach, Steiermark (Austria), showing suspended eavestrough from dished out half-log with decorative end treatment. The shingles clearly show the warping resulting from working of the wood.

146

Fig 146
Nailed-shingle roof from Reinersdorf, Kreuzburg district, Silesia. The rows of grooved shingles are run over the hips in continuous bands. Since the shingles are inclined at the hips, they must be narrower at the top than at the bottom. To maintain the rhythm of the shingle widths, that is to say, to prevent the hip shingles from becoming too wide at the bottom and too narrow at the top, the butt line of the courses is pulled up slightly over the hips.

Fig 147
Roofs of grooved shingles from the Transylvanian *Erzgebirge*. To assure a tight weatherproof roof at the eaves, the starter course has been doubled. At the hip, the usual shingles have been used, but cut back toward the top on the narrow side with only a drawknife. This has preserved a uniform rhythm in the visible width of the shingles. To keep the hip shingles from having to be too narrow at the top, while maintaining the same butt width over the hip, short undercourses resembling the peak of a cap were added.

148

Figs 148, 149 and 150
Roofs of groove-edged shingles from Transylvania.
Fig **148** East Germanic style polygon barn from the Transylvanian *Erzgebirge*. Fig **149** From a farmstead in the Törzburger Pass, with gable roof joining at the hip. Fig **150** Dwelling in the Transylvanian *Erzgebirge*, showing valley shingling and eyebrow dormer.

149

150

151

152

Figs 151 and 152
Shingle roofs including decorative motifs from the *Széklerland* in Transylvania. The hips are covered by pairs of shingles running up and down the roof. At the ridge, the shingles on the weather side have been run over the peak and cut into decorative patterns consistent with the thin material of the shingle. In Fig **152**, which incorporates an East Germanic overhanging entryway, the roof has been given an exuberant touch by doubling the roof boarding roughly one third the way up, creating an interesting stepped effect.

Fig 153
Shingled eyebrow dormer from the Törzburger Pass in
Transylvania. The eaves board is in two pieces,
overlapped like the shingles.

Fig 153a
Nailed shingle roof with dormers and eyebrows from
Dürnstein an der Donau (Austria). Note how the
horizontal rows of shingles have been carried on over the
arching eyebrows.

154

Fig 154
Hip and half-hip covered with large shingles, from Arriach
(Kärnten), Austria. Because of the difficulty of achieving a
weatherproof fit using ridge boards, the ridge has been
extended beyond the top of the hip in both instances.

156

155

157

Figs 155, 156 and 157
Nailed-shingle roofs, showing a cut-back gable edge and a
sweeping eaves line. Fig **155** from the Millstätter See,
Kärnten. Fig **156** from the Black Forest (Germany).
Fig **157** from Ebene Reichenau (Kärnten), Austria.

Boarded Roofs

The boarded roof as we know it today is the most recent form of wooden roofing, as the boards are obtained by sawing. The earlier form used planks, two of which would be riven and broadaxed from a log.

Because of a board's larger dimensions, the impact of warping is more severe and the tendency to check is more pronounced than with shingles; something which must be borne in mind when the boards are sawn from the logs. Roof boards may be overlapped (Figs **158** and **159**) or applied in double layers (Figs **160** and **161**), with no more than a single nail per board in the horizontal nailing pattern.

158

Figs 158 to 161
Boarded roofs from the *Széklerland* in Transylvania (Figs **158** to **160**) and from Ebene Reichenau in Austria (Fig **161**). The boards are overlapped in the first three examples, while the roof of the fourth is a double layer of boards, touching one another side by side. With its several rows of roof boards, Fig **158** represents an intermediate stage between shingled and boarded roofs. In Fig **159**, a second row has been nailed on only at the ridge, setting it out in frieze-like fashion. Here, as in Figs **158** and **160**, the

159

160

161

boards on the weather side have been extended beyond
the ridge line. In Fig **160**, the boards have been
overlapped in a herring-bone pattern at the ridge, creating
a distinctive and interesting effect. The roofing in Fig **161**
is simply two layers of boards laid side by side. The peak is
capped by two ridge boards running lengthwise.

Roofs of Stone

A unique form of roofing is found in the southern cantons of Switzerland, where slabs of gneiss are used, somewhat in the manner of loose-laid shingles. Usually about 6 cm in thickness (Fig **162**), these slabs of stone may be as much as 90 cm long when carefully cut, and 60 cm wide (Fig **163**). The material is laid over very stout horizontal roof battens, with either one or two layers interposed between the pieces actually touching the supports. This makes them lie flatter than the pitch of the roof, a feature which, in combination with the great inherent weight of the material, prevents them from slipping out of place. To make the slabs lie flat at the eaves as well, a transition into the horizontal must be created by extending the ceiling beams (Fig **163**).

In Norway, roofs of stone may also be found here and there, their large slabs slightly overlapped and applied much in the fashion of the slate roofs of Germany (Fig **164**).

Fig 162
Stone roofed hay sheds from Kippel (Lötschberg) in the Valais, Switzerland. The gneiss roofing has been applied in extremely primitive fashion, and wooden shingles have had to be added as patching because of the rough cut of the stone.

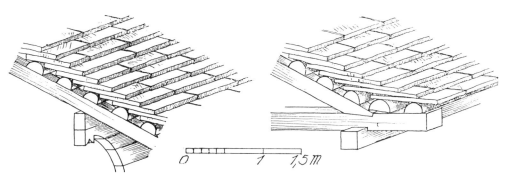

Fig 163
Stone roof of gneiss slabs from Canton Ticino, Switzerland. The great weight of the material and the fact that the individual slabs lie almost flat preclude any need for additional fastening.

Fig 164
Log hut with slate covered roof from Hardanger, Norway.

123

Roof Framing

When gables are of log construction, the settling of the logwork affects the entire structure right up to the roof framing. For this reason, the supports for the roof purlins within the roof area must settle accordingly, meaning that they must rest on a full-log or stub-log wall (Fig 165). If, however, the roof framing consists of uprights and purlins or is of collar-tie design with angled bracing, the reverse is the case, and the gable must be built so as to preclude settling (Fig 166).

In the first mentioned situation, where the design is a purely log-built one, the rafters rest on purlins and are free to move as the building settles; being held firmly only at the ridge purlin (Figs 165 and 167 to 171). In Sweden, some builders used a type of framing in which the rafters are seated firmly into the plate log, with the freedom of movement being allowed at the ridge (Fig 168/5 and 168/6). However, this technique causes problems with the roofing and is therefore only acceptable on sod roofs.

One additional point in this context is that settling is more pronounced on the sunny side of a building than on the shaded side.

By themselves, log gables are not structurally stable, and hence require some form of lateral reinforcement. This is clearly demonstrated by Fig 172, where, in effect, two log walls connected by short log ties have been placed side by side. In addition to partition walls and log-built stub-walls or cross-walls, purlins generally provide the necessary bracing and support (Fig 165). In the absence of purlins, gables must be braced by keying-in a longitudinal tie beam (Fig 173).

Over the years, a wide variety of approaches has been used to combine the roof rafters with log-built gables (Figs 174 and 175). However, all of these old framing techniques demand that the timber be fully air dried, and that the log walls have completely settled. The most advisable approach is to set a pair of rafters against the outside of the gable wall, so that the log wall can settle unhindered (Fig 175/2).

Originally, the houses built by the Germanic peoples were of open ceiling design. It

Fig 165 (opposite)
Purlin roof framing, supported by log walls or stub-wall uprights of logwork, thus assuring uniform settling. To reduce the distance spanned by the purlins, they have been set on head trees. In item **1**, a short stub wall has been combined with the head trees, simultaneously providing reinforcement for the gable walls. In **2**, the head

165

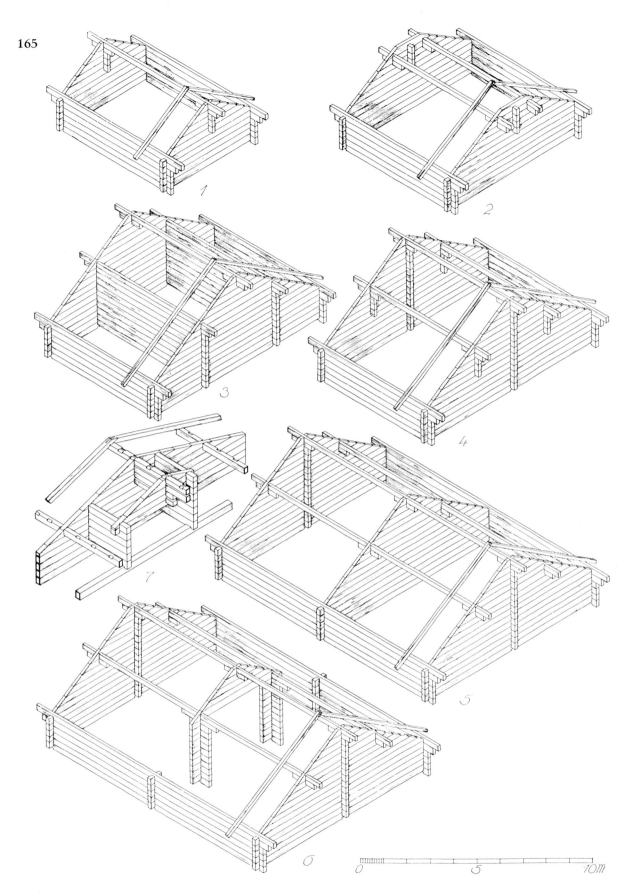

trees and the keyed-in stub walls are separate. In **3**, the middle purlins are carried by longitudinal partition walls. In **4**, the head tree under the ridge purlin rests on a stub-wall of short keyed-in cross-pieces running the full height of the building, while only a short stub-wall in the gables supports the middle purlins. Item **5** shows half-span support provided by a partition wall parallel to the gables, making it possible to dispense with the short stub-wall supports for the secondary purlins. In **6**, stub-walls of interlocked cross-pieces were used instead of a full partition wall of logs. In **7** (from a farm house in Eggstetten, Upper Bavaria), a system of beautifully designed logwork has been used to support the ridge purlin.

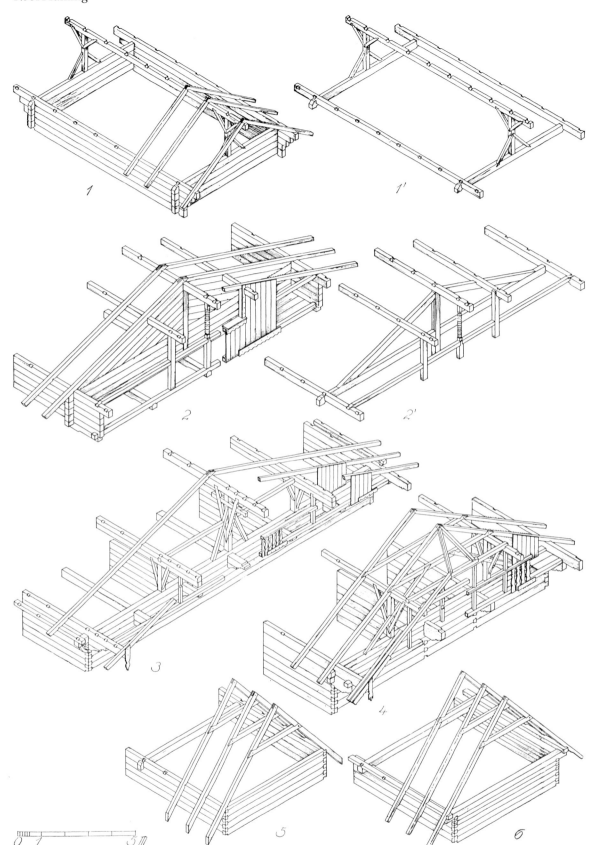

Fig 166
Roof framing techniques relatively independent of shrinkage in the logwork. As the log walls settle, these roof structures come down with them, while retaining their shape (**1**). This applies even to a design such as that shown in **2**, from the Oberpfalz region of Bavaria, where the gable is of diagonal logwork, because when the lower ends of the logs on which the middle purlins rest are held fast,

they act like a brace, which, combined with the king post, forms a firmly interlocked unit. In **3** and **4** (both from Salzburg province, Austria) provision for settling can also be seen in the framing of the overhanging roofs. While the eaves plates and their supports form a unit with the log walls, bracing is used on the middle purlins. Because these structures do not move, the rafters can be notch-fitted into the purlins. Like the previous examples, **5** from

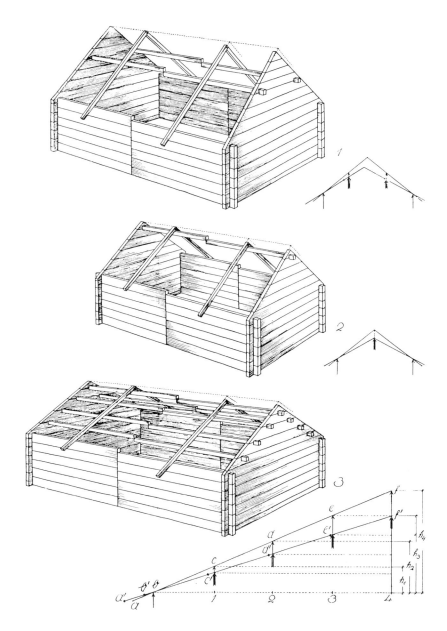

Fig 167 (above)
Showing how the shrinking of the log walls affects the rafters in purlin-style roof framing. When the purlins rest on a log wall, they too change position as the logwork settles. Expressed in terms of a triangle, this means a reduction in height and hence a shortening of the sides. In this illustration, the rafters form the sides of the triangle. During settling, the point at which the rafters rest on the purlins also changes. To prevent this from causing problems, the rafters must be free to move; being held fast only at the ridge (**2** and **3**). If no ridge purlin is used, and the rafters simply rested on the other purlins without notching, the stability of the roof will suffer (**1**), since the rafters are now without any firm support. To more clearly illustrate the situation, shrinkage equal to one quarter of the height has been assumed in the accompanying diagrams.

Oberösterreich province and **6** from the Transylvanian *Erzgebirge* are also examples of rigid roof framing. The difference highlighted here between log walls which settle and rigid roof framing which does not precludes a log gable in the latter case. With rigid roof framing, the gables must be sheathed or timber-framed (**3** and **4**).

● 127

is highly lamentable that we have abandoned this feature, as its value is not merely aesthetic, but economical as well. In the following sequence of illustrations from Figs **176** to **197**, the reader will find a wealth of design possibilities which are not only economical in terms of construction, but which at the same time surpass the boxed-in structures of today in beauty and comfort.

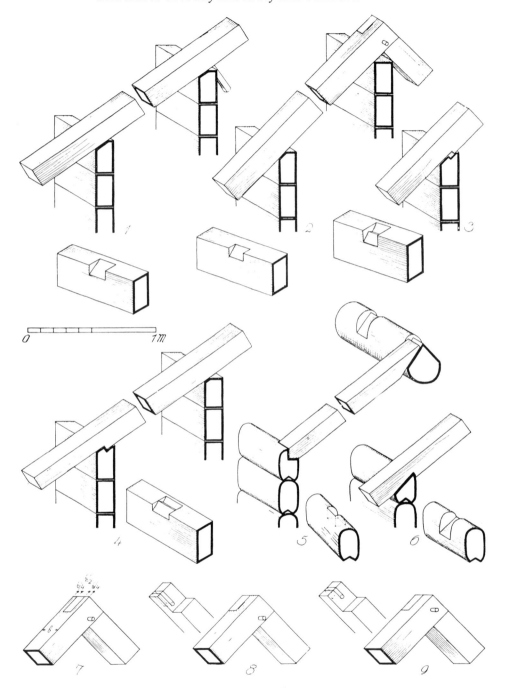

Fig 168

Fitting rafters to allow for settling. On a shed roof (**1**), the rafters are hung from the ridge using wooden pegs and notched into the lengthwise support members to keep them in place as they slide downward. The reverse approach may also be taken by cutting a birdsmouth into the rafter and securing it at the foot, so that the movement is upward toward the peak as the building settles (**4**). Similar methods are employed on gable roofs (**2**, **5** and **6**). At the ridge, rafters may be halved and pinned, or notch-fitted. Alternatively, a birdsmouth or lock notch may be cut into the foot of the rafter. In this latter case, an especially sturdy ridge purlin is called for. However, the upward-moving rafters may also be secured at the foot (**3**), but only after the log walls have completely settled, which involves allowing room for this process. In tenoned or half-lapped joints at the ridge (**7** to **9**), it is important that the distance from the peg hole to the end grain of the rafters be as great as possible to provide maximum strength.

Fig 169
Dwelling with shed roof from Münster (Valais),
Switzerland. The rafters are hung by (crooked) wooden
pegs at the ridge. The ceilings of both storeys are built in
the style known in Switzerland as the *Wölbi*, meaning a
sloped design in which the ceiling boards are groove-fitted
into a joist on the longer side of the house. A regular level
board floor is then laid atop this upward sloping ceiling.
The joists, which resemble ridge beams here, are visible
externally.

170a

170b

Figs 170a and 170b
Shed-roofed utility buildings from Kärnten province,
Austria. In **170a**, loose-laid shingles rest on wall and
purlins. The side walls carrying the purlins add to the
sense of upward motion. In **170b**, the place of the log side
walls has been taken by rafters resting on posts and the
hillside itself, while stout roof slats or battens have been
used instead of purlins. These two structures, while
makeshift, nonetheless illustrate the two alternative
approaches to framing a shed-type roof in log
construction.

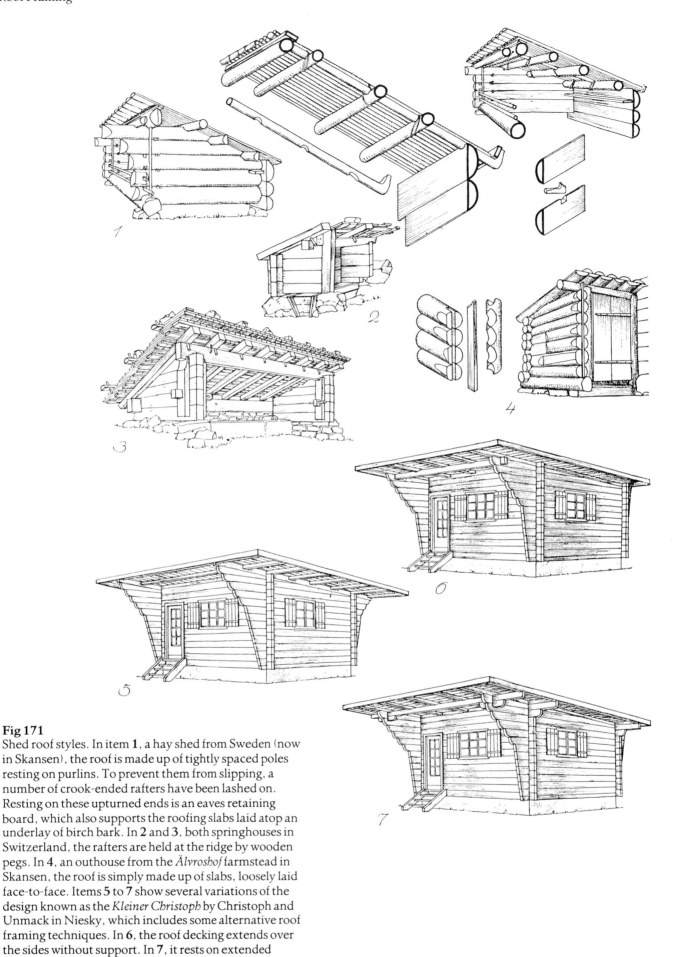

Fig 171
Shed roof styles. In item **1**, a hay shed from Sweden (now in Skansen), the roof is made up of tightly spaced poles resting on purlins. To prevent them from slipping, a number of crook-ended rafters have been lashed on. Resting on these upturned ends is an eaves retaining board, which also supports the roofing slabs laid atop an underlay of birch bark. In **2** and **3**, both springhouses in Switzerland, the rafters are held at the ridge by wooden pegs. In **4**, an outhouse from the *Älvroshof* farmstead in Skansen, the roof is simply made up of slabs, loosely laid face-to-face. Items **5** to **7** show several variations of the design known as the *Kleiner Christoph* by Christoph and Unmack in Niesky, which includes some alternative roof framing techniques. In **6**, the roof decking extends over the sides without support. In **7**, it rests on extended rafters, and in **5** it is carried by purlins alone in the style of the Scandinavian purlin roof.

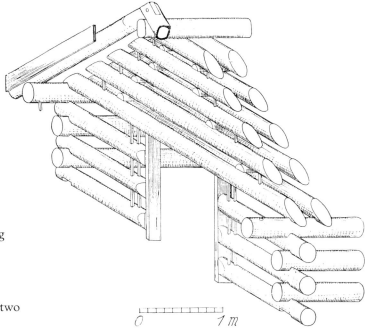

Fig 172
Double log gable on a hay barn in Zell am See, Salzburg
province (Austria). Since simple dowelling would not
provide adequate structural stability for the gable
logwork, two log walls were erected at the gable and
joined by short cross-members. The construction
technique is akin to that used to tie together and brace two
opposite walls, or two walls set close together.

0 [........] 1 m

Fig 173
Norwegian storehouse (*bur*) from Snartland, and a log
house (*arestue*) from Grove, dating from 1704. In the
upper building, both gable walls are strengthened and
reinforced by a longitudinal tie-beam. In the lower one,
two purlins serve the same function. In addition, the
weight of the roof in this case necessitated the inclusion of
a cross-tie.

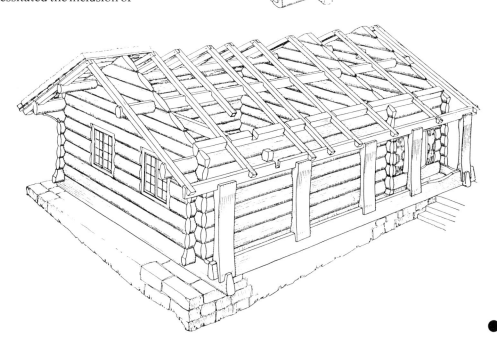

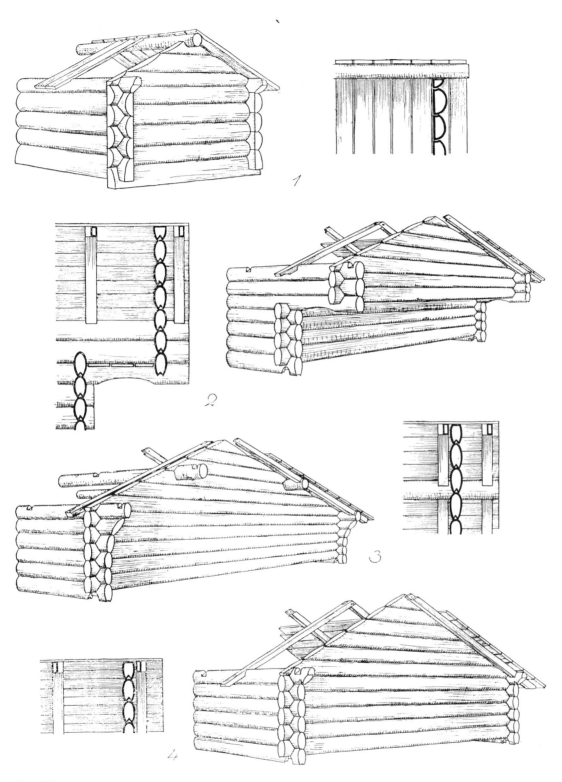

Fig 174
Gable-roof systems. In item **1**, from the Setesdal valley
(Norway), the plank roof extends beyond the gable. In **2**,
from Vest-Agder, one pair of rafters sits out beyond the
gable wall, with the roof boarding touching the edge of the
gable. Item **3**, from Morgedal, involves a pair of rafters
laid against the inside of the gable wall to make a tight and
secure fit where the roof meets the gable. Item **4** shows the
same on the outside.

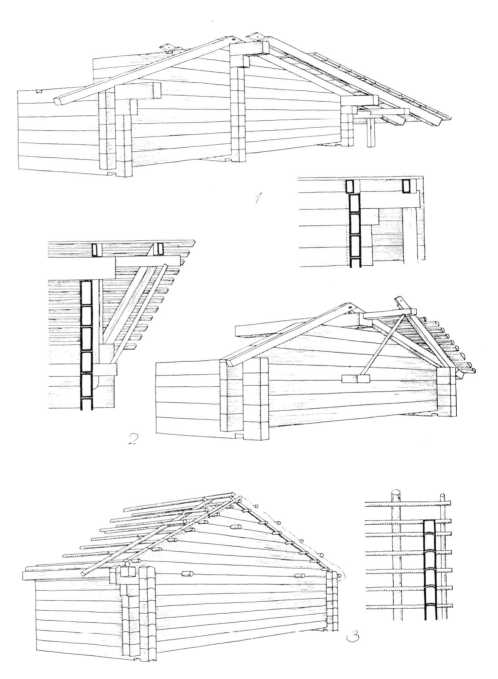

Fig 175
Additional roof-gable systems. In item **1**, from the Valais,
one pair of rafters is laid flush with the log wall, requiring
that the logwork have fully dried and settled. In **2**, from
Kippel, also in the Valais (Switzerland), a pair of rafters is
touching the outer wall surface. Notice also the makeshift
arrangement in which the overhanging roof, which is
covered with slabs of stone, is supported by a pair of
rafters inclined outward from the plate. In **3**, from
Uppland (Sweden), the roof of loose-laid thatch rests on
the edge of the gable.

Fig 176

Storehouse or *härbre* from Kråkberg (Sweden). The roof system is of split logs running parallel to the sides of the structure. The rounded logwork of the side walls is blended into the slab ceiling, forming a sloping log wall, as it were. Over the ceiling slabs are sheathing boards seated on crook-ended spur rafters which rest on purlins. Over these, in turn, is a layer of birch bark, followed by sheathing boards running up and down the roof, and finally saddle boards interlocked at the peak and covering the gaps in the underlying boarding. A retaining board resting on crook-ended rafters at the eaves prevents the entire roof skin from slipping.

The floor planks of the ground storey extend under the walls right out to the exterior wall line. In the upper storey, the fact that the logs all appear similar in shape and are all horizontal creates an impression of exceptional unity. However, because the walls and ceiling look exactly the same, a closed-in and oppressive atmosphere is created. The sloping ceiling of the upstairs gives the impression of log walls on a tilt.

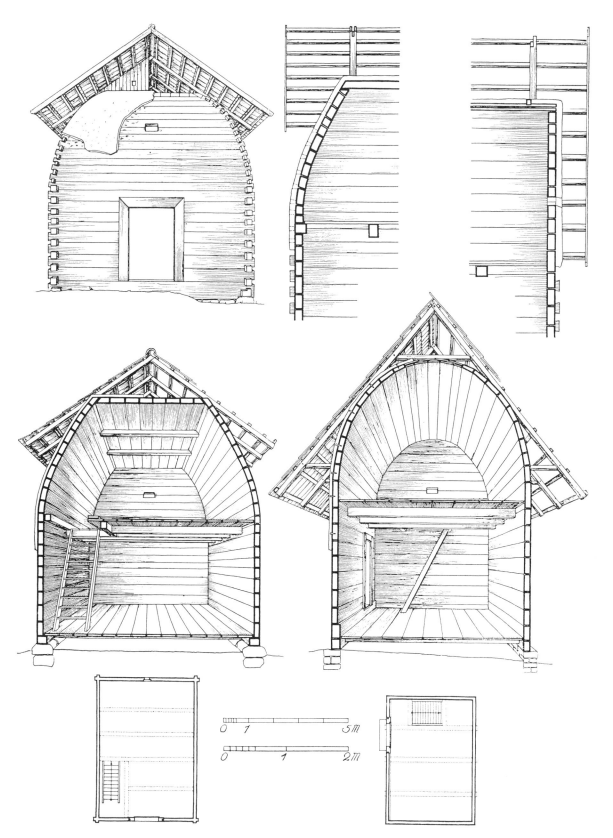

Fig 177
Corn granaries from Mittenbrück (left) and Leschane (right), both in Cosel district, Silesia. The unique design consists of a separate enclosed structure with a roof perched atop it like a wide-brimmed hat. The granary at left originally had a hip roof of straw. The exterior is completely plastered over with a 6 cm thick coating of mud and chaff, held in one case by a roughened surface and by wooden pegs in the other. In the building at right, a double layer of overlapped boards has been inserted at the top of the arched ceiling in place of logs to allow for shrinkage. The two beams which intrude into the upper storey of the granary at left give special accent to the ceiling, emphasizing their supporting function, and thus eliminating the danger of a closed-in appearance. Notice the arched ceiling of the right hand structure. The atmosphere created by this design suffers from the arch starting down too low on the wall, as it should always start above head height. As it is here, the impression created is that of being inside a huge barrel.

Fig 178
Fruit storehouse from Altreu, Canton Solothurn. The
rafters rest on the ridge purlin and two eaves plates carried
by extensions of the gable wall. The straw roof is sheathed
from the inside. Below this protective sheathing, a tongue-
and-groove plank ceiling has been installed running from
gable to gable and generally following the incline of the
roof. The wide boards make an effective contrast to the
wall logs. This avoids the problem of them having the
same appearance as the log walls.

Fig 179
Log house with central hearth or *eldhus* from Fåsås. The rafters of half-logs are placed side by side in the age-old manner, and carried by a ridge purlin and the plate logs. On top of this, which in itself forms a complete roof, a layer of birch bark is laid, in turn covered by closely spaced saddle logs. Because the rafters which form the ceiling run in a different direction from the main logwork, and since the support provided by the ridge purlin is clearly visible, the whole is sure to provide a pleasing and striking impression.

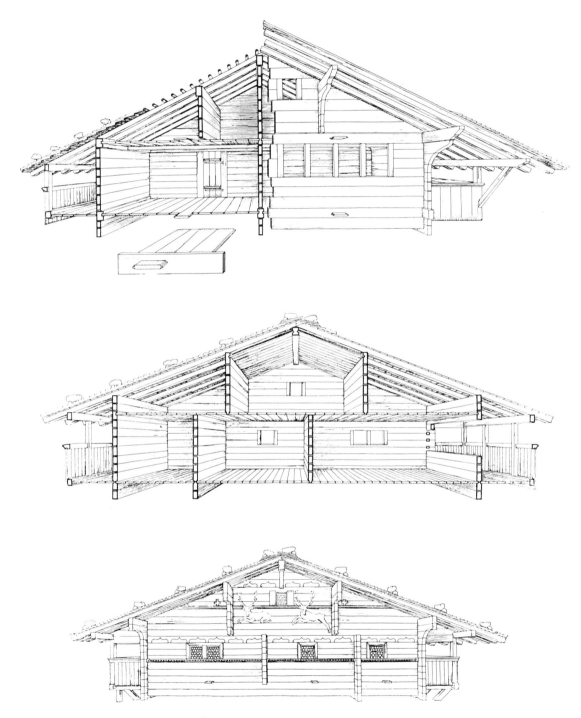

Fig 180
Swiss farm houses from Matten, Interlaken (above) and Ernen, in the Valais (middle and below). The upper floor, which is covered by a roof of weighted and loose-laid shingles, has been utilized to its full height in both buildings. In the top house, no special attention has yet been devoted to the layout or floor plan of this upper area; this being dictated rather by the interior framing system. In the second building, on the other hand, the centre wall has been omitted to create a pleasant room. The roof-supporting function of this wall has been taken over by a ridge purlin. Also added, despite the fact that the shingles are resting on sheathing boards, is a board ceiling matching the slope of the roof. In addition to the insulation against heat and cold which this ceiling provides, it helps create a room with a most attractive appearance.

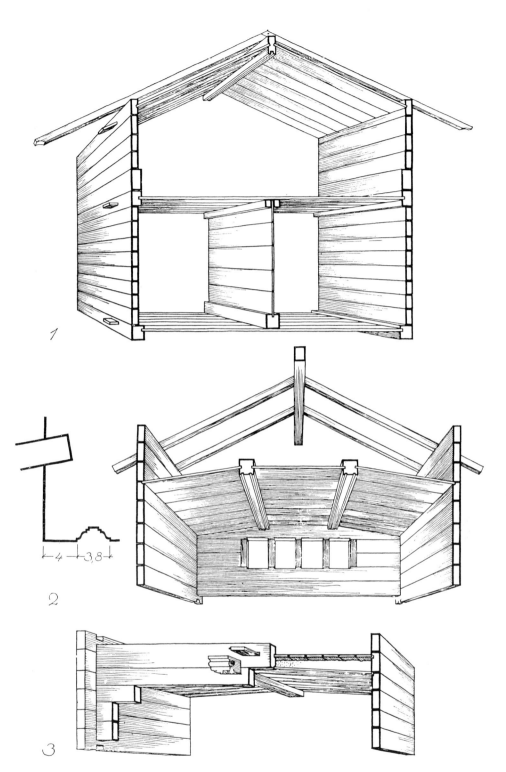

Fig 181
Sectional detail of a cheese shed from: **1** Böningen, Canton Bern; **2** a dwelling in Stalden, Valais; and **3** a house from Kippel, Valais.

The building in **1** has a boarded ceiling following the incline of the roof beneath a four-ply loose-laid shingle roof on sheathing boards. Just as in the horizontal ceiling and floor below it, this ceiling features a set of tapered boards fitted into the middle of the ceiling, one of which is left protruding, to be gradually driven in to keep the boards tightly together. The East Germanic peoples who emigrated to the Valais of Switzerland brought with them the ancient Germanic tradition of the open ceiling, which appeared in the form of a ceiling angled upward slightly toward the middle rather than being horizontal. The design is known in the vernacular of this region as a *Wölbi* (**2** and **3**). If the floor above this ceiling houses living or storage space, a separate horizontal floor is added above the *Wölbi* (**3**). Although angled only slightly, the effect of this design feature is sufficient to take from the ceiling any feeling of oppressiveness.

● 139

183

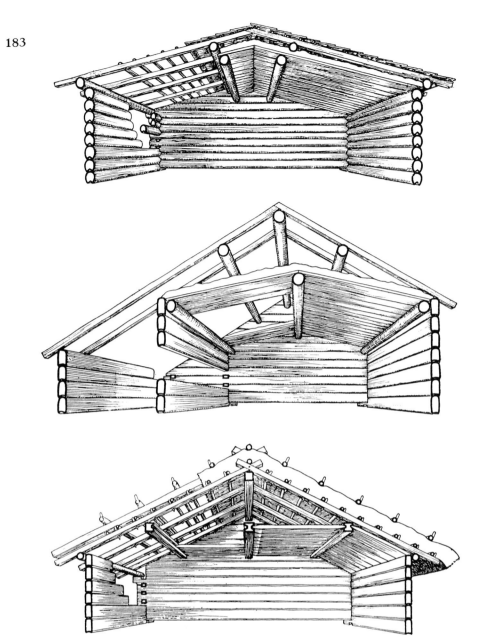

Fig 182
Interior of a dwelling from Stalden, featuring the inclined ceiling known as the *Wölbi*.

Fig 183
Woodsworker's cabin from Hälsingland, Norrland (above) and saunas from Väddö Island (middle) and Tallet, Aspnäs, Östervåla (below) in Uppland (Sweden).

The cabin is 4.90 m in width with a shingled roof. The foot of the rafters rests on an eaves purlin or plate set out slightly from the walls. This provides a broad base for a plank ceiling, each side of which is supported by an additional purlin. A layer of earth on top gives this extremely natural-looking structure effective and inexpensive insulation against heat and cold (in the drawing, a chimney opening in the middle of the roof has been omitted).

In the middle building, the interior width of which is 3.70 m, the ceiling rests on a centre purlin and two purlins pushed out against the walls. Insulation is the same as above.

In the lower building, we find a reoccurrence of several design elements from the previous buildings. The eaves plates, for example, are again set outward as in the woodsman's cabin. Also, the ceiling features a centre beam, as in the second building of this series. One refinement which occurs in this building is that the middle

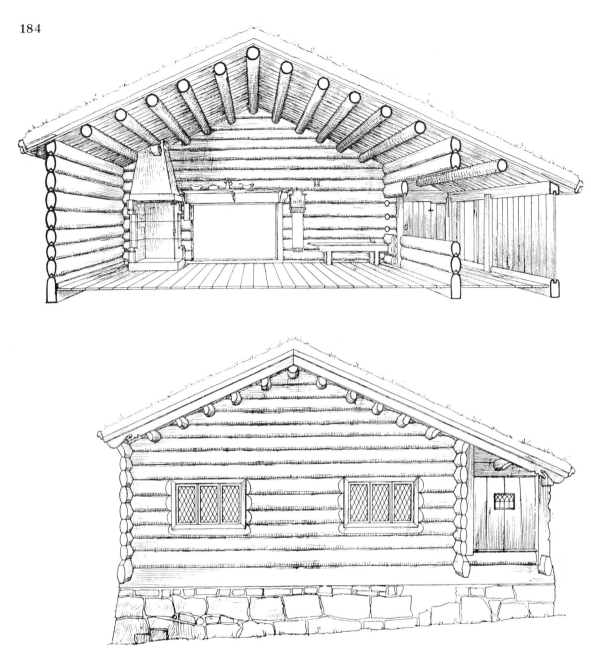

184

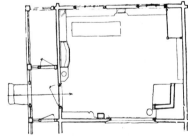

purlins which support the straw-thatched roof also hold
the ceiling boards, which are groove-fitted into them and
the central beam.

All three buildings show full utilization of the space
enclosed by roof and walls. To use this style as a basis for
modern-day applications, additional interior support
would be called for to create partitions, etc.

Fig 184
Summer house from Lökre, dating from 1663, now in the
Sandvig Collection in Lillehammer. Main living area with
its room to the rear and porch (*sval*) are covered by a
unique type of purlin type roof, which excludes rafters.
The sheathing boards running parallel to the gable edge
rest directly on the purlins. The eaves retaining board is
held by oversize wooden pegs, which penetrate the bark
covering, thus being protected against rain and snow. The

heads of these pegs are covered by an eaves board fitted
with a drip-cap. The design of the ceiling seems to set it
apart in picturesque fashion as an entity unto itself. The
manner in which the purlins rise toward the ridge dispels
the closed-in atmosphere inherent in a ceiling with low
horizontal beams. The walls of the side porch are timber-
framed with vertical staving in the old Norwegian style
known as *reisverk*.

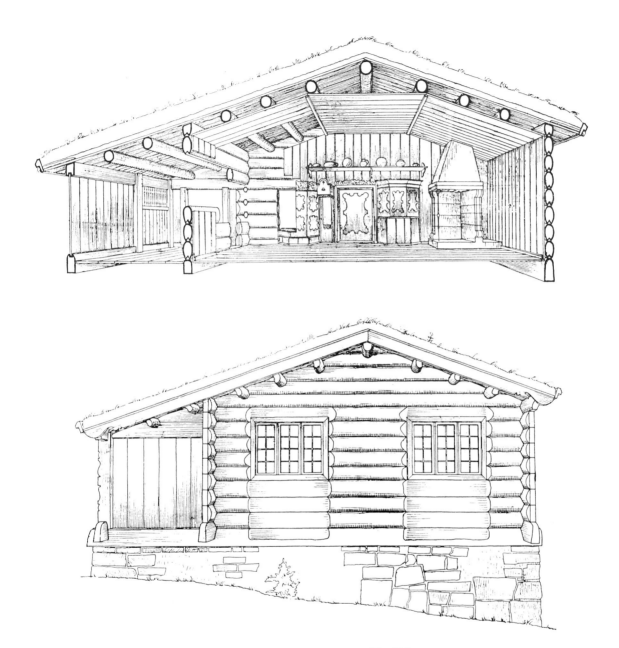

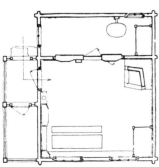

Fig 185

Winter house from Vigstad, dating from 1709, now in the Sandvig Collection in Lillehammer. Main living area and side porch (*sval*) are covered by a purlin roof. During alterations in 1811, the walls of the living room were vertically panelled; the theme being continued in a board ceiling nailed to the purlins. Wooden strips cover the two joints in the ceiling where the boards change direction. Excluding the gable walls, all of the sheathing boards run in the same direction, vertical, horizontal and inclined alike. Because of this, the interior seems too much like a wooden crate. If the main logwork of the building could be seen instead of being hidden, this unsettling appearance would vanish, to be replaced by one of hominess.

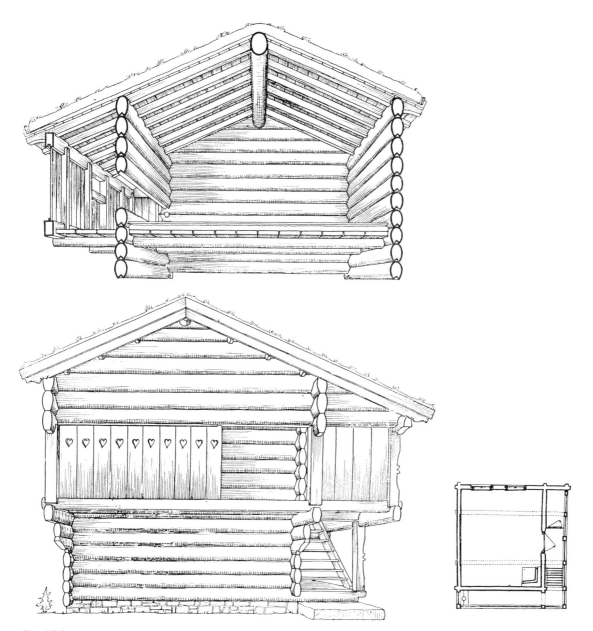

Fig 186
Elevated cabin, known as the Per Gynt House, from
Nordgard Hågå, near Vinstra; c. 1700. Now in the
Sandvig Collection in Lillehammer (Norway). The roof is
a single purlin structure, with the rafters resting on a ridge
purlin. Accordingly, the sheathing runs parallel to the
eaves. The retaining board at the eaves is held by crooked
wooden pegs, which are kept dry by the layer of birch bark
covering them. The wall of the side porch, carried by the
extended ceiling joists of the storey below, is timber
framed with the spaces between the uprights filled by
vertical planking in the Norwegian style. From the inside,
the rising rafters create an impression of increased space.
The heavy ridge purlin assures the eye of solid support for
the roof structure, the lightness of which stands out in
contrast to the heaviness of the log walls.

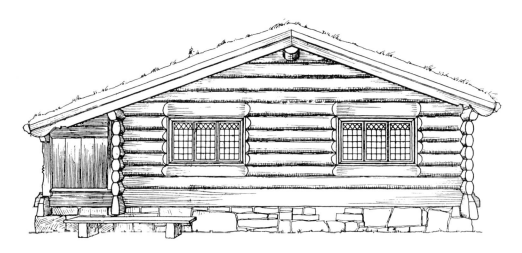

Fig 187
Guest house from the Hjeltar farmstead, from the year
1565, now in the Sandvig Collection in Lillehammer. The
rafters of the roof rest on a ridge purlin; in this instance a
markedly heavy log, required to bridge the long span. The
interplay between this heavy beam, the square-hewn
rafters and the sheathing provides a distinctive
counterpoint to the smoothed and chamfered logwork of
the interior. The outside wall of the covered porch (*sval*) is
again timber-framed and vertically boarded. At one end of
the living area, a narrow overhead balcony has been
created between the gable wall and a lateral tie beam,
beneath which a cosy dining nook has been set. The
balcony itself provides an effective storage area. This is an
excellent example of space utilization without impairing
the warm and homey atmosphere of the whole.

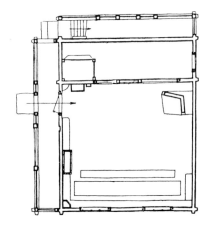

Fig 188
Main living area of the Mora house, Dalarna (Sweden),
now in Skansen (Stockholm). Seen suspended beneath the
rafters is one of two *kronstänger* which usually took the
form of decorated beams or bars and served to divide the
interior into three areas.

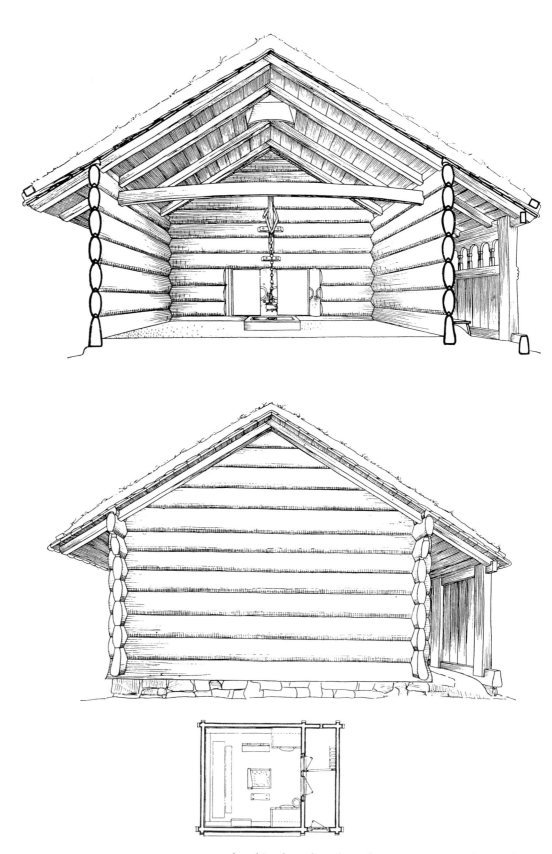

Fig 189
Open-hearthed interior of the Aamli house from Valle in the Setesdal valley from the end of the 17th century. Now in the *Norsk Folkemuseum* in Oslo. This *arestue* is covered by a rafters-only roof, which includes an opening above the hearth to allow both smoke to exit and light to enter (*Ljore*). The visible upreaching rafters and their covering of sheathing boards make a pleasant contrast to the nearly-oval profile of the wall logs. There is a hint of freedom in the slightly upward bow of the tie beam just above head height. Had the beam been run horizontal, it would have given an oppressive and closed-in feeling to the room, spoiling its agreeable atmosphere.

Fig 190
Interior of the Hjeltar house from Gudbrandsdalen,
Norway (1565) with *peis* or corner fireplace. Now in
Lillehammer.

Fig 191
Front parlor of the Bergmann house in Laxbro,
Västmanland (Sweden), *c.* 1650, now in Skansen,
Stockholm.

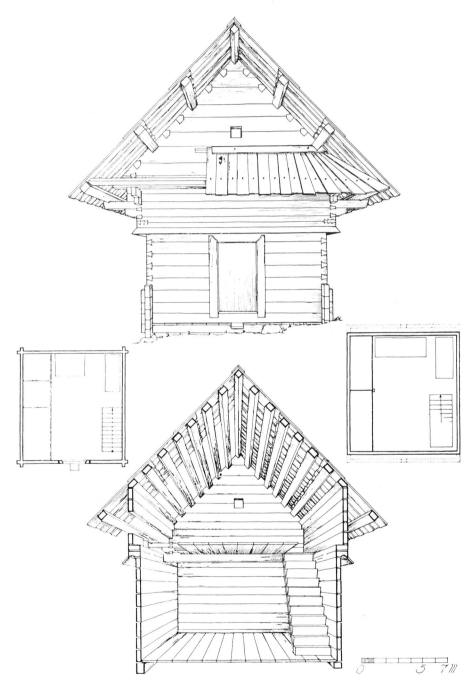

Fig 192

Grain storehouse or *Troadkasten* from the *Bodnerhof* farmstead in St. Oswald (Kärnten, Austria). The roof framing is reminiscent of the Scandinavian purlin roof. Here, too, no rafters have been used. The roof covering is a double layer of wooden shingles. To prevent entry from above, two smaller purlins have been placed between each of the main ones. One interesting feature is the five-sided member, half plate-log and half roof purlin, which is used to make the transition from wall to roof. The overhang of the upper storey was created by using two courses of wider logs as a base. To deter mice, the lower of the two logs forming the start of the overhang has been scooped out and fitted with a nailed-on board, known in the vernacular as a *Mauswihr* or mouse-guard.

Fig 193

The log storehouse *Zum Turken*, near Summiswald, Switzerland. This beautiful example of building in wood combines a purlin roof (without rafters) over the upper storey with two shed-type roofs of rafter construction covering side balconies or walkways. The former is sheathed with boards running parallel to the gable edge. On the shed roofs, the builder has contented himself with shingles over spaced boards or battens. The rafters of these side roofs have been notched into the plate logs of the main structure, the top ends flush with the inside wall. They receive added support from the headers of the galleries. The entire gallery structure is held upright by extensions of the gable logwork.

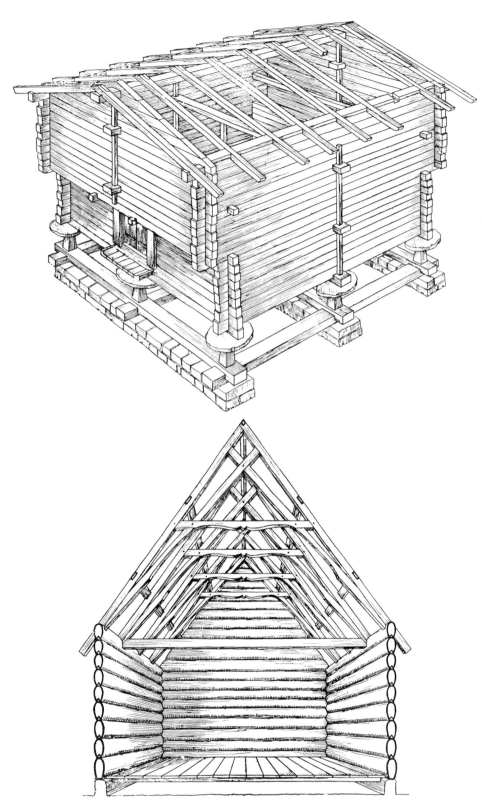

Fig 194
Structural detail of a barn from Ernen (Valais),
Switzerland, and the chapel of St. Olaf and the Blessed
Virgin Mary, dating from 1459, now in the outdoor
museum in Lillehammer. The log walls of the barn are
braced by vertical ties, and further strengthened by a
triple system of tie beams, the middle one of which is
interlocked at both ends with a vertical tie.

In the second structure, the tie beam has been notched
into the plate logs. In the first example, the rafters tend to
exert an inward force on the walls. In the second,
however, the pressure of the steep and typically
Scandinavian-style self-supporting roof is outward.
Unconsciously, the eye senses this interplay of structural
forces, without finding the tie beam an intrusion.

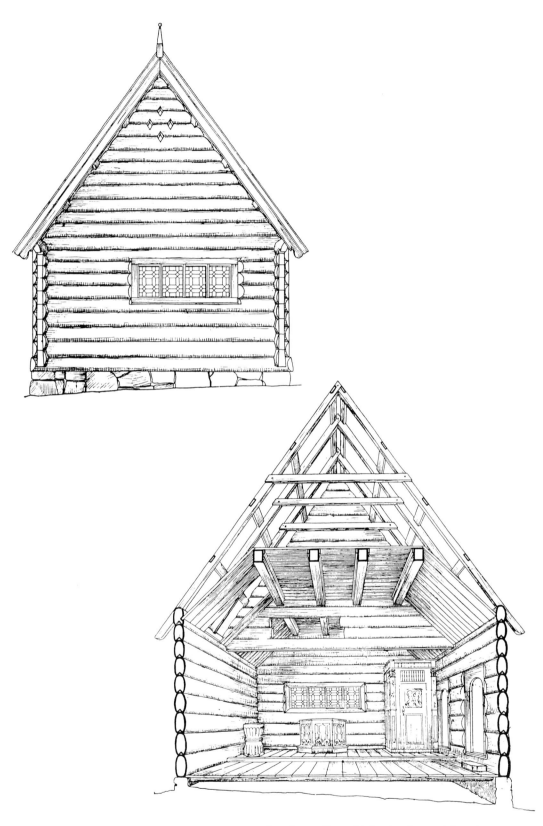

Fig 195
The Isum chapel on the *Bjrnstadhof* farmstead from Lalm in Vaagaa, Gudbrandsdalen (Norway) from the 16th century. Now in the outdoor museum in Lillehammer. The roof framing of the chapel is of collar beam construction, beneath which is a unique log wall rising upward from the tie log and filling the upper portion of the structure. This wall fulfills two functions; firstly, by supporting the purlins which take the roof sheathing, it removes some of the strain on the rafters. Secondly, it provides support for the four ceiling beams. Because it also reflects the division of the chapel into two parts, it appears appropriate to the interior design.

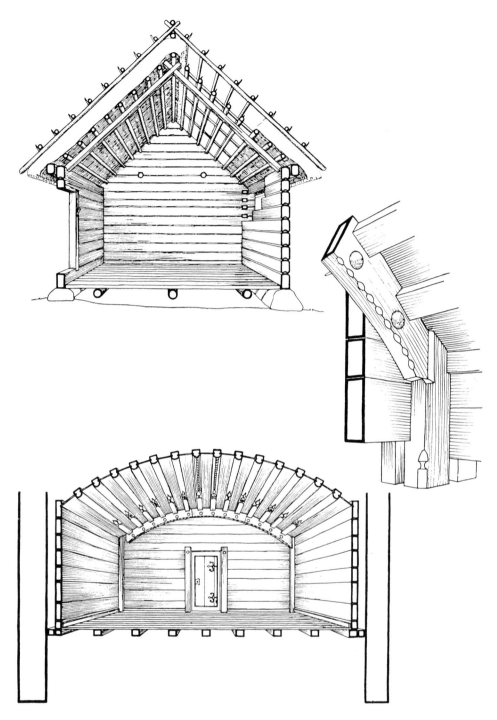

Fig 196
Fisherman's shanty from Marviken, Väddö Island
(Sweden) and a room from a solid masonry structure in
Villanders, near Klausen, Tirol (Austria), c. 1500. In the
shanty, which is 3.30 m wide inside, the poles carrying the
roof of straw thatch are notched into the joints between
the logs in the gable walls, and supported in the middle
by a pair of rafters. The style is reminiscent of the
Scandinavian purlin roof. The spacing of the poles is
governed on the one hand by the nature of the stalks of
straw, and by the size of the logs in the gable on the other.

The beams of the room depicted below (which measures
4.80 m across) rest on a curved beam spiked to the logwork
of the end walls. In this instance, spacing conforms to the

width of the groove-fitted boards paralleling the beams. In
evolutionary terms, if we neglect the Romans, this ceiling
was preceded by the pure plank ceiling. Here, every other
plank has given way to a beam. One notable feature here is
the size of the heads on the hand-forged spikes, and the
fact that they have been used to create a striking and lively
motif.

Fig 196a (opposite)
Late Gothic interior from Villanders, now in the *Tiroler
Volkskunstmuseum* in Innsbruck (*cf.* also Fig. **196** in which
a cutaway drawing of this room is shown, and Figs **278**,

196a

196b

280 and 281 which show the doors and door detail). These log walls are really nothing more than a covering over the outer walls of solid masonry; a striking illustration of how strongly the custom of living in a timber-built home persisted. However, the arched styling of the ceiling also points to the past. Its uplifting design hearkens back to the ancestral open ceiling of the early Germanic peoples.

Fig 196b
Late Gothic interior from Villanders in Tirol.

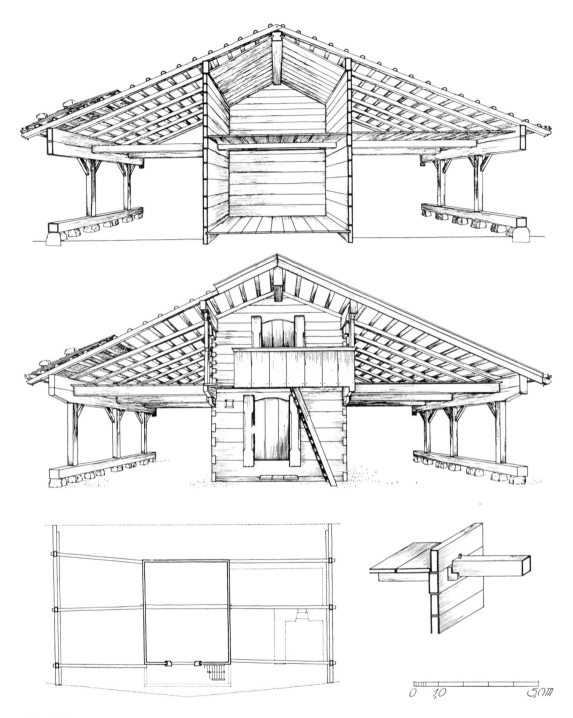

Fig 197
Storehouse from Schleching near Marquartstein,
Chiemgau, dating from 1675. The enclosed storehouse in
the centre is an entity unto itself, linked to the side bays
only by virtue of the rafters and the beams, which have
subsequently been inset and pegged to the sides of the
building. Upstairs in the storehouse, one end of the
boards forming the sloping ceiling is fitted into the
grooved-out ridge purlin, while the other is nailed to the
top logs, which in this case simultaneously represent
intermediate purlins. The structure as it stands now must
154 ● represent later additions to an original building.

Eaves Framing without Supporting Beams

In open-ceiling structures, the eaves framing is dictated by the nature of the roof system. Since the roof deck must be carried beyond the log walls to protect them, rafter-and-purlin framing, in which the rafters may be of any desired length, quite naturally provides the answer (*cf.* Figs **186** and **189**). On rafter type roofs, where the rafter is birdsmouth-seated at the plate, short angled tail-pieces have to be added (Fig **200/1**). On purlin roofs, lengthwise members serving the same purpose may also be used (Figs **176** and **192**). Log ends may also be carried out beyond the wall to take an eaves plate. If the upper storey is closed in by a boarded or planked floor, this does not mean any need to change the construction at the eaves (*cf.* Figs **198** and **199**). To provide greater headroom in the attic floor of a building, the floor was lowered some distance below the plate, where it may be set into grooves cut into the logwork (Fig **199/2**). Log building in Russia produced some unique eaves constructions. One such, featured in this book, involved log walls bowed outward to both form the eaves and carry the roof covering at the same time (Fig **201**).

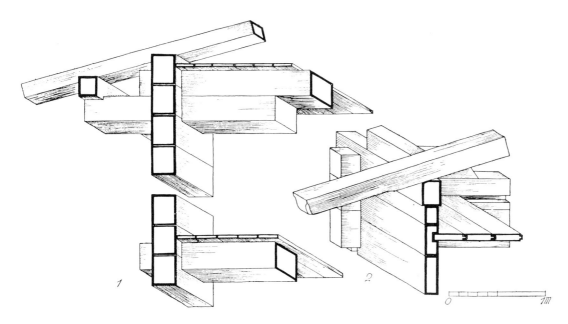

Fig 198
Eaves framing incorporating support from the log walls.
1 from Eggenstein, Lower Bavaria; **2** from Graubünden (Grisons), Switzerland. To provide the needed support for the long overhang of the rafter in **1**, a saddle or head tree has been placed under the joist and notch-fitted with the eaves plate. Since the broad overhang of this roof provides excellent protection from the rain, the ends of the logs beneath it may safely be extended. In the second piece of framing shown, the top log is also the eaves plate, which is why a heftier log has been used. To prevent it from being forced over, it has been interlocked with a short cross-piece at the partition wall.

● 155

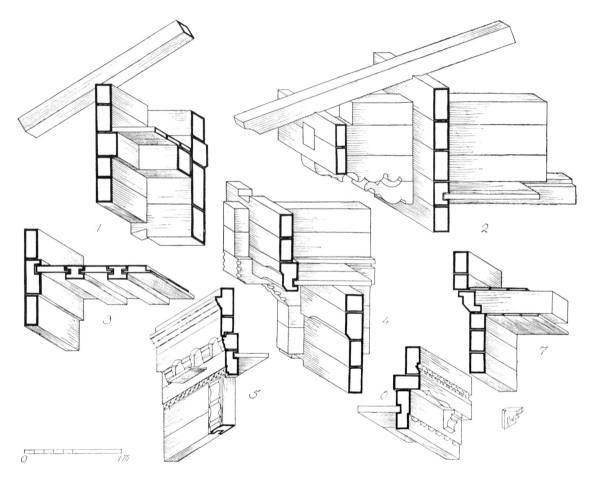

Fig 199

Ceiling and beam detail. **1** Berg, near Söllstein (Salzburg province, Austria); **2** Tegernsee, Germany; **3** Gösis, Wallgau (Vorarlberg province, Austria); **4** Brienz, Canton Bern (1602); **5** Meiringen, Canton Bern; **6** Böningen, Canton Bern; **7** Reuthe, Vorarlberg.

To allow greater headroom in the upper storey, the ceiling is set below the level of the plate. This applies equally to ceilings of boarded (**2**) or board-and-beam construction (**1**). Boarded ceilings are frequently grooved into the log walls. Accordingly, builders were fond of using a heavier log at this point, with the extra thickness of the log either on the inside (**3** and **4**) or on the outside (**5** and **6**). In the latter case, decorative patterns would at times be carved into this protruding woodwork. Obviously, timberframe and post-and-beam construction, which are related, were bound to exert their influence. Because the

necessary features for this type of embellishment are not present in boared ceilings, the logs themselves were simply shifted outward slightly to provide accent (**5**). If the centre line of the logs began to move dangerously close to the exterior wall line, console-like brackets would be notched into the logwork for added support (**6**). Only when the span between exterior and partition wall was short, as in **4**, where it is only 2.80 meters, would a builder venture to extend the upper floor out over these vertically intersecting walls. This slight overhang, formed only by the lengthwise logs, may also be found in conjunction with board-and-beam ceiling construction (**7**). During the Renaissance, ornamentation ruled the scene to such a great extent that some even went so far as to attempt imitation of the arched corbel table of stone architecture, an ill-fated departure which produced the most tangled compositions (**5**).

Eaves Framing with Beam Support

The dynamism clearly embodied in horizontal logwork may also be captured by ceiling beams when extended to carry rafters, rafter tail-pieces or eaves plates (Fig **200**). Anyone with a feel for the vitality and expressiveness of timber joinery will concur that protruding beam ends have great potential for visual appeal. After all, not even the Greeks and Romans of classical antiquity were able to create in their exclusively stone architecture anything like the eloquence of a beam of solid timber, having been compelled to imitate it in stone instead. Although the ends of the beams are boarded over in Fig **200/6**, this is somewhat atoned for by the fact that the skillfully worked tail-pieces are still visible.

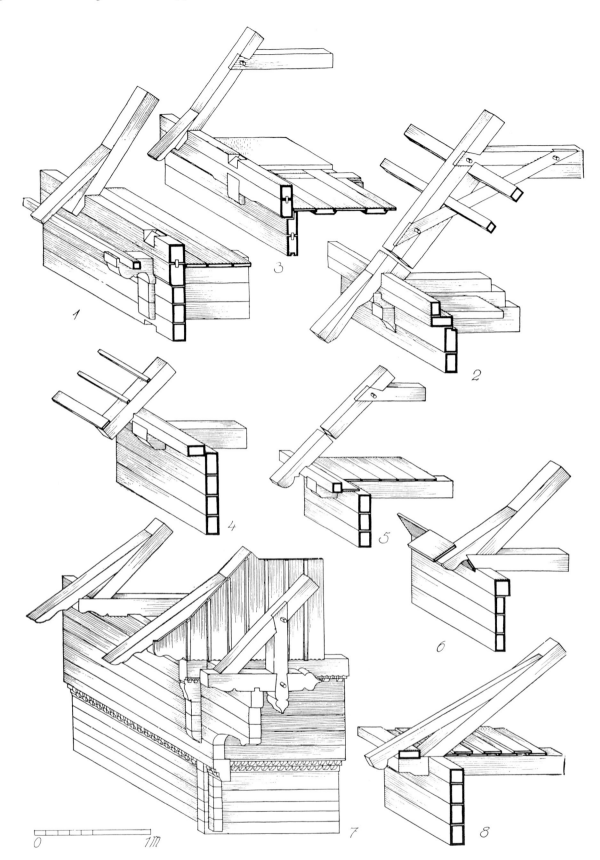

0   1m

Fig 200
Eaves framing. **1** Friedersdorf, Oberfranken, Germany
(1686); **2** Niederneuching, Upper Bavaria, Germany
(1581); **3** Neukenroth, Oberfranken (1606); **4** Willkassen,
Oletzko District, East Prussia; **5** Pempen, Memel District,
East Prussia; **6** Sonneborn, Mohrungen District, East
Prussia; **7** Rheintal, Vorarlberg; **8** Gilge, Labiau District,
East Prussia.

In **1** to **5**, the rafters are seated on an eaves plate, either
placed as a regular wall plate (**1**) or set out beyond the wall
and supported by projecting beams or joists. This
encompassed a broad array of alternative framing
techniques. For example, a wide underplate might be laid
beneath the wall plate to form the connection (**2**), or the
plate might be doubled and rabbeted into the log below,
as shown in **3**. Another style is to simply edge-butt the

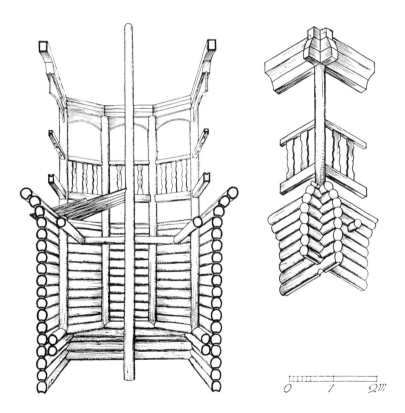

slightly overhanging plate against the exterior wall, as in
4. A similar approach involved the addition of a covering
board between plate and wall (5).

Item 1 includes a special extended purlin, designed
solely for support of the angled tail pieces. Items 6 to 8
show rafters tenoned into beams, the ends of which are
left showing (7 and 8) or bashfully boarded over (6). Here
as well, techniques were used which involved supporting
the rafter tail-pieces on a purlin (8), which at the same
time represents a transition from the main wall to the
eaves.

Fig 201 (above)
Beautifully flared-out logwork forming integral eaves on a
bell tower in Ouneyma, Archangel Territory, Russia. The
flared logwork is structurally secured by the interlocking
corners. As it supports only a light boarded ceiling, with
the major load carried by interior timber framing and
transmitted to a four-sided substructure, no further
strengthening or reinforcement was called for at this
point. In terms of their function above the sills of the
interior framework, the log walls simply provide an
enclosure.

● 159

Floor and Ceiling Construction

Floor and ceiling systems are used to provide the horizontal divisions within log structures (Figs **202** and **203**). When plank ceilings are grooved into the walls and hence are not discernible from the exterior, the only differences occasioned by such construction occur when logs of larger dimension are used. If larger logs are placed so that their additional bulk is on the inside, this will only be externally noticeable at the protruding corners. If the extra material is on the outside, however, cornice-like projections are created (Fig **199**). In the log-built storehouses of Kärnten (Austria), flooring planks are at times laid on top of a course of logs, extended out over the walls, and used as support for the storey above (Fig **204**).

In ceilings of beam construction, care must be taken to assure that the beam is seated on an ample bearing surface, and that the beam-ends do not jut out unprotected beyond the exterior wall line. If the upper storey overhangs, beam-ends flush with its walls will be protected by them. At the same time, the beams themselves receive full support according to the thickness of the wall logs. If the upper and lower storeys are in line, however, the butt ends of the beams must not project beyond the wall surface. If a beam is notched out, there is not adequate thickness between the end face of the beam and the shoulder to effectively resist shearing forces. Consequently, the best approach is to dovetail the beam full thickness into the log-work, while increasing the thickness of the bearing log on the inside (Figs **199** and **203**).

Over the years, a vast array of techniques developed for handling the beams of an overhanging upper storey, most particularly on log granaries and storehouses, as evidenced by the Austrian and Norwegian timberwork shown in Figs **204** and **205**.

Fig 203 (opposite)
Beam-style ceiling framing, both flush with wall and extended. To shield the end grain against moisture, rain must be able to run off rapidly. Consequently, the end of the beam must never protrude completely on its own beyond the wall line. To provide the needed bearing surface when upper and lower storeys are vertically in line, the log on which the beam rests is increased in thickness, and the beam keyed into the wall with a locking dovetail. Larger logs thus used may show in the extended corners without appearing out of place. If a beam is extended, the wall of the storey above must be flush with its end surface. This provides the necessary protection against moisture. Since it can be notch-fitted full thickness onto the log

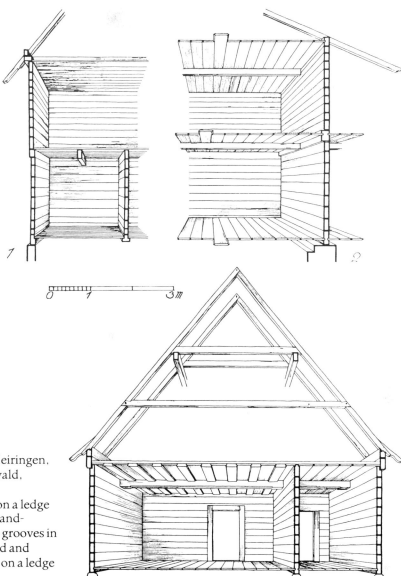

Fig 202
Planked ceilings resting on joists or tie beams.
1 Niederneuching (1581), Upper Bavaria; **2** Meiringen,
Canton Bern (1785); **3** Neukenroth, Frankenwald,
Oberfranken (1606).

In **1**, the planks are laid side by side and rest on a ledge
created by the walls. In **2**, they are laid tongue-and-
groove, including a tapered plank, and set into grooves in
the walls. In **3**, boards and planks are alternated and
rabbeted together to form a ceiling which rests on a ledge
at the walls.

203

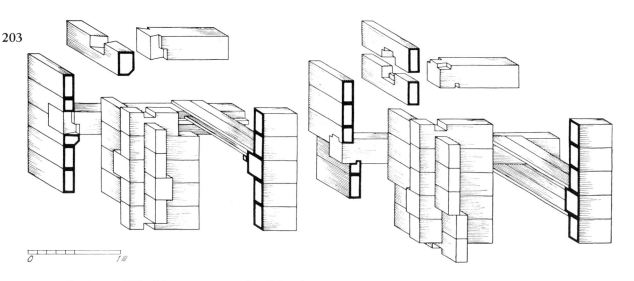

supporting it, no difficulties are presented at this point.
Problems only occur at the corners where the protruding
cornerwork must also accommodate the overhang. To
assure structural stability in this instance, the logs of the
upper storey must rest on those of the lower one, even if
only on a narrow ledge.

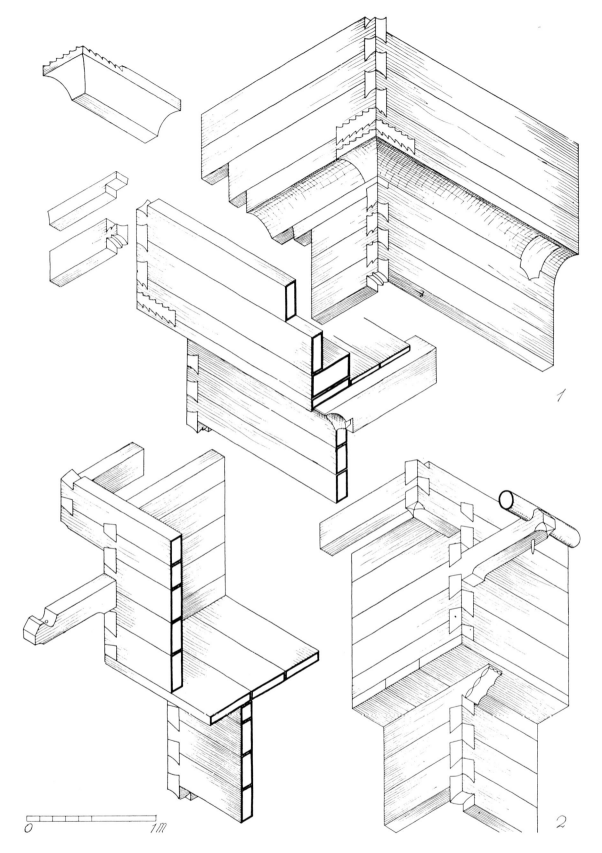

Fig 204
Overhanging upper storey construction on storehouses in Kärnten. **1** is from the *Brugger-Hof* farmstead in Radenthein (1707), while **2** is from a granary in St. Oswald (1563). In the first building, the transition between storeys is made by a course of heavier logs dished out to blend the two wall lines into one another. In addition to this feature, in itself load-bearing to a degree, the ends of the ceiling beams have also been worked into the design, cut and shaped to match the hollowed-out contour. While the logwork of this building follows strictly log upon log, a floor of planks 7 cm in thickness has been inserted between the upper and lower storeys of the second structure. Supported on each of the side walls by a console bracket and one beam, this both carries the upper storey and forms its floor.

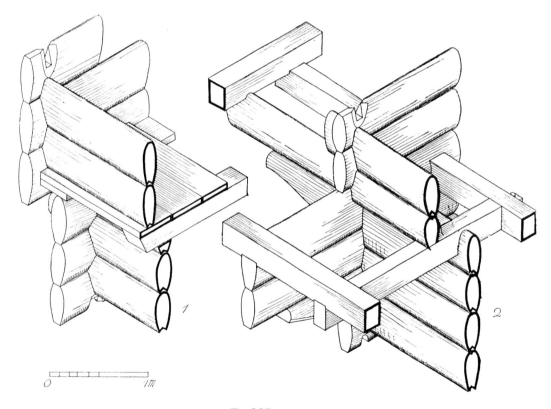

Fig 205
Overhangs on Norwegian log structures. **1** Brottweit. Valle.
Setesdal; **2** Ljosland, Åseral, Vest-Agder. In item **1**, the
overhanging storey is carried on one side by beams and
projecting log ends, and on the other solely by the
extended cornerwork. It is interesting to note that one of
the upper log walls sits on the plank flooring, while on the
other wall, a plank is used as a shim. In the post and beam
construction of the Alemannic people, the flooring of the
upper storey likewise extends out to the end face of the
beams. In **2**, the beam-ends appear on both sides as load-
bearing supports. In this case, the builders have used
lookout or tail beams, locked into the closest main beam
via a shouldered tenon.

● 163

Doors and Doorways

Historically, doorways existed before windows and once played an important role in permitting the entry of light. Formerly, they were something like half a meter lower than they are today. When it is cut, the opening for the doorway substantially reduces the structural stability of the wall, necessitating the use of special forms of reinforcement at this point.

The most readily apparent solution is to increase the dowelling near the opening, an alternative which has led to double-dowelling at times (Fig **206**). However, such measures begin to fail as soon as more than two logs are cut away, with the result that the wall logs shift out of plumb. To avert this, stout splines or trimmers must be set into the logwork. Because these vertical members are at right angles to the horizontal logwork of the building, new concerns over settling arise, and with them the need for new framing techniques to accommodate this problem (Fig **207**). At first glance, this issue appears simple to resolve, and of no special significance. It is useful, however, to notice the variety of the solutions which appeared, and to observe the wealth of different building customs and styles developed by various cultural groups as a result. In the case of doors and doorways, for example, we can distinguish Scandinavian, Celtic (or Celtic-Germanic) and Bavarian styles.

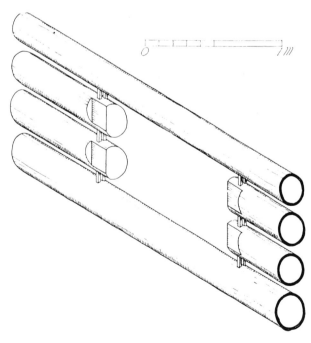

Fig 206
Wall opening in a barn from Radenthein, Kärnten, showing double dowelling. This feature is only used near openings in the logwork; otherwise, only single dowels are driven into the logs.

Fig 207
Doorway of a farmhouse in Kürnbach, Waldsee, Württemberg (Germany). This illustration clearly shows the different degrees of shrinkage; being about thirty times greater along the medullary rays than along the grain. Because the lintel or header log sits on the corner posts and door posts, as well as the intermediate uprights, it cannot settle with the other logs, resulting in a gaping crack above the top log.

Scandinavian Door Framing

In Scandinavian style door framing, trimmers, originally in plank form, were inserted in a corresponding slot mortised into the ends of the logs at the opening, with space for settling left above them in the lintel log, into which they were also mortised, usually full thickness. Fig 208 provides a purely conceptual look at the mechanics of this type of framing, while Fig 209 shows the evolutionary stages in its development, using Swedish log structures as examples. The beautiful and varied work pictured in Figs 209 to 217 provides some idea of the creative energy and skill of the old-time carpenter-craftsmen.

Traces of this distinctive technique may be found as far south as Switzerland and the Tirol, although here in only a few rare examples (Fig 217). These do show however that even the East Germanic peoples used this joinery technique. Vestiges of a Slavic settlement dating from the early Middle Ages found in Oppeln, Poland attest to the cultural influence of the Vikings, which at that time extended as far as the Oder (Figs 217 and 225).

Scandinavian log building produced a marvel of form in its bowed-out door posts, which portray in graphic fashion the strain imposed upon them by the logwork of the building (Figs 213 to 216). These posts are the equivalent of the bulged-out shafts of the columns of classical antiquity, although curiously, art historians have thus far turned a blind eye to this relationship.

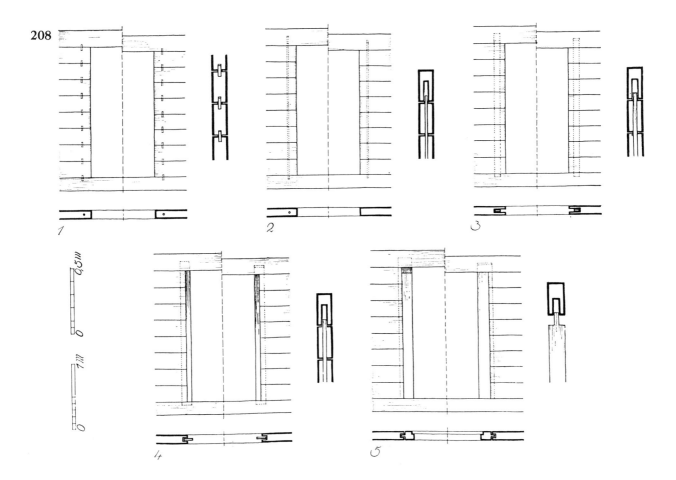

208

1   2   3   4   5

Fig 208
Conceptualized view of Scandinavian-style door framing.
The left half of each sketch shows the wall as it is once
erected, while the right half represents the situation after
settling. To prevent the logs from shifting out of plumb,
dowels must be inserted in addition to the interlocking
notching at the corners. The need for this reinforcement is
most serious where the logwork has to be cut away to
allow for openings. When openings took in more than two
rounds of logs (**1**), even dowelling could not provide
adequate support. Purely conceptually, it now became
necessary to link up the individual dowels to form a single
rod or pole (**2**). However, this would have made erecting
the logwork difficult. The solution was to adopt the use of
a wooden spline, mortised into both sill and header, and
set into a channel grooved out of the ends of the logs (**3**).
The mortise in the header was cut deep enough to allow
space for settling above the vertical spline. To provide a
stop for the door itself, the spline was increased in size
until it became a sturdy plank (**4**). When this in turn
became a door post of thickness nearing that of the wall
logs, its top had to be tenoned or tapered to be mortised
into the header with space for settling (**5**). The protruding
tongue on one side of the door post which fits into the log
ends shows the form of its evolutionary predecessor.

Fig 209 (opposite)
Door framing on Swedish log buildings. In item **1**, a hay
barn from Aelvros parish in Härjedalen, splines 6 cm
square have been inserted into the grooves cut out of the
ends of the logs on either side of the door opening. These
are let into the sill log and through-mortised at the lintel or
header to allow settling. Wedges are placed between the
individual logs to maintain the gaps for ventilation, while
serving at the same time to hold the logs firmly in place.
Item **2**, from a blacksmith's shop in the same area, is of
kindred construction, except that the gaps between the
logs have been chinked. In addition, the narrow spline has
been replaced by a plank which also functions as a door
stop. To make the tightest possible fit with the wall logs,
the side of the door plank is V-grooved and the end of the
mortised slot has been cut to a W-groove contour. Space
has been left in the header log above both sides to allow for
settling. Item **3** from a farm kitchen in central Jämtland,
shows a further evolutionary stage in the form of a stop in
the header flush with the side planks. Notice also how the
logwork has been nicely cut back around the opening.
In **4**, from a smokehouse originally in the parish of
Lekvattnet, an area of northern Värmland peopled by
Finns, door posts with an integral spline set into grooved-
out logwork enter the scene. As these posts are tenoned

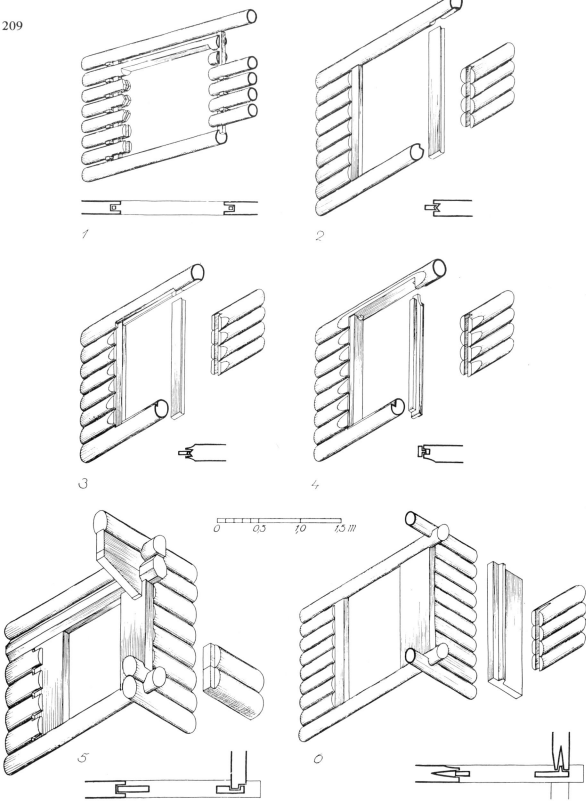

1

2

3

4

0   0,5   1,0   1,5 m

5

0

into the header, just enough space was left above them to give a tight fit when settling was completed. In **5**, a corner door from the *Morahof* farmstead (Dalarna), the side planks are tenoned full-size into the header log with settling space. Allowance was also left for settling of the protruding endwork, which fits into a slot mortised out of the corner upright. While the side plank on the left is set into the logwork in Scandinavian style, the situation is

reversed on the right side, where a tongue fits into a corresponding slot. Here we may see the influence of Norwegian style *reisverk*, in which the vertical staving is fitted into the grooved-out timberframe. Item **6**, from an *eldhus* or farm-kitchen building in Fageråsen, is free from such derivation, since in this case a tongue on the doorway upright sits in a slot cut in the log-ends.

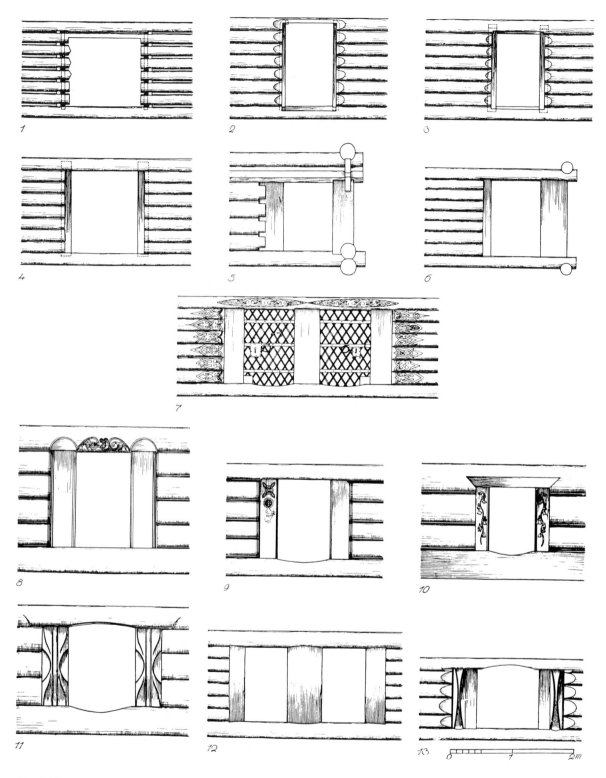

Fig 210
Scandinavian doorways. The numbers in brackets refer to
the figures in which the item is treated in detail. **1** Aelvros
(Fig **209**); **2** Lekvattnet (Fig **209**); **3** Jämtland (Fig **209**);
4 Aelvros (Fig **209**); **5** Mora (Fig **209**); **6** Fageråsen
(Fig **209**); **7** Aelvdalen (Fig **212**); **8** Vindlaus (Fig **211**);
9 Midgarden (Fig **211**); **10** Snartland (Fig **211**);
11 Haugen (Fig **213**); **12** Kråkberg (Fig **213**);
13 Dagsgård (Fig **213**). Items **1** to **7** are from Sweden;
8 to **13** from Norway.

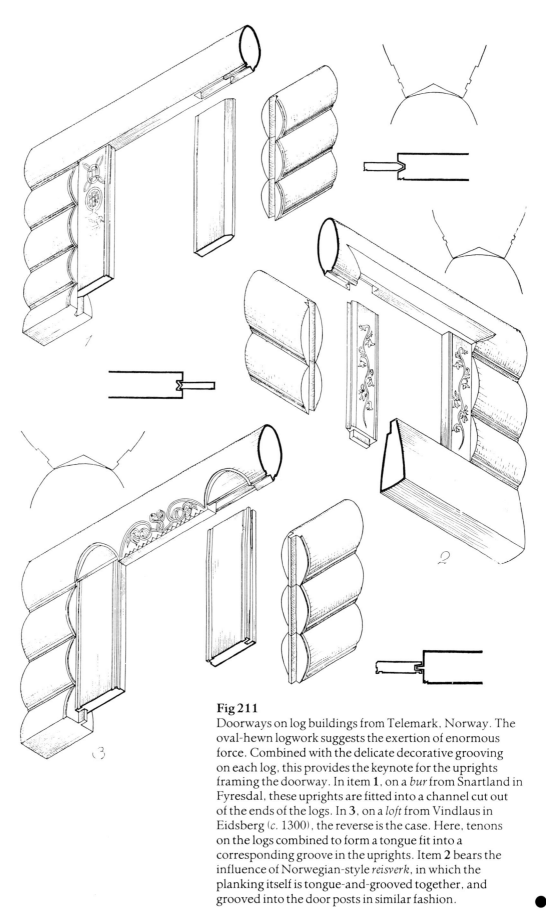

Fig 211

Doorways on log buildings from Telemark, Norway. The oval-hewn logwork suggests the exertion of enormous force. Combined with the delicate decorative grooving on each log, this provides the keynote for the uprights framing the doorway. In item **1**, on a *bur* from Snartland in Fyresdal, these uprights are fitted into a channel cut out of the ends of the logs. In **3**, on a *loft* from Vindlaus in Eidsberg (*c.* 1300), the reverse is the case. Here, tenons on the logs combined to form a tongue fit into a corresponding groove in the uprights. Item **2** bears the influence of Norwegian-style *reisverk*, in which the planking itself is tongue-and-grooved together, and grooved into the door posts in similar fashion.

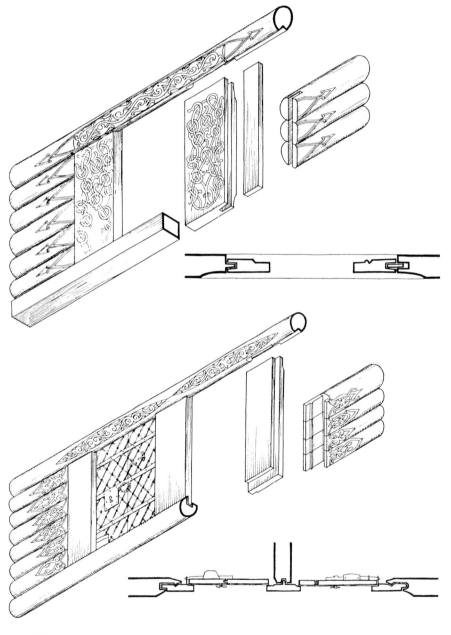

Fig 212
Doorways on Swedish log buildings, above from Fåsås
and below from Aelvdalen. Of special note is the manner
of connecting the doorway uprights and the log walls;
above right via a separate inserted spline, and below,
incorporating a special locking key into the grooved-out
logwork.

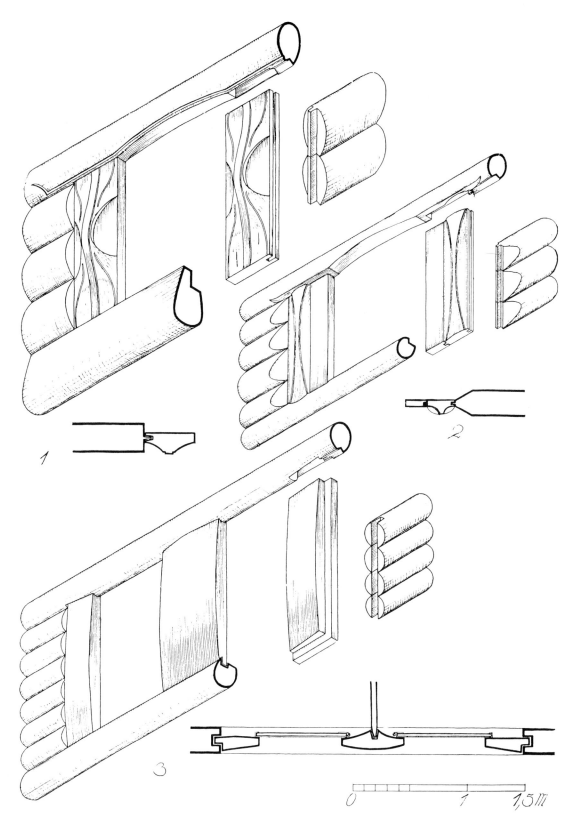

Fig 213

Doorways on Norwegian log buildings including bowed-out door posts. The oval profile of the wall intimates the exertion of extreme force in the vertical plane; a phenomenon which we may equate with the flexing or bulging of muscles. This portrayal of the forces exerted upon the log walls was also carried over onto the door posts, which were given an outward bow from top to bottom. This concept, which was transplanted from the North to the South, represents the epitome of architectural eloquence in an individual feature. This idea reoccurs, transposed in stone, on the bulged-out shaft of the classical column. In item **1**, from a *loft* in Haugen (Setesdal) dating from the Middle Ages, delicate half-round scoops have been made in the side posts to bring the high point of the bow back to the wall line. Item **2**, on a loft from Dagsgård (17th century) is related to the former, except that in this case, the transition from the bow to the wall extends all the way from top to bottom, producing a gently curving contour line. In **3**, from Kråkberg, the sloped sides are omitted, although, by way of compensation, the bow of the post is less accentuated.

● 171

214

215

Fig 214
Door from the attic floor of the *Oseloft*, a log storehouse now in Bygdö. Like the horizontal logwork, the upright door posts also depict in their design the strain of the building's weight. The graceful tendrils hand-forged onto the iron strap hinges are a much beloved feature of the Scandinavian blacksmith's craft.

Fig 215
Double doors on the house known as the *Åmlistue*, now in Bygdö. The decorative carving on these door posts faces inward to the *arestue* or open-hearthed interior.

Fig 216
A comparative look at Scandinavian timberwork and
classical architecture in stone, both of which display in
their design lines a vivid depiction of forces at work. In
item **1**, the uprights framing the doorway give the
impression of straining muscles, as do the wall logs with
their oval cross-section. In the second item, by contrast,
the keynote is sounded by the vertical staving. Hence the
accent on gripping at the door posts, which at the same
time nestle against the building. With its bulged-out shaft,
the Doric column at **3** clearly demands comparison with
its precursors which these door posts represent. This
language, born of intimacy between craftsman and
medium, was even extended to the human form, used as a
support column in the fourth example.

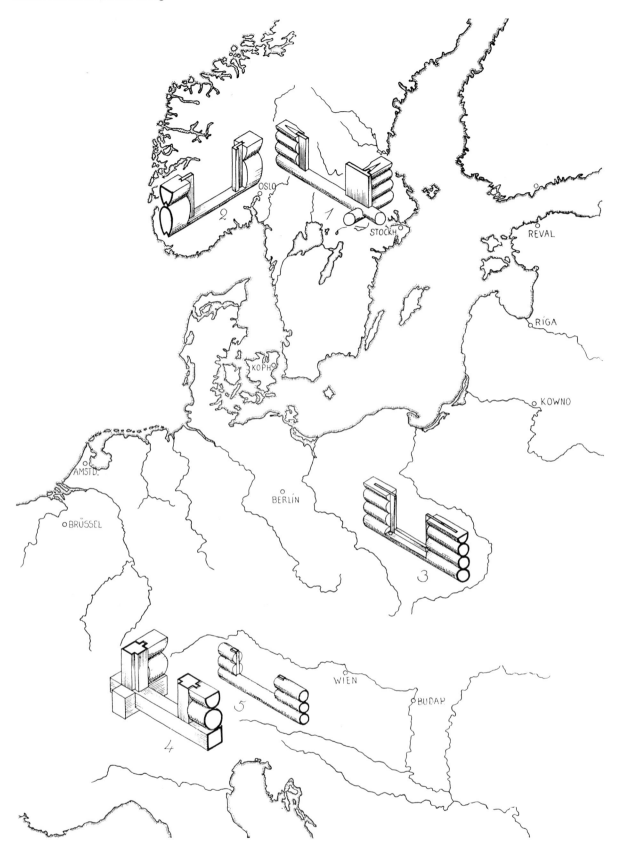

Fig 217
Showing the range of Scandinavian door framing. The salient feature of this technique is that the door posts, originally in plank form, are set into a slot mortised out of the log ends (*cf.* Fig 208). Where planks give way to full or half logs at the opening, the portion set into the logwork retained its effectiveness in the form of a tongue. In Scandinavia, this approach has endured right up to the present. Elsewhere, its influence may be traced into Silesia and on down into Switzerland and the Tirol. **1** from an *eldhus* in Fageråsen, Sweden; **2** from a *loft* in Valle (Setesdal), Norway; **3** from a dwelling in the settlement on Oder Island, near Oppeln, dating from the early Middle Ages (11th to 12th century); **4** from an upland dairyherd's hut in Seewis, Graubünden, Switzerland; **5** from a barn in Unterlängenfeld, Ötztal, Tirol. Item **4** suggests Burgundian roots, while **5** indicates Gothic background.

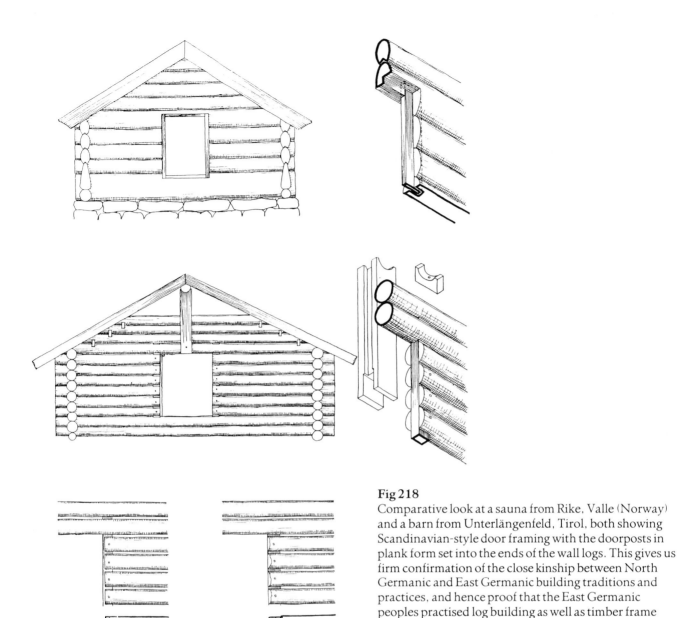

Fig 218
Comparative look at a sauna from Rike, Valle (Norway) and a barn from Unterlängenfeld, Tirol, both showing Scandinavian-style door framing with the doorposts in plank form set into the ends of the wall logs. This gives us firm confirmation of the close kinship between North Germanic and East Germanic building traditions and practices, and hence proof that the East Germanic peoples practised log building as well as timber frame construction. The wooden pins on the barn from Tirol were added at a later date, having been completely omitted from the top log on the right hand side of the opening. Below: variations of this technique from the Ötztal valley, Austria.

Fig 219
Comparison of small hay barns from: **1** Åseral, Norway; **2** Narbotten, Sweden; and **3** Kleis, Upper Bavaria with king posts from the Mittenwald (Germany) area which bear a striking resemblance to one another, and which confirm the kinship between the building practices of the North Germanic and East Germanic peoples. Apart from the log construction itself, the king posts of items **1** and **2**

are framed in the same fashion as the columns (*stolper* in Norwegian) of timberframe-and-staving construction. Notice also the outward cant of the walls in **2** and **3**. The gently sloping roof of all three is dictated by the nature of the materials used for the roof covering and the fact that structural stability is provided by both added weighting and the inherent weight of the roof proper.

Fig 220
Comparison of a *loft* from the *Hofe Halvorgaard* farmstead,
Gol, Hallingdal (Norway), from the early 18th century
(left) and a barn from Untertauersteinhof in Alpbach,
Tirol, revealing the close kinship between North
Germanic and East Germanic building traditions. The
latter structure, which illustrates the sad effect of the
framesaw and the iron nail on creative timberwork, likely
goes back to Gothic origins. The further back we go
chronologically, the greater must be the similarity to its
Scandinavian sister, with the upper storey sheathed in
vertical staving.

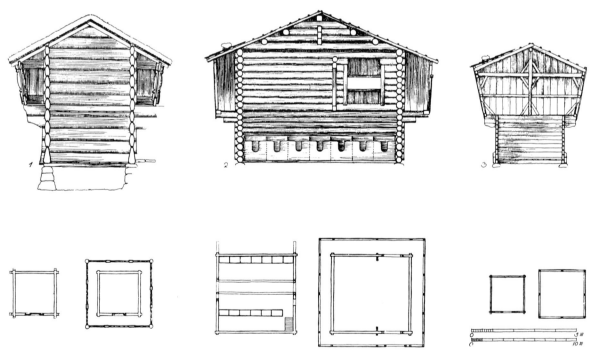

Fig 221
Floor plans and elevations of **1** a *loft* from Dale (Valle),
Setesdal; **2** a combined barn and stalls from Alpbach; and
3 a storehouse from Vorderbrand, near Berchtesgaden,
Upper Bavaria. Item **1** shows the characteristic shape and
form of the North Germanic storehouse, used to house
provisions and store farm equipment, and even to provide
sleeping quarters in the upstairs portion. The second
structure may be traced to East Germanic origins. Stalls
are located on the ground floor, and a barn on the upper
storey. Item **3**, with the upper storey in the West Germanic
post and beam style, reveals a combination of the two
preceding ones. A storeroom makes up the ground floor,
while the second storey is a barn. Missing here is the *sval*
or elevated walkway of the other two.

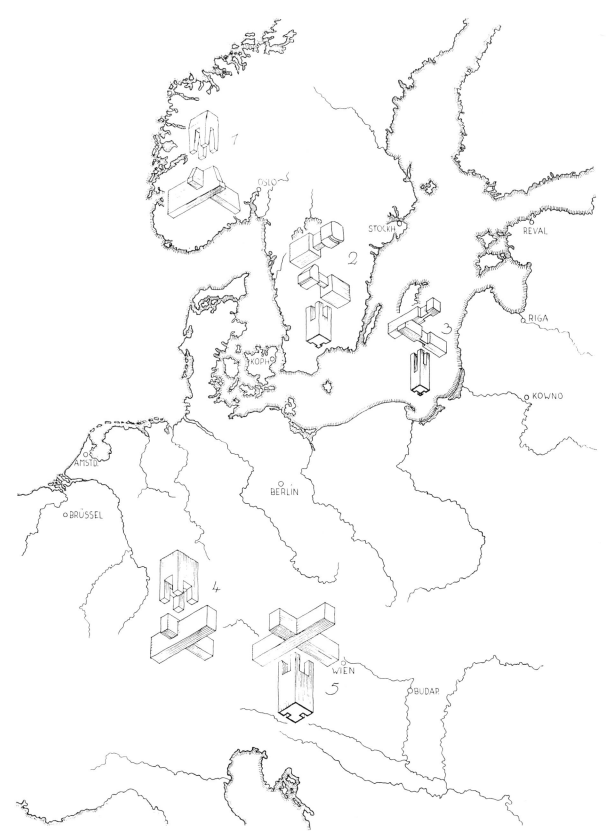

Fig 222
Showing the range of double-forked mortising, which developed with Scandinavian timberframe and staving techniques, and was transposed to log building as well.
1 from a *loft* in Totakoygarden, Telemark, Norway (1722);
2 from Västergötland, Sweden; **3** from the island of Farö, near Gotland; **4** from Münster, Switzerland and **5** from Sölden, Ötztal valley, Austrian Tirol.

In addition to this type of notching with its visible mortises, there exists another style in which the end grain of the sill course or the frame timber is concealed. Double-forked mortising swings from Scandinavia across to Denmark and down into Schleswig. Contrasted with this North Germanic current is the East Germanic one, the Burgundian branch of which is discernible in isolated examples to the north, south, and south-west of Lake Constance and in the Valais of Switzerland, while the Gothic branch appears in the Tirol.

Fig 223
Two storey farmshed from Sölden, Ötztal, Tirol. The structure's configuration and its boarded roof point strongly to Swedish origins.

Fig 224
Threshing floor of a hay barn from Sölden, Ötztal, Tirol. Notice the mortised-in spline holding the cutaway log wall in place; a typically Scandinavian technique.

Fig 225
Remains of a house doorway unearthed in 1930 at the site of the ancient habitation on Oder Island near Oppeln (11th to 12th century). The shaded portion represents the find unearthed by Georg Raschke; the rest has been added by the author. Like the Scandinavian structures, this building also featured the doorframe planks fitted into a slot mortised out of the log ends. This is further substantiation of the assumption that the ''Rus'' cited by the Arabian merchant Ibrahim-ibn-Jakub in his travel diary dating from the 10th century must have been the Sweden of Viking times.

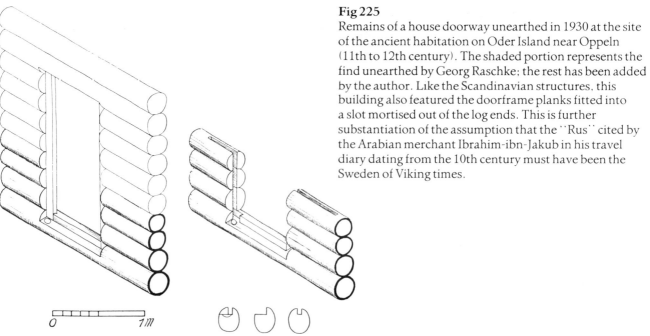

Celtic and Celtic-Germanic Door Framing

In this style, the wall logs are tenoned into a corresponding groove cut out of the door posts, creating what is essentially a tongue. Similarly, the door posts themselves are tenoned into sill and header. The need to provide settling space in the lintel created a problem not encountered in the Scandinavian style, where the posts could be fitted full size into the header log. The resulting designs which emerged as a solution to this were many and varied (Fig **226**). The name ''Celtic'' has been chosen because it has been shown that this type of doorway structure existed even in pre-Celtic times (Fig **227**), and because its evolution was richest in those areas formerly inhabited by Celts. It spread far beyond these areas, and is today considered the most commonly used joinery technique in log building (Fig **228**).

In Switzerland alone, this method witnessed the most diverse variation (Figs **229** to **251**), both in terms of individual joinery techniques and in terms of creative designs, which, with few exceptions (Fig **238/2**), were invariably a credit to the nature and the character of wood. On the door posts, the groove originally cut only on the sides and forming a long slot is carried over onto the ends of the posts as well. The inspiration for this came from Scandinavian-style timberframe-and-staving construction, where the vertical planking sits in a groove running completely around the perimeter of the panels. This is to say, the stimulus was from the Germanic side. It is thus fitting that the style be referred to as Celtic-Germanic.

Fig 226 (overleaf)
Details of Celtic and Celtic-Germanic style door framing. In each of the drawings, the left half depicts the situation at completion of construction, the right hand following settling. In item **1**, the door posts are tenoned into both sill and header, being set in place as the walls go up. The log walls follow this same idea. Because here tenon upon tenon combine to form a continuous tongue, the door post must be grooved out accordingly. To allow for settling, the mortise in the header is made deep enough so that ample space is left above the tenons of the posts. This concept occurs as far back as the Bronze Age redoubt-habitation of Buchau in Württemberg (Germany). Hence, the framing style which features it should be referred to as ''Celtic''. In **2**, a purely hypothetical example, the groove is carried over onto the ends of the posts both top and bottom. This produces slots on both ends. Here too, space must be allowed for settling. As obvious as this may at first glance appear, this modification nonetheless required impetus emanating from another building tradition before it materialized. This came from the Germanic side, where the planking which fills the timber framing of the North,

179

226

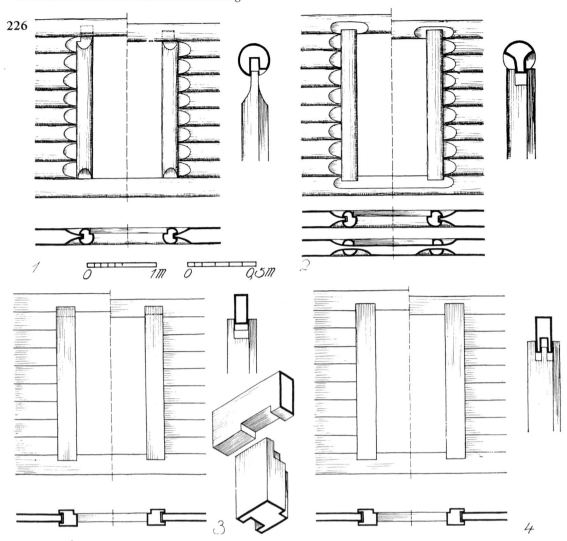

East, and West Germanic building styles fits into a groove which runs completely around the framework. Item **3** shows a style related to the former, but now transposed to squared timber. This represents the basic form of Swiss doorway framing, which may be called Celtic-Germanic. In the fourth item, the conceptual features of the first and second styles are blended into a unified whole, in which the sides of the grooves conceal the gap left for settling.

Fig 227

Projected reconstruction of a doorway as found on the log buildings of Buchau, the fortified habitation in the marshland near Lake Federsee, Württemberg, Germany (c. 1100 to 800 BC). Artist's conception from data by Hans Reinerth, the leader of the archaeological dig. The portion sketched in with fine lines shows the author's projected version of a complete doorway. The location of the doorway on the unearthed sill was identified from two mortises and a hole for the door pin. Since the door posts were fitted into these mortises, they must have been set in place at the same time as the logwork was erected. It is obvious that with further slight modification, the same joinery technique was used to fit the ends of the wall logs into the sides of the door posts. In this case, the tenons on the ends of the main logs became a tongue and the individual mortises a groove. Because the walls and door posts were erected simultaneously, space must have been left in the lintel log to allow for settling.

227

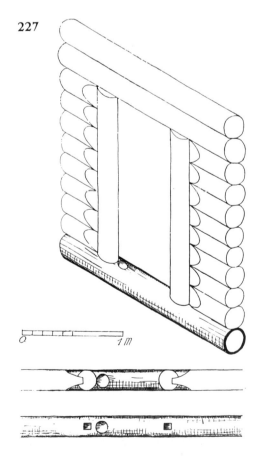

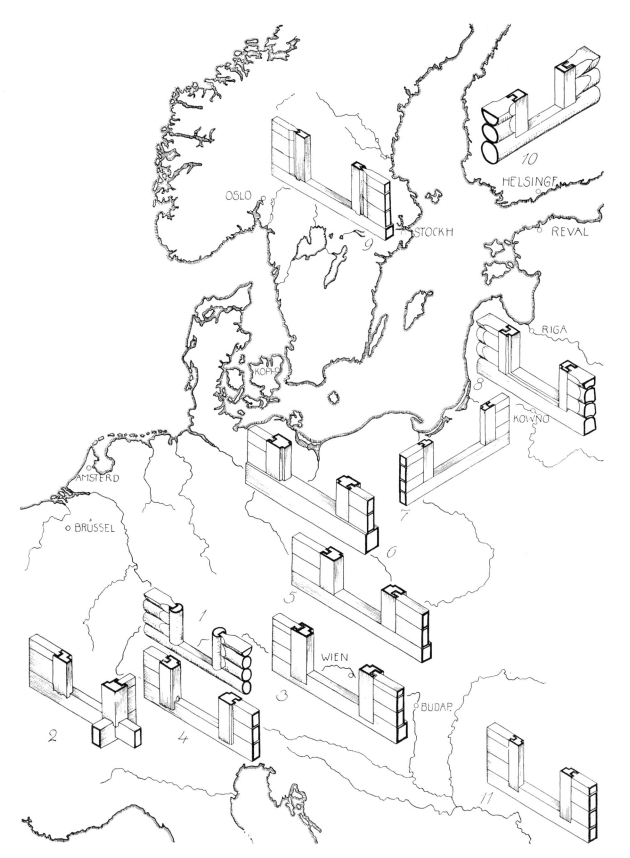

Fig 228

The range of Celtic style door framing. The term Celtic has been chosen since this technique originated in the region once populated by the Celts, although it may be traced back as far as the Bronze Age. The characteristic features are that, at the doorway opening, the ends of the wall logs, either full size or tenoned, are fitted into a space chiselled out of the sides of the door posts, as in a mortise or a groove. Secondly, these posts are erected at the same time as the logwork. **1** from the redoubt-habitation of Buchau (c. 1100 to 800 BC); **2** from Stalden, Valais; **3** from Peuerbach, Oberösterreich province; **4** from Upper Bavaria (hybrid form, since in this instance the door posts have been added subsequently and hence not tenoned); **5** from Cosel District, Silesia; **6** from the province of Brandenburg; **7** from East Prussia; **8** from the Lithuanian-Belorussian border region; **9** from western Blekinge, Sweden; **10** from Finland; **11** from the Transylvanian *Erzgebirge*.

● 181

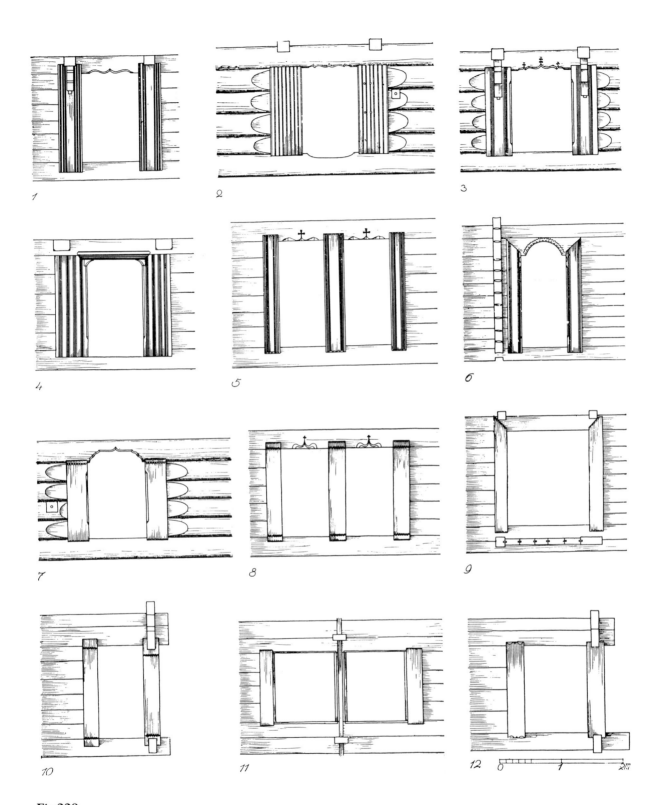

Fig 229
Doorways from Switzerland. The numbers in brackets
refer to the figures in which the particular item is discussed
in detail. The origins of the doorways shown here are as
follows: **1** Ried (Figs **238, 239**); **2** Egisvyl (Fig **230**);
3 Waldhaus (Figs **230, 235, 236**); **4** Ried (Figs **238, 240**);
5 Naters (Fig **241**); **6** Naters (Figs **244, 246, 247**);
7 Waldhaus (Fig **230**); **8** Fiesch (Figs **241, 243**); **9** Naters
(Fig **244**); **10** Fiesch (Fig **251**); **11** Kippel (Fig **251**);
12 Stalden (Fig **277**).

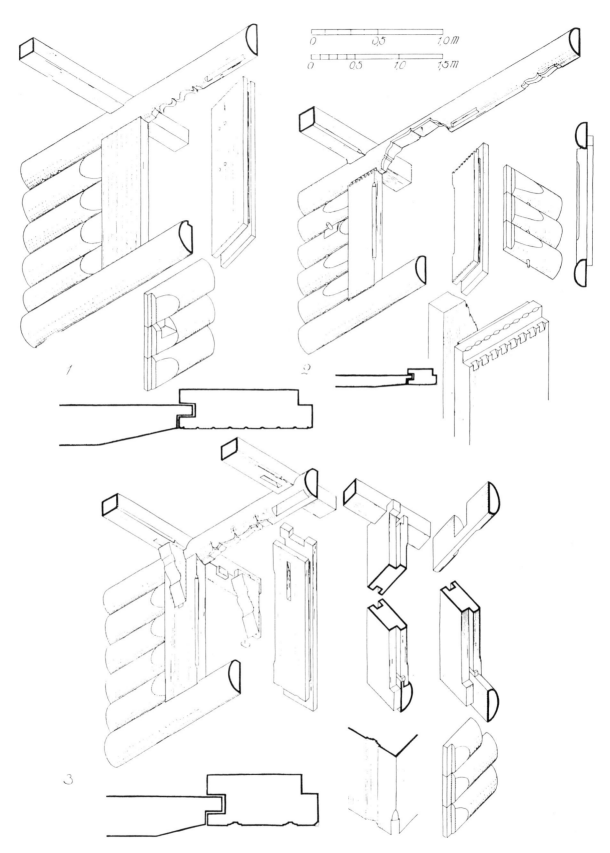

Fig 230

Doorway framing from Canton Bern. **1** from Egisvyl;
2 from the *Lüthihof* farmstead in Waldhaus (1629); **3** from
the *Kipferhof* farmstead in Waldhaus (1701). The walls are
of half-logs, split from fir logs using axe and wedges. The
ends of the broad door posts are held in mortises; the sides
by the tenoned wall logs, with allowance left for settling in

each case. In item **3**, the support brackets would not have
been fitted until after settling, then being tenoned and
wedged in place. Notice that neither sill nor header is
rabbeted for the door. In **1**, the door posts are of oak, an
uncommon feature manifested even by the nature of the
decorative grooving, which distinguishes it from **3**.

● 183

231

232

Figs 231 and 232
Granary doors from Egisvyl, Canton Bern.

Fig 233
Granary door from Waldhaus, Canton Bern.

Fig 234
Attic door on the granary from Waldhaus, Canton Bern.

Figs 235 and 236
Granary door from Waldhaus, Canton Bern.

Fig 237
Granary door from Waldhaus, Canton Bern.

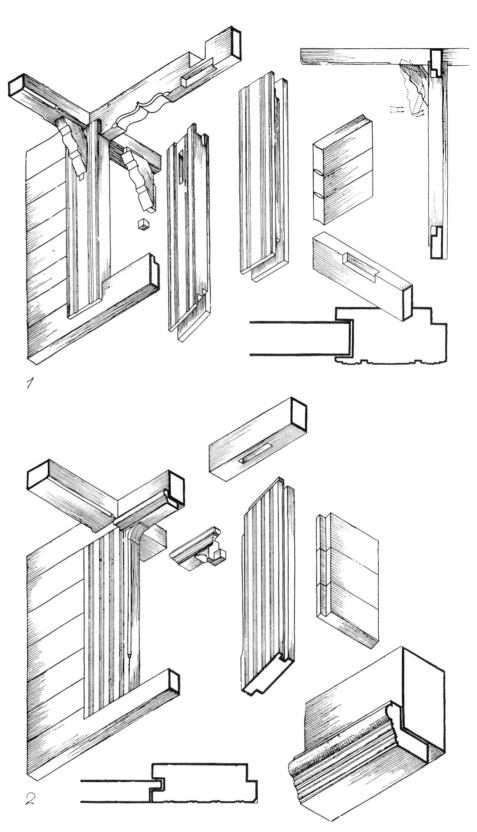

Fig 238

Granary doorways from Ried, Canton Bern. **1** from 1722; **2** from 1772. In item **1**, the square-hewn logs are fitted full size into a slot mortised out of the door posts, while in **2**, the log ends are tenoned into the uprights. In **1**, the ends of the posts are mortised, while the upright is tenoned into the header in **2**, with allowance for settling in both cases. Fully in keeping with the nature of wood, shallow decorative grooving has been cut into the face of the posts. By contrast, the contouring of the decorative header piece added to the doorway in **2** suggests an imitation of stone architecture.

Fig 239
Granary door from Ried, Canton Bern.

Fig 240
Granary door from Ried, Canton Bern.

241

2

Fig 242
Granary door from Naters, Valais.

Fig 241 (left)
Doorway framing from granaries in the Valais.
Switzerland. **1** from Naters; **2** from Fiesch. In both cases,
the door posts take the wall logs in a mortised slot. As they
are also set into the sill and the header log, and as the end
of the post fits tightly against the cutout portion of the
overhead log, we have some evidence of just how
accurately the old-time log builders were able to calculate
the proper allowance for settling. The rabbet for the door
extends the full way around the opening. The decorative
treatment of the header logs is interesting in that,
although the designs are somewhat similar, that of **1** uses
chamfering as its motif, while a plane surface has served
the purpose in **2**. On the first set of door posts, surface
grooving has been used for a decorative touch, while saw
and gouge have produced the ornamentation on the
second.

Fig 243
Granary door from Fiesch (Valais), Switzerland.

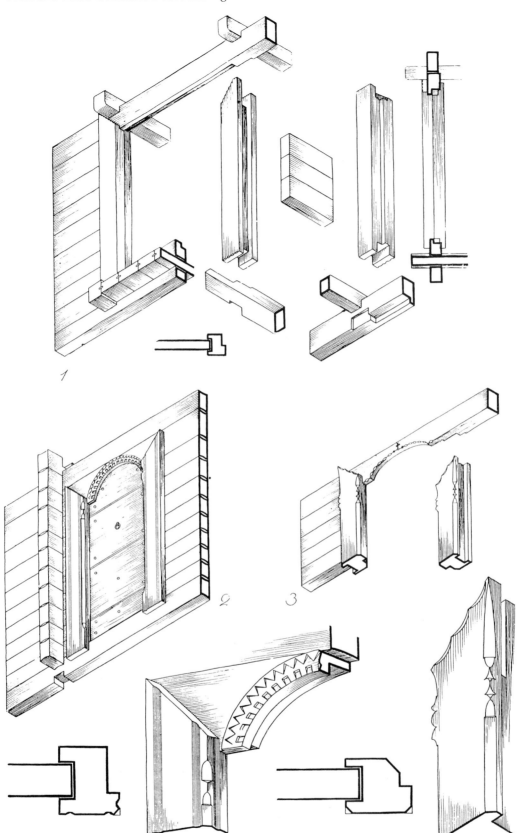

Fig 244
Doorway framing: **1** from a stable; **2** a dwelling in Naters; **3** and a house in St. Nikolaus, Valais. In all three, the door posts are mortised out to take the wall logs, and mitred outward at the top on the outside. One interesting feature is the decorative work on these posts. In **1**, the embellishment is confined to gougework on the end surfaces. In **2**, contoured and shaped edges have been chosen, while in **3**, emphasis was placed on detailed chamfering of the edges, both on the sides and tops.

Fig 245
Granary door from Naters, Valais, Switzerland.

246

247

Figs 246 and 247
Door of a home in Naters, Valais.

248

249

250

Figs 248 to 250
Doors on homes in Fiesch, Valais.

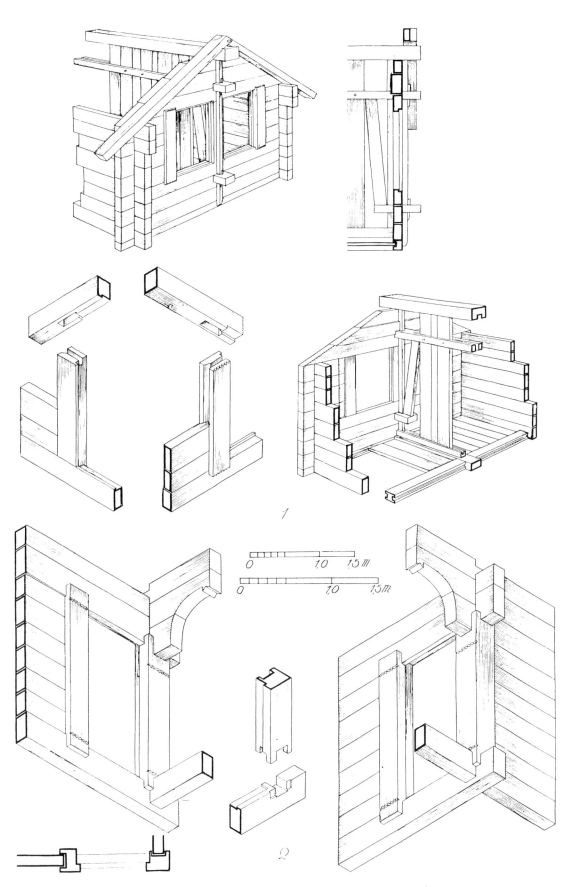

Fig 251

Stable from Kippel (**1**) and door framing from the upper floor of a granary from Fiesch (**2**), both in the Valais. On both buildings, the sill and header logs sit in a mortise cut out of the door posts. This mortise is offset by the thickness of one cheek so that the other, which now becomes a tenon, fits into a corresponding mortised hole. Double-forked mortising is used on the corner post of the second item shown. Notable in the first building is the manner in which the vertical tie-beam bracing the gable wall has been linked with the framing of the interior partition.

Bavarian Door Framing

Unlike Scandinavian and Celtic door framing, in which the door posts were added at the same time as the walls went up, the Bavarian approach was to delay installation of the posts until after the walls had fully settled, at which point these door posts were fastened in place by wooden pegs driven in at an angle (Fig 252). This suggests the immigration of a people who must have made extensive use of pegging techniques throughout their building practice. It turns out that in West Germanic post-and-beam construction, such skew pegging was the oldest and most common joinery technique (Figs 253, 254 and 255). Consequently, it must have been a West Germanic group which contributed to the development of the Bavarian method of door framing. In fact, this was what actually happened. The particular people were the Marcomanni, who pushed into the region of Celtic log building tradition, where they continued, however, to cling to their ancestral post-and-beam ways for the initial centuries of their settlement, as documented in the *Leges Baiuvariorum*. Their conversion to log building took place gradually, and although the change did occur, these people clung to their age-old method of securing the door posts for so long that, to this day, skew pegging at this point coincides with the movements of the Bavarian ethnic group (Fig 256).

The custom of delaying installation of the door posts or door frame until after the walls had settled remained in practice even longer than skew pegging. In the Alpine regions of Austria, for example, log buildings are still given a chance to dry and season for a winter and a summer (or at least a full summer) before door and window frames are installed and the interior work gets under way. In these areas, logs are not used until two years after they are felled.

One consequence of not adding the door posts until after settling was that builders tended to be most restrained here in their use of artistic work in general (Figs 257 to 272), confining embellishment to the lintel log or header, which was itself sometimes cut away along sweeping lines (Figs 261 and 266). Alternatively, trim boards decorated with similar patterns might simply be added (Figs 263, 264 and 265). Surface decoration may also be found, but only when carried over onto the header log, thus providing embellishment completely around the door frame. When trim was added, either full (Fig 267) or partial (Fig 268), numerous different techniques were used to fit the uprights into the horizontal header.

Skew pegging was also used on corner posts, as shown in Fig 271. To demonstrate the origins of skew pegging as outlined earlier, we shall look at another set of barn doors from the region into which this practice found its way. In Fig 272, notice the pegging firmly securing the bevelled blocks on which the doors are hung. Skew pegging even appeared on barns in which the logs are kept well apart by stout dowels placed between them. Here too, they helped hold door posts firmly in place (Figs 252 and 273 to 275).

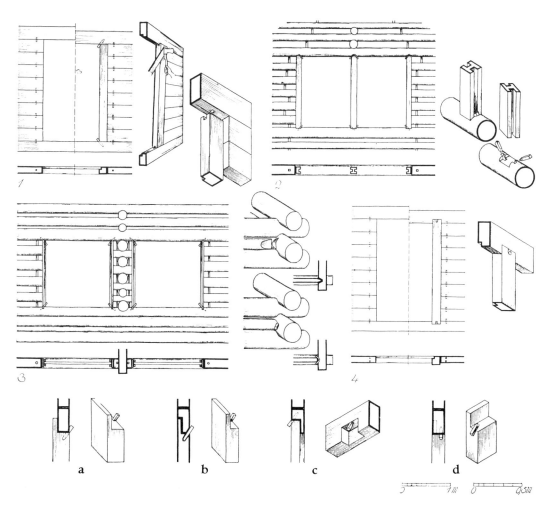

Fig 252
Details of door framing Bavarian style. Using this approach, door posts are not installed until after the building has settled. First, the walls are put up, with dowels (1), not infrequently in pairs (4) being driven in around openings in the walls. The door posts are then installed only after settling is completed. To hold the posts in place, pegs are driven in at an angle; a process which takes the place of tenoning. Widespread use of skew pegging originated in another timber-building tradition, namely the post-and-beam construction of the West Germanic peoples. This technique was brought to Celtic-style log building during the migrations of the Marcomanni, a West Germanic group. The clearest

example of this joinery technique may be found on barns such as those shown in 2 and 3 above, both from Hofgastein, Austria. Here, skew pegging was also used to secure the poles inserted in the log walls (3). At its most advanced stage of evolution, the technique is combined with half-lapping, either offset (4a) or flush-fit (4b, 4c, 4d). The pegs themselves may appear in the face of a wall (4a, 4b, 4c) or on a jamb (4d). If the peg is on the side opposite the tongue of the half-lap (4a, 4b), it is driven in so as to angle downward, creating a kind of clamp on the end of the post. If, however, it goes directly into the tongue of the half-lap, as in 4c, it is angled upward, in which case the clamping action occurs on the header (4c).

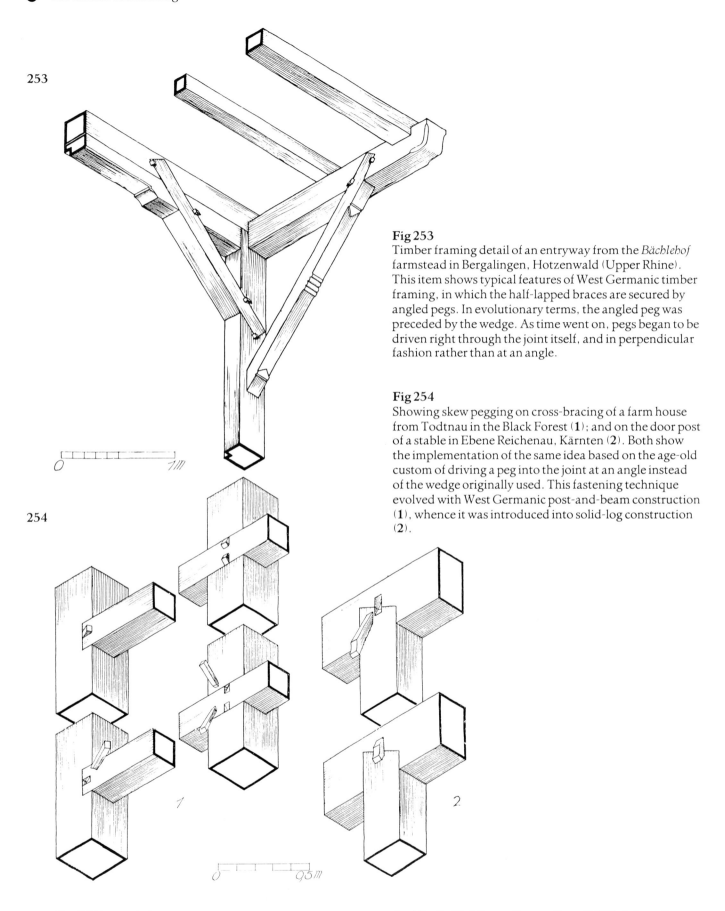

253

Fig 253
Timber framing detail of an entryway from the *Bächlehof* farmstead in Bergalingen, Hotzenwald (Upper Rhine). This item shows typical features of West Germanic timber framing, in which the half-lapped braces are secured by angled pegs. In evolutionary terms, the angled peg was preceded by the wedge. As time went on, pegs began to be driven right through the joint itself, and in perpendicular fashion rather than at an angle.

Fig 254
Showing skew pegging on cross-bracing of a farm house from Todtnau in the Black Forest (**1**); and on the door post of a stable in Ebene Reichenau, Kärnten (**2**). Both show the implementation of the same idea based on the age-old custom of driving a peg into the joint at an angle instead of the wedge originally used. This fastening technique evolved with West Germanic post-and-beam construction (**1**), whence it was introduced into solid-log construction (**2**).

254

Fig 255 (opposite)
The range of pegged timber joints, both straight and skew, as well as plank doors with cross-battens and wooden pins integral to the inside plank. **1** from the stave church in Hedal, Norway (c. 1200–1250); **2** from the granary of the *Lüthihof* in Waldhaus, Canton Bern (1629); **3** from Strom, near Bremen (Germany); **4** from Rötenbach in the Black Forest, Germany; **5** from Petersdorf in Transylvania, carried there in the middle of the twelfth century; **6** from Bergalingen, Hotzenwald (Upper Rhine, Germany);

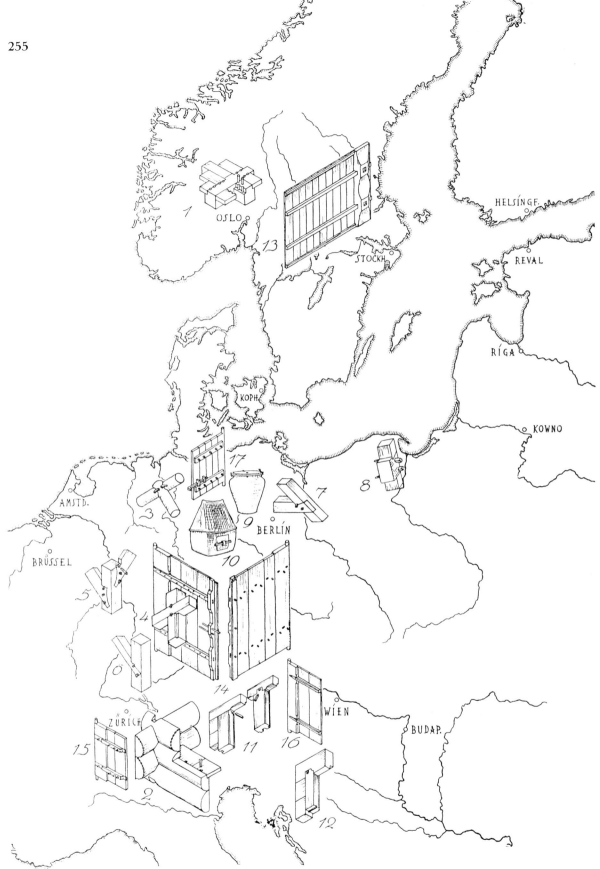

HELSÍNGF.

OSLO

REVAL

STOCKH.

RÍGA

KOWNO

KOPH.

AMSTD.

BERLÍN

BRÜSSEL

ZÜRICH

WÍEN

BUDAP.

7 from Grimnitz, near Eberswalde, Germany; 8 from Klein-Zünder, near Danzig (here, the pegs have been driven directly into the halved member, although still at an angle); 9 clay urn from the king's tomb near Seddin, Germany (800 BC); 10 house urn from Königsau near Aschersleben, Germany (c. 600 BC); 11 door framing from the *Hirtenhaus* near Erding, Germany (c. 1600); 12 from a door of the *Schmied-Hof* in Arriach, Austria; 13 barn door from Östnor, Mora parish, Dalarna (Sweden); 14 barn door from the *Martin-Meyerhof* farmstead in Rötenbach; 15 window shutter from Enge, Canton Zürich (1565); 16 door from the mill at Steegen, near Peuerbach, Oberösterreich province (Austria); 17 dormer door from Nienhagen, near Teterow, Mecklenburg-Schwerin, Germany (here, the one-piece doorplank-and-pins has with evolution been reduced to no more than board thickness, and the cross-battens now rather fastened by nailing).

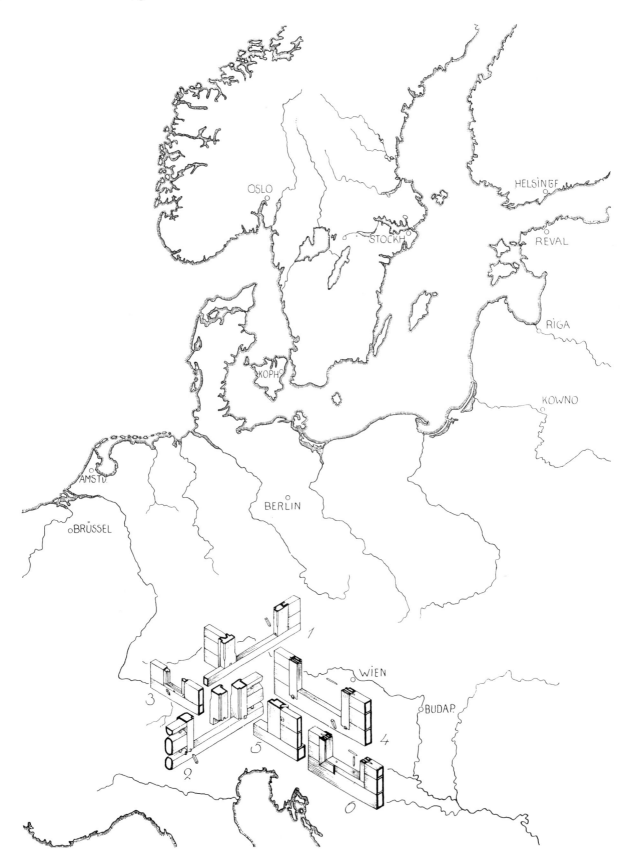

Fig 256
The range of Bavarian door and window framing. The distinctive feature of this style of building is that the door posts are not added until after the logwork has seasoned and the walls have completely settled, at which point the posts are fastened in place by angled wooden pegs. This technique may be found wherever Bavarian groups moved into areas which were culturally Celtic. Skew pegging,

which originated in West Germanic post-and-beam construction, thus merged with Celtic log building. **1** doorway of a *Hirtenhaus* or shepherd's cabin near Erding, Germany (17th century); **2** doorway of a barn from Ramsau-Schüttlehen, Steiermark province, Austria (1598); **3** window frame of a farm house from Wegscheid, near Lenggries, Upper Bavaria; **4** doorway from the *Schmied-Hof* farmstead in Arriach, Kärnten province,

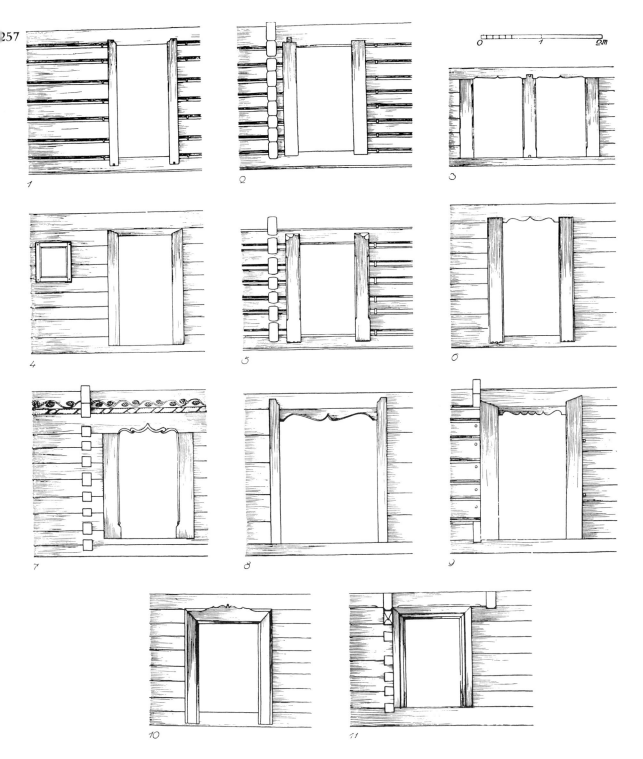

Austria; **5** house doorway from the *Meislitzer Hof* farmstead in Arriach; **6** window frame from the *Schmied-Hof* in Arriach.

In item **4**, the oldest structure, the logwork is simply butted up against the door posts, which are secured not only by skew pegs, but by others driven straight into the end grain of the logs. Item **6** is related, but without the skew pegs. In **5**, the logs are prevented from shifting out of position by wooden pegs driven at an angle into the sides of the door posts. In **2**, the logs are butted up against the rabbeted posts. Item **3** shows the reverse, where the rabbet has been cut into the end surfaces of the logs. In **1**, the wall logs are fitted into a groove in the door posts.

Fig 257 (above)
Bavarian style doorways. **1**, **2**, **4**, **8**, **9** and **10** are from Kärnten province (Austria); **3**, **6** and **11** are from Upper Bavaria (Germany) and **5** is from Steiermark province, Austria.

The numbers in brackets refer to the figures where the items are dealt with in detail. **1** Arriach (Fig **258**);
2 Winkel (Figs **258**, **259**); **3** Erding (Fig **261**);
4 Obermillstatt (Fig **262**); **5** Ramsau (Figs **262**, **13**);
6 Upper Bavaria (Fig **285**); **7** Niederneuching (Fig **266**);
8 St. Oswald (Figs **263**, **264**); **9** Arriach (Fig **263**);
10 Winkel (Fig **267**); **11** Lein (Fig **266**).

258

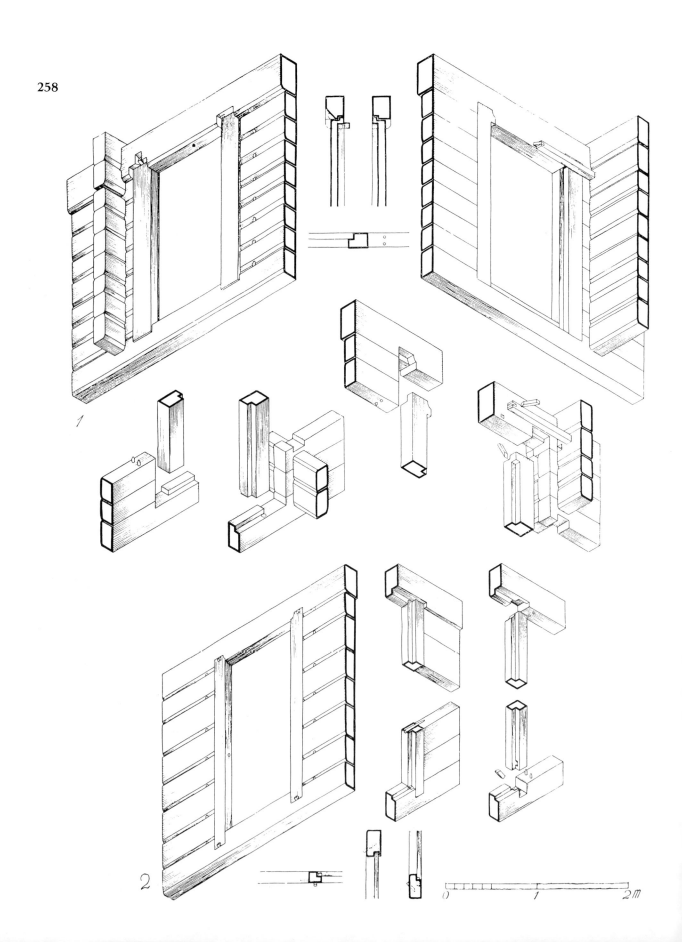

1

2

0   1   2 m

Fig 259
Skew pegging on the farmstead Poltl-Hof in Winkel,
Ebene Reichenau, Austria.

Fig 258 (left)
Detail of doorway framing from: **1** the farmstead *Poltl-Hof*
in Winkel, Ebene Reichenau; and **2** the *Schmiedwirt* in
Arriach; both in Kärnten, Austria. In both cases we
can see that some joinery technique other than that
exemplified by long-log construction must have crept in.
This came in fact from the post-and-beam construction of
the West Germanic Bavarians, who were able to artfully
combine their own knowledge of skew pegging with the
practices of Celtic log building. In item **1**, the posts (added
after settling) are fitted full size into the sill, but halved
into the lintel log. On the left side, an additional angled
peg was used for the final fastening. On the right,
however, being the side against which the door closed, the
peg is noticeably absent. Here, the shrinkage of the wood
became an issue. In all likelihood, this right hand post
would have been dried, and thus reduced to a minimum
section. In this condition, it would then be fitted as tightly
as possible, so that it would be wedged firmly in place once
it had swelled as a result of absorbing moisture from the
air. In **2**, the top of the post is fitted full-size into the lintel
log, where it closes against a similarly scooped shoulder; a
feature omitted at the sill. Thus, while a single peg driven
into the joint at an angle from the front was adequate at the
top, an extra peg had to be inserted from the side at the
bottom of the post.

Fig 260
Door posts secured by angled pegs from Patergassen in the
Nockgebiet area of Kärnten. The technique used here is
similar to that indicated in Fig **252/4c**. This method of
joinery continued to hold despite the sinking of the door
posts.

● 201

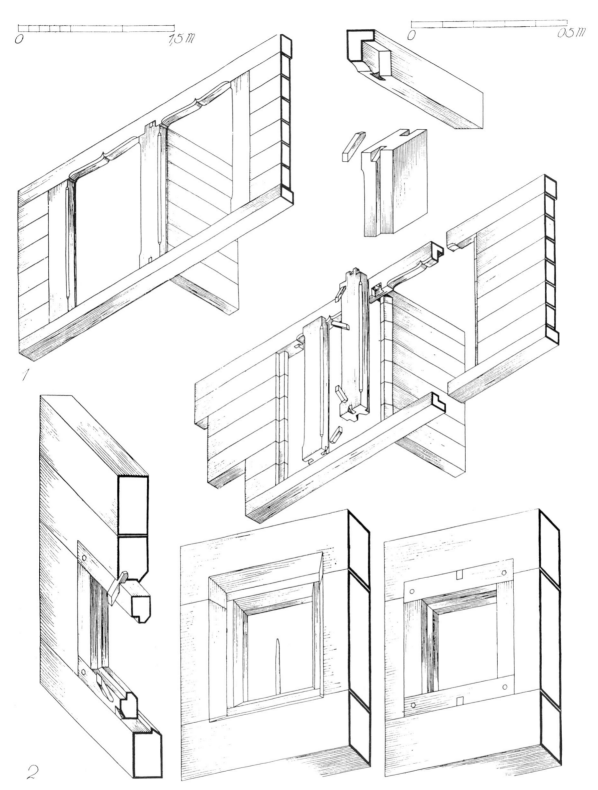

0   1,5 m

0   0,5 m

1

2

Fig 261

1 Doorway framing system on a shepherd's cabin near Erding (17th century); and 2 window framing from the *Wiham-Hof* farmstead in Wegscheid dating from 1758; both in Upper Bavaria, Germany. In both instances, we can see the blending of West Germanic-Bavarian skew pegging with Celtic style log building in a number of variations. First, in the case of the door framing, the middle post (installed following settling) is grooved out to take the partition wall, and half-lapped into the lintel log. Finally, pegs are driven in at an angle both top and bottom. The side posts, likewise added after settling, had to first be brought out flush with the wall surface, then forced onto the tongue formed by the ends of the wall logs. Here, too, the pegging was from the sides of the door posts. The window frame in 2 is set into a rabbet and held in place by pegs driven in at an angle from the side on which it was installed.

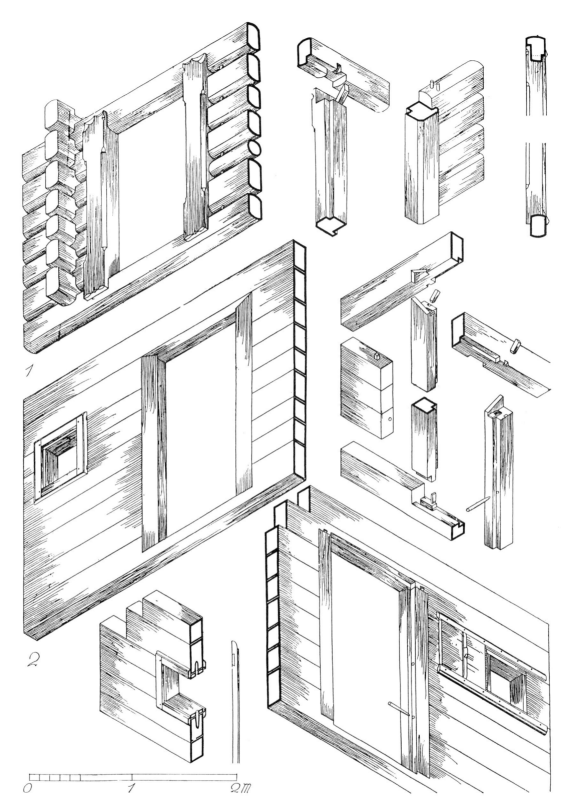

Fig 262
1 Doorway framing from a barn in Schüttlehen (Ramsau), Steiermark, from 1598; and **2** from a mill in Obermillstatt (Kärnten). In both, the logs are butted up against a rabbet in the door posts. In **1**, the posts are halved on the outside and skew-pegged on the inside. In **2**, by contrast, they are tenoned into the sill and fitted into the header with an inset half-lap, pegged at an angle on the inside. Since the door posts in **2** had to be mitre-tenoned into place, wedging was needed. An interesting feature is the decorative work on the tops of the protruding door posts, carved with drawknife and *klingeisen*.

203

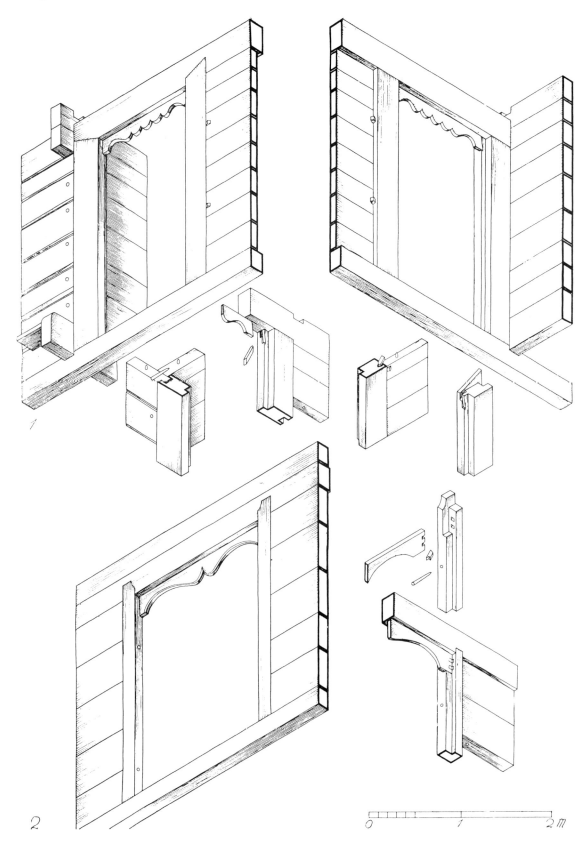

Fig 263
Doorways including distinctive overhead stop board, from Kärnten. **1** from the *Weislitzer-Hof* farmstead in Arriach; **2** from the *Hofer-Hof* farm in St. Oswald. In both cases, the ends of the decorative header board sit in a rabbet, while the upper edge simply fits flush against the lintel log. In **1**, the builder was content with this system, but in **2** both ends are further secured by two skew-pegs. Although this board did serve the function of a rabbet in the lintel log, it was a desire for decorative styling at this point which led to the addition of this item. Notice the varied ways in which wooden pegs are used; in one case angled to secure the door posts at sill and header, in another to prevent the wall logs from moving out of alignment – the latter in the form of pairs hammered in at an angle. In a third application, they are used to tie the partition wall to the exterior logwork.

Fig 264
Doorway of the *Hofer-Hof* farmstead in St. Oswald,
Kärnten.

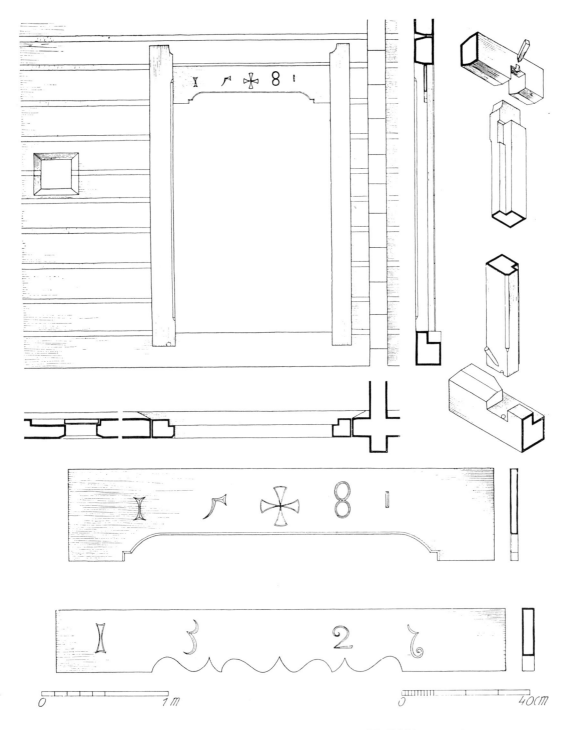

0 — 1 m

0 — 40 cm

Fig 265
Doorway framing with overhead stop board from the
Scherer-Hof farm in Ebene Reichenau, Kärnten and a stop
board from the *Moritz-Hof* farmstead in St. Lorenzen, near
Ebene Reichenau. In both cases, the ends of the boards sit
in a rabbet, while the upper edge fits flush against the
lintel log. The date of construction carved into the boards
gives them a special accent.

Fig 266 (opposite)
Doorway framing: **1** from the *Beindel-Hof* farm in Lein,
near Lenggries; and **2** from the so-called *Kasten* (granary),
originally in Niederneuching, now on the publicly-owned
Grub property near Munich (from 1581). The door posts
of both buildings have been added after the logwork had
settled, and skew-pegged into sill and lintel. In item **1**, this
is combined with a half-lap set into the header log, with

0   0,5

0   1   2 m

the moulded contouring of the side post carried over onto the lintel. On the example below, the lintel log was cut into a saddle-shaped arch, which, while borrowed from stone architecture, has nonetheless been nicely transposed onto wood. An interesting feature of both is

the system for holding the door-bolt on the inside, consisting of a sturdy upright pegged into place. Notice too how the manner of pegging has been turned into a decorative motif. The notch, used to guide the peg, was enlarged in very appropriate fashion.

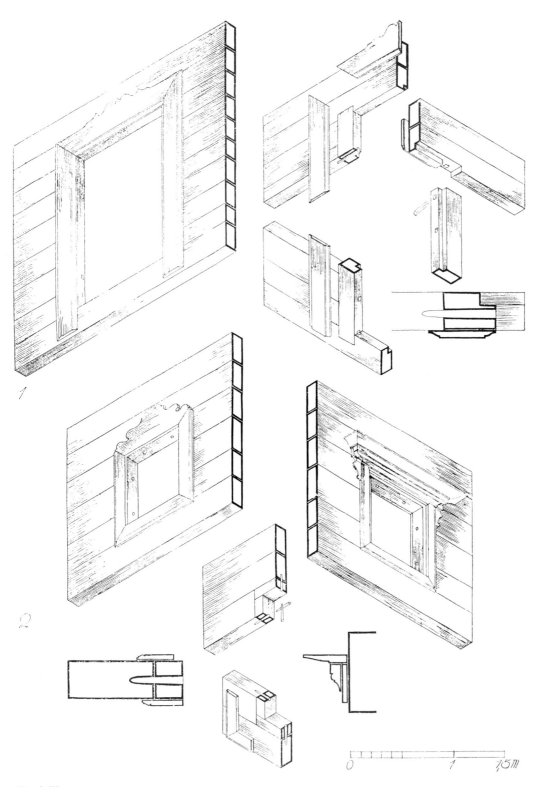

Fig 267
Door and window framing with trim from Kärnten
province: **1** from the granary of the *Poltl-Hof* in Winkel,
near Ebene Reichenau; **2** from the *Schmied-Hof* in Arriach.
In item **1**, the angled pegs are set inside the door jamb.
Worth noting in both cases is the manner in which the
moulded edgework of the side trim boards has been
worked into the upper board.

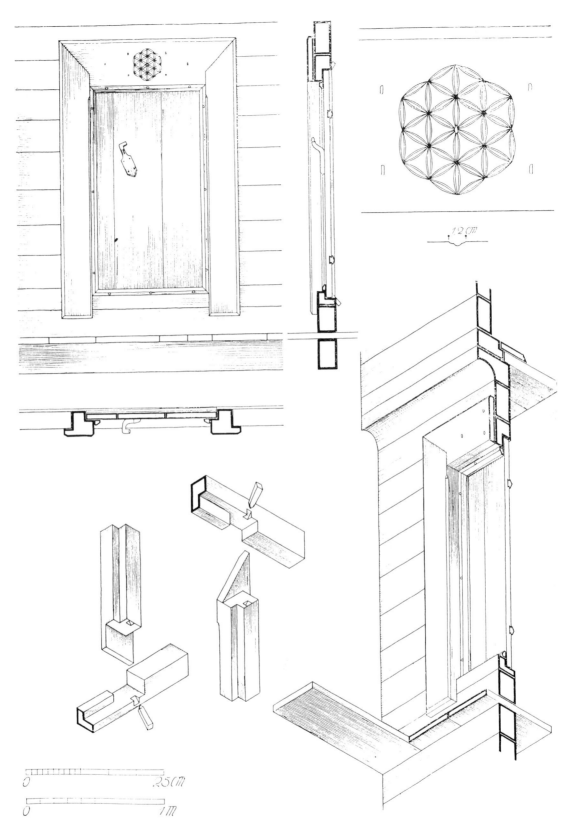

Fig 268
Door detail of the granary on the *Scherer-Hof* farm in Ebene Reichenau. The wall logs are butted into a rabbet in the door posts. These are halved and secured from the inside by angled pegs. Above the door, the trim board has been fastened with hand-forged iron nails. The board is flush with the door posts, combining with them to produce a single uniform frame. The iron nails are set in a decorative pattern. One, in fact, sits in the centre of the rosette, which has been chiselled out and outlined in red, representing the sun.

Fig 269
Doorway of a granary from Hofgastein. The lower portion of the brackets, which are pegged to the building, has a shoulder cut into it. The sill resting on it is tenoned into the brackets.

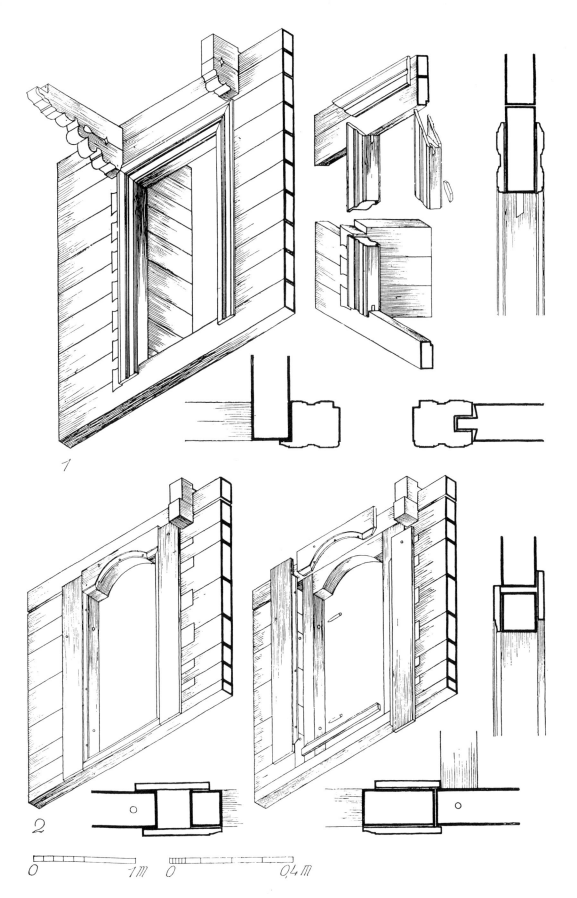

Fig 270
Doorway framing from Upper Bavaria, Germany: **1** from
Greiling; **2** from Arzbach. In **1**, the slightly protruding
door posts, fastened with skew pegs, are decoratively
contoured and combined with a similarly featured trim
board nailed to the lintel to form a complete frame. In **2**,
the door frame was installed as a single unit, following
which trim was added both inside and out.

211

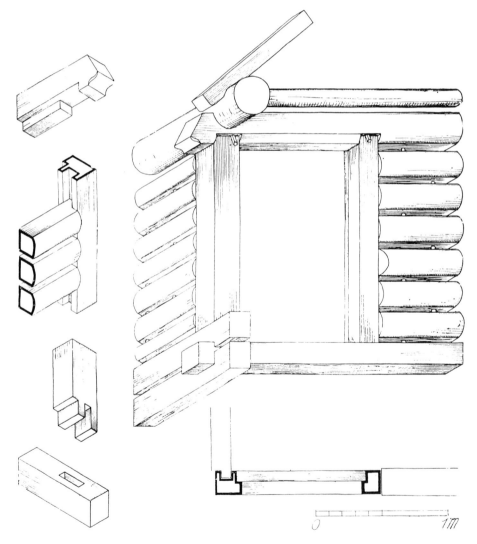

Fig 271
Doorway detail of a mill from Seeboden on the *Millstätter
See*. The wall logs are simply butted up against the right-
hand door post, while they fit into a groove in the left hand
one, which doubles as a corner post. Although in this case
the posts were put up at the same time as the logwork, they
have still been secured with skew pegs instead of tenons,
out of traditional custom.

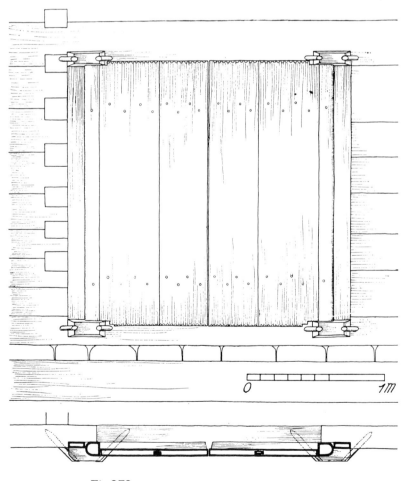

Fig 272
Barn door from Hirschegg, Vorarlberg, Austria. The
skillful use of skew pegging developed with West
Germanic post-and-beam construction is evident here in
the manner of fastening the beveled blocks of wood
holding the door pins.

273

274

275

Figs 273, 274 and 275
Barns from Hofgastein, Austria. Both the side posts of the double doors and the centre posts have been fastened with angled pegs.

Special Types of Door Framing

Of special interest is the practice of installing the doorframe as a single unit, an approach found in numerous different areas all the way up to Norway (Figs **282** and **283**). Here too, space had to be left for settling. The illustrations and accompanying texts on the following pages indicate how this was done.

One curious arrangement found on the door framing of a log granary in the Chiemgau region involved the use of a different joinery technique on each of the door posts (Figs **285/1** and **286**). Another doorway unusual in its framing and decoration occurs on a farm house in Villanders (south Tirol) dating from the Middle Ages. The covering board atop the door posts is secured by conspicuously oversize hand-wrought spike-heads, and features a fanciful border design (Figs **278**, **280**, **281** and **196a**). We may see as a kindred spirit the door shown in Fig **284** (left). An interesting point to ponder in all of this is that handcrafting buildings from solid unhewn timber gave the log builder of old greater scope for creativity and imagination than is possible for the builder of today with the lumber from sawmills.

Another noteworthy framing technique is one common in Latvia, where the door posts of plank thickness are groove-fitted into both sill and header logs (Fig **292**). In allowing space for settling, door posts were either set full-size into the header log, as in Scandinavian door framing, in which case the header had to be kept thick enough (Fig **288**), or the tops of the posts would be halved in various ways to conceal the gaps above them (Figs **287** and **288**). The former method points to the East Germanic peoples, who had the same building tradition as the North Germanic group. Indeed, the old-time craftsman's intimate feel for wood was such that, at times, doorway framing would not be fashioned straight-sided and of uniform thickness; instead sometimes displaying a venturesome inward bow toward the top, both in Scandinavian and Bavarian log building practice. The result was a singular motif only imaginable in wood (Figs **289**, **292** and **291**).

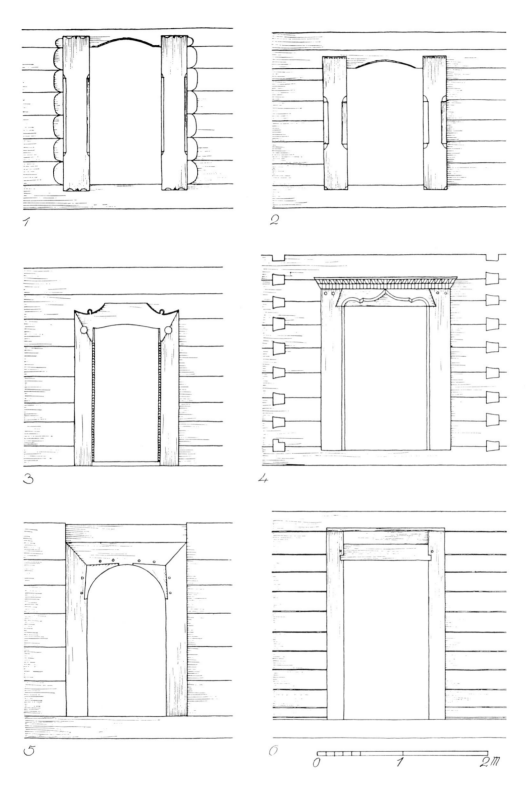

Fig 276
Some outstanding examples of doorway framing from: **1**
and **2** Upper Bavaria; **3** southern Tirol; **4** Oberfranken
(Upper Franconia); **5** Danzig; **6** East Prussia. The
numbers in brackets refer to the figures in which the items
are dealt with in detail. **1** Mettenham; **2** Schleching;
3 Villanders (Figs **278**, **280**, **281**); **4** Neukenroth (Fig
282); **5** Klein-Zünder (Fig **282**); **6** Königsberg (Fig **282**).

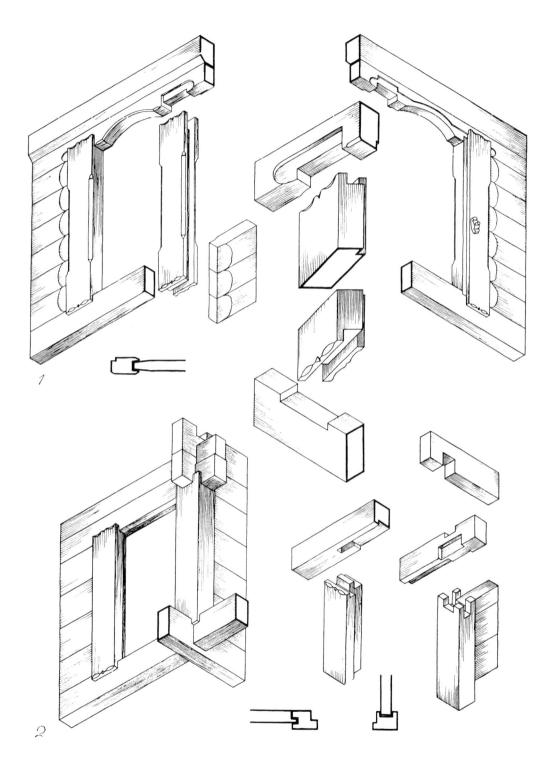

Fig 277
Details of doorway framing from a farmhouse: **1** in
Mettenham, Chiemgau region, Upper Bavaria; and **2** a
stable in Stalden, Valais, Switzerland. In item **1**, the door
posts hold the wall logs in a groove, while a tenon has been
added as well at the left post of **2**. Notice the skillful
joinery on the corner post, with its double-forked
mortises.

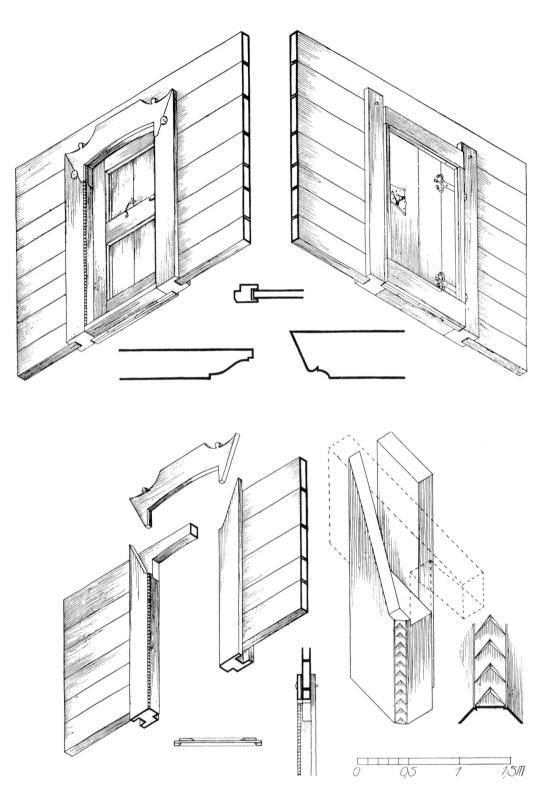

Fig 278
Interior door of a farmhouse in Villanders, near Klausen in southern Tirol (*c.* 1500). The wall logs are set full-size into a mortised slot in the door posts. On one side of the wall, a trim board has been added above the doorway, flush with the outer surfaces of the two door posts, thus completing the frame. The broad heads of the spikes, peened on a swage, also act as extremely effective decorative highlights.

280

281

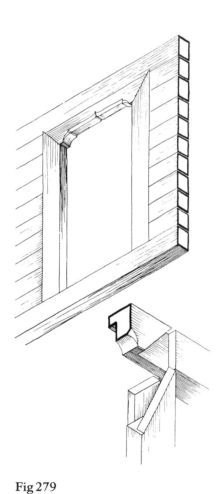

Fig 279
Doorway of a stable on the *Berghof* farm in Sölden, Tirol.
Here, the mitred side of the open mortise on the door
posts has been fully lapped into the lintel and the log
above it. The post has been mortised out and the mortise
cut so as to match the rabbet. This represents a late form,
since visible space for settling had to be left above the
posts when the building was constructed.

Figs 280 and 281
Interior door from Villanders, Tirol (Austria), from within
and without.

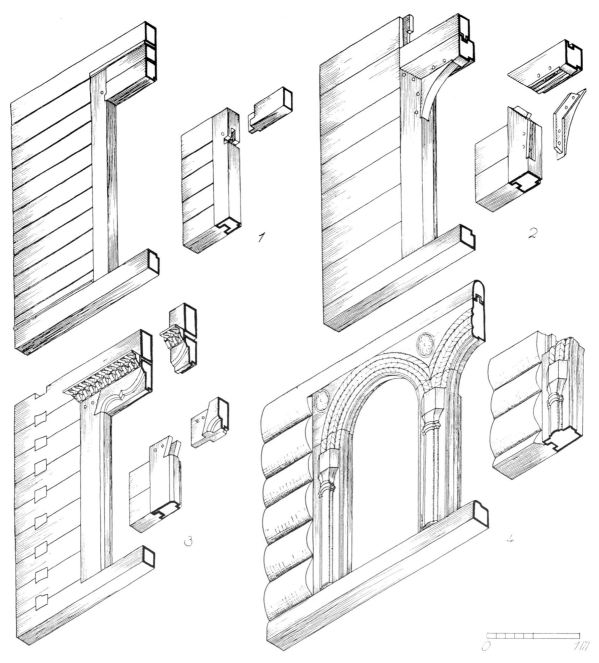

Fig 282
Doorways featuring single-unit door frames. **1** from a
klete (storehouse) in the open air museum in Königsberg,
Prussia; **2** from a farmhouse in Klein-Zünder near
Danzig; **3** from a farmhouse in Neukenroth in the
Frankenwald forest (1606); **4** from a *bjaelkestue* in Nikor
Sogn, Hardanger, Norway. In all four examples, tenons
on the log ends combine to form a tongue which is fitted
into a slot mortised out of the door frame. So much space
for settling was left in item **1** that a board had to be driven
into the crack at a later date to seal it. In **2**, the lateral
tongue extends all the way to the plate. In **3**, the builder
nailed a saw-toothed cornice moulding above the door to
cover the gap left for settling. In **4**, however, which is
conspicuously modelled after Romanesque stone
architecture, the extent to which the building would settle
had been calculated so precisely that when the logwork
did come to rest, the gap above the lintel was tightly
sealed.

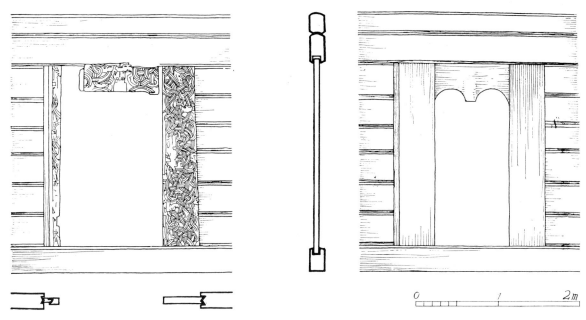

Fig 283
Doorway of the west portal of the *Blomskops-Kyrka* church in Värmland, Sweden (at left as it presently exists; at right in its original form without the intricate carving). The door frame, with its panels of carved tracery, is from an older building done in timberframe-and-staving and belonging to the thirteenth century.

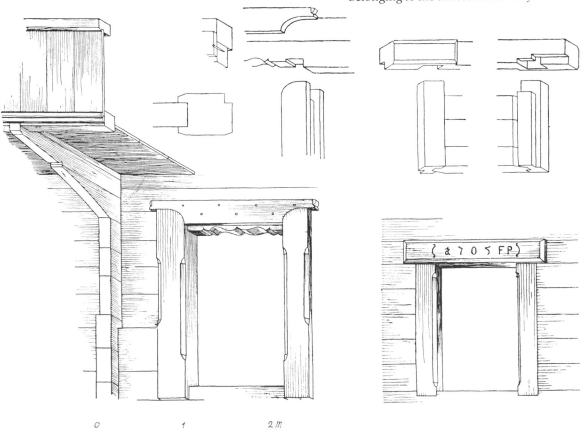

Fig 284
Doorways from the *Inneraltenhof* farmstead in Alpbach (Tirol) and a granary in Vorderbrand near Berchtesgaden, Germany. In the left-hand illustration, the wall logs are fitted full size into the door posts, which were left stout enough so that a groove of appropriate width as well as a mortise could be cut into them. Worth noting is the manner in which the covering board above the doorway (fastened with wooden pegs) has been organically blended with the protruding door posts. In the right-hand example, the door posts sit flush with the face of the wall. To provide a way to leave space for settling, a portion of the log above the door was left thicker and worked into a decorative motif.

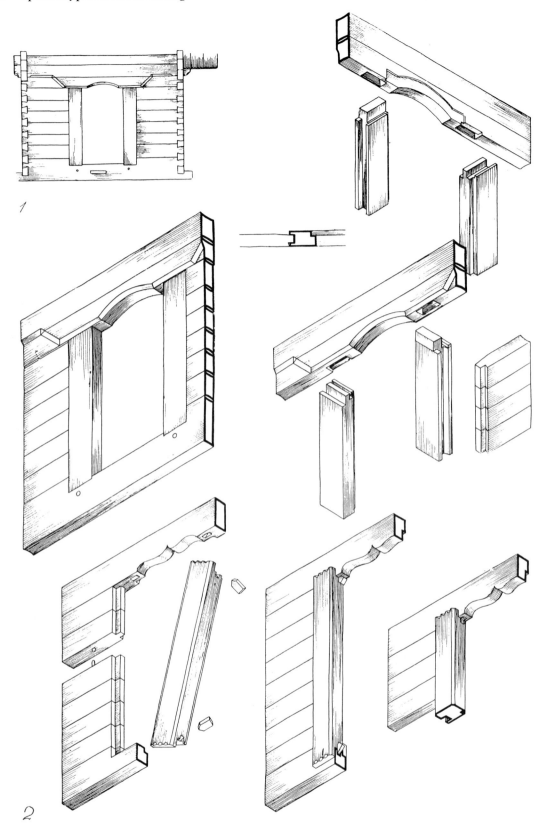

1

2

Fig 285
Detail of Upper Bavarian door framing from:
1 Landershausen near Schleching, Chiemgau. The lower item shows a blending of Bavarian joinery technique, with its characteristic skew pegging, and Celtic-style logwork. Notice how the builders have nicely tenoned the ends of the wall logs in the Celtic manner, despite the posts having been installed after the walls went up. The upper structure bespeaks an imaginative and at the same time a questing rural carpenter. He abandoned the traditional skew

pegging in favour of tenoned posts erected at the same time as the main logwork. It is the lintel, however, which shows the most remarkable aspect of all. The tenon on the left post is cut back on the outside, but only slightly bevelled on the right-hand one. This meant that a gaping crack had to result above the left post. From a compositional viewpoint as well, the protruding lintel piece and the artistic manner in which the log above it has been blended into the face of the main logwork show an innovative and creative mind.

Fig 286
Granary door from Landershausen, near Schleching, Chiemgau (Germany).

Fig 287
Doorway construction from the *Obertalerhof* farmstead, Alpbach, Tirol (Austria). The lower door is the older of the two. Different approaches have been taken to decoration on the tops of the posts concealing the gap left for settling. A gouge has been used on the lower one, while saw and skew chisel have been called upon for the upper door. Combined with the chamfered arch of the lintel, both create a unique architecture consonant with the nature of wood. Added effect is provided by the heavier logs over the doors, the lower one of which has been given a special accent with the addition of a small window which seems to have grown there of its own accord.

Fig 288
Architectural designwork on door framing from the Tirol and Vorarlberg, Austria. **1** from Pertisau, Tirol; **2** from Egg in Vorarlberg; **3** from Vals in Tirol. These beautiful examples illustrate the vast design potential inherent in the nature of wood, particularly when the material involved is timber in the round.

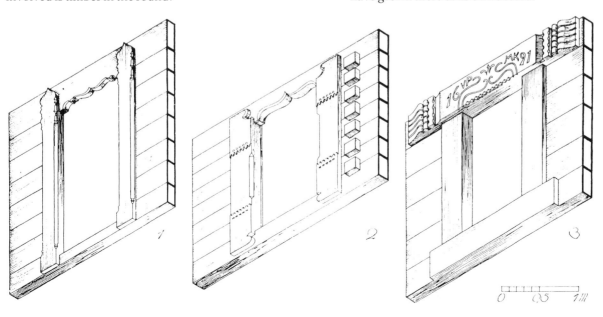

Fig 289
Doorway framing from the log-built granary on the
Aelvros-Hof farm in southwest Härjedalen, Sweden, now
in Skansen (Stockholm), and from the *kasten* (granary),
originally from Niederneuching, near Erding (1581) and
now on the grounds of the Grub property near Munich.
The inward-bowing door frames sound an elegant and
distinctive note, deriving entirely from the nature of
wood. Notice too how skillful axework has been used to
taper the logwork of the Swedish granary toward the door
posts, affording natural and extremely effective
embellishment.

Fig 290
Door construction of the log granary on the *Aelvroshof*
farmstead, Sweden.

Fig 291
Doors on the upper floor of the *kasten* (granary) from
Niederneuching.

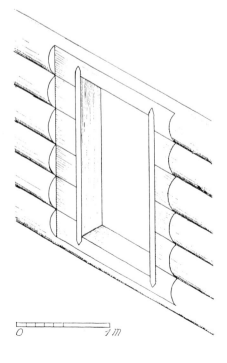

Fig 292
Doorway of a Latvian log house. The two door jambs were
not installed until after the walls had settled, and serve
only to cover the end grain of the logs.

Windows

Windows did not make their appearance in log buildings until well after door framing had reached an advanced stage of evolution. As indicated even by the latin root of the German word *fenster*, they emerged with the stone architecture borrowed from the Romans and came to log building by way of ecclesiastical architecture. A number of factors occasioned their adoption, among them the addition of a first-floor ceiling and the installation of chimneys, thus closing off the opening in the roof for the exit of smoke and the entry of light.

In early times, narrow slits would simply be chopped or cut out of the walls, enabling those inside to see out (Fig 293). These openings would start from the joint between two logs and take in only one log or those on either side of it. Gradually, they grew in size to become small apertures fitted with sliding shutters (Figs 293 and 294). In Gothic, such openings were called *auga-dauro*; in Old High German *auga-tora*; and in Old Norse *vind-auga*.

It is amazing to see the array of different sizes and shapes created by imaginative builders in this regard, and to consider that these are solely a product of their intimate feel for their craft. Because no more than one log would be cut all the way through to make these early openings, the dowels in the walls continued to provide adequate structural support.

The situation was somewhat different when windows of larger size came to be involved. In this case, special care had to be exercised in the design of the framing, simply to assure that the logwork would remain tight in the joints. A number of options were used, including vertical trimmer posts (Figs 295 to 298), splines (Figs 299 to 302), heavy timber frames (Figs 303 to 306) which in Upper Bavaria were at times set into a recess in the logwork, and lighter wooden frames (Fig 307).

To seal joints, trim and covering boards were nailed on, these in turn being the subject of innumerable designs and variations, as illustrated in Figs 297, 299, 300 to 303, 305 to 313.

To assure proper runoff of rain driven against window panes, window sills were also extended outward (Figs 300, 306, 307 and 312), or a special drip board would be nailed in place beneath the window, as pictured in Fig 300. In Silesia and the neighbouring areas of Bohemia and Saxony, a frame might also include a stout sill member which protruded well beyond the wall surface. Occasionally, a split-log would even be pressed into service here (Figs 308 and 309).

One fundamental design rule for windows fitted into log walls is that the moveable

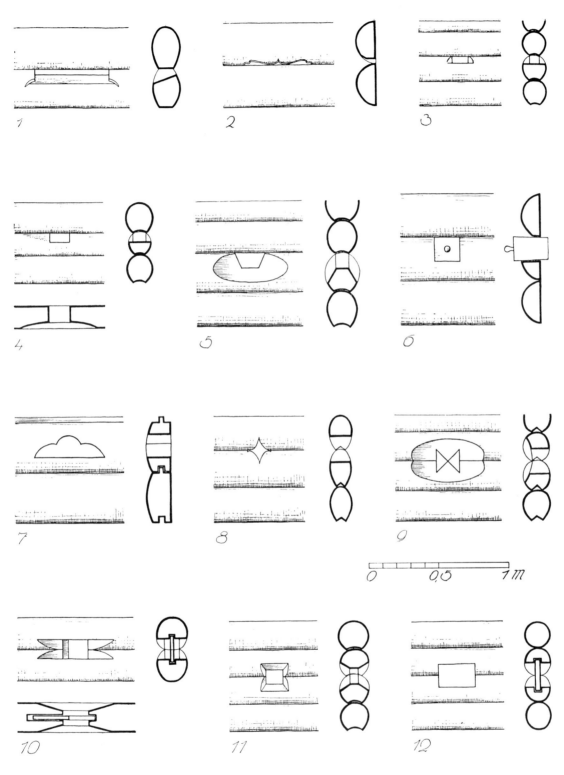

Fig 293
Loop-holes for light, some with covers, from log building countries. Items **1** and **8** are from Norway, **3** to **5** and **9** to **12** from Sweden; **2**, **6** and **7** from Switzerland. In **1** to **6**, the aperture has been cut from one log only. Even here, however, we see the variety and the variation inspired by a craftsmanlike working of the material, be it in the flared or scooped sides of the openings, or the distinctive shapes themselves. Item **7** shows an affected-looking opening cut in the middle of a log, a design copied from stone architecture. Items **8** to **12** show several different designs which include the logs both above and below a joint. Items **6**, **10** and **12** show some early means of closing the opening.

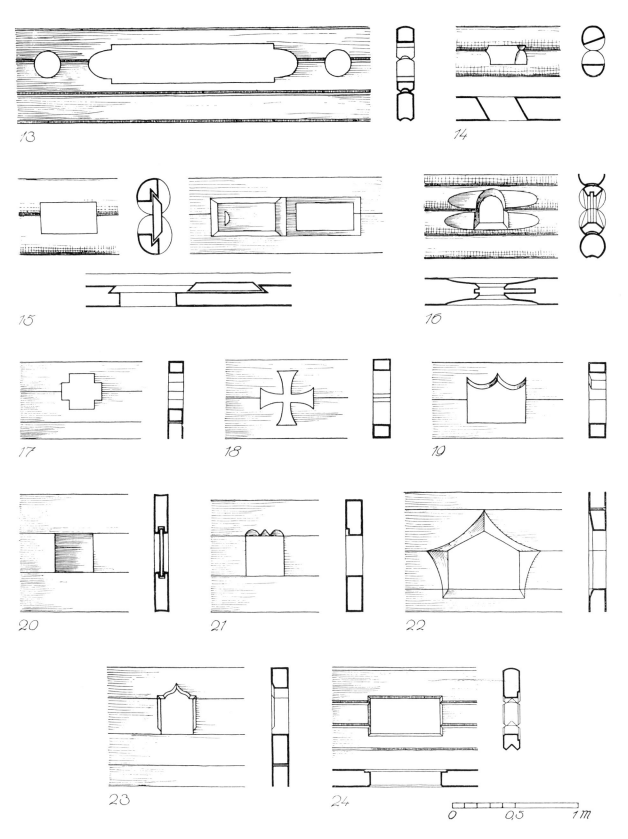

Fig 294

Window apertures from log building countries: **13** from Finland, **14** to **17** and **24** from Sweden, **18** to **21** and **23** from Switzerland, and **22** from Steiermark (Austria). In **13** to **19**, the openings were cut both above and below the joint between two logs and in a rich variety of shapes and sizes, without completely cutting away any one log. In **20** to **24** by contrast, a log had to be completely cut through.

When this was the approach, the adjacent logs might be left intact (as in **20** and **21**), or the cutaway portion might be enlarged to include the log above (**22** and **23**). Occasionally, the logs both above and below would be included to make the opening (**24**). The small sliding shutters shown in **15**, **16** and **20** were installed as the logwork was erected.

window itself and the frame surrounding it form a single unit, installed so as not to be affected by the settling of the logwork. This applies equally to window shutters, which must always be mounted on the window frame proper.

When multi-unit windows are installed and hence the window opening becomes fairly wide, deflection of the lintel log can readily occur. In this case, some form of steel reinforcement is acceptable (Fig **313**). Special mention need not be made of the fact that space for settling must be left above windows just as above doors (Fig **295**).

Fig 295
Showing a window before application of exterior trim. From Switzerland. Settling allowance has been left above the trimmers and the frame itself, in the latter case including a chinking of oakum. Trim is not added until after the logwork has fully settled.

Fig 296
Multi-window unit from Stalden, Canton Valais. These windows are set into a groove cut directly into the logs and the posts.

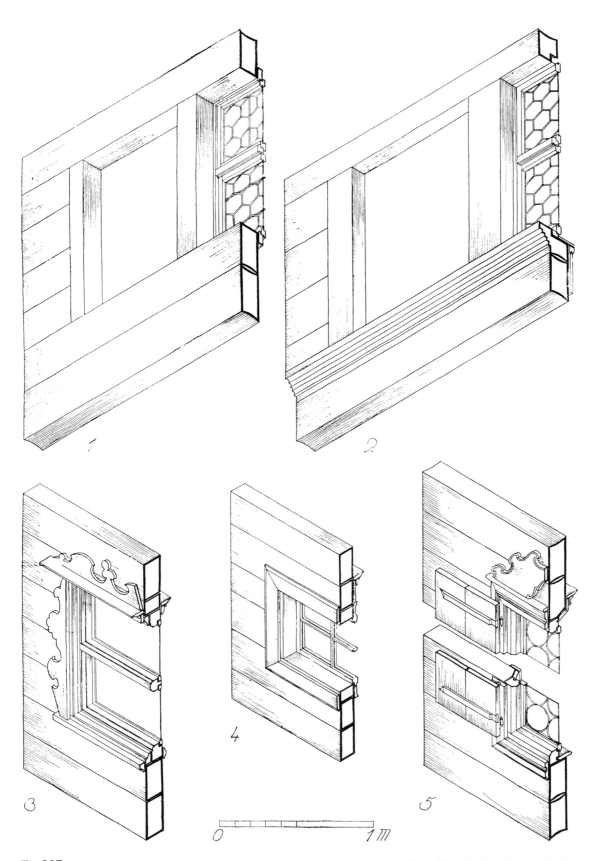

Fig 297

A variety of window designs from: **1** Rothenturm, Canton Schwyz; **2** from Erstfeld, Canton Uri; **3** from Pertisau, Tirol, Austria; **4** from Feistritz an der Drau; **5** from Bernlohe in Upper Bavaria. The windows in **1** and **2** are divided into two units, the upper one of which swings open, while the other slides. The frame is nailed to the interior logwork in **1**, while the unit in **2** is properly fitted into a rabbet. The windows in **3** to **5** all swing open, closing against a heavy frame. The rabbet against which they close is either cut out of the heavy frame itself (**3** and **5**) or formed by the frame and the trim boards (**4**). Because all of the examples shown are protected by a wide roof overhang, no special provision has been made for runoff from the sills.

Fig 298
Architectural styling on window frames of Swiss log
buildings. **1** from Meiringen; **2** from Wittigen near
Meiringen. Of the two richly adorned examples shown
here, both befitting the nature and character of wood, the
second is the more desirable design. Here, the builder has
confined himself to fluted grooving, and successfully
combined it vertically and horizontally into a unified
whole of the most vivid and striking eloquence. Notice
how the posts above the sill cornice come forward at this
point, and how their contouring blends into that of the

lintel.

Fig 299

Light wooden framing on windows from: **1** the roadhouse
Zur Sonne in Tschagguns; **2** from a farmhouse in Klein-
Zünder near Danzig; **3** from the *kyrkulthaus* in western
Blekinge, now in Skansen, Stockholm; **4** from a house
in Steiner; **5** from a farmhouse in Obereidisch in
Transylvania. In items **1**, **2**, and **3**, the frame fits flush

against the sides of the opening. In **4**, by contrast, the
frame has been replaced by two strips of wood which hold
the sash. While the rabbet against which the actual
window closes is cut out of the frame in **1**, **2** and **3**, it is the
window trim which is rabbeted in **5**. An interesting feature
of **2** and **3** is the manner in which provision has been made
to deal with runoff.

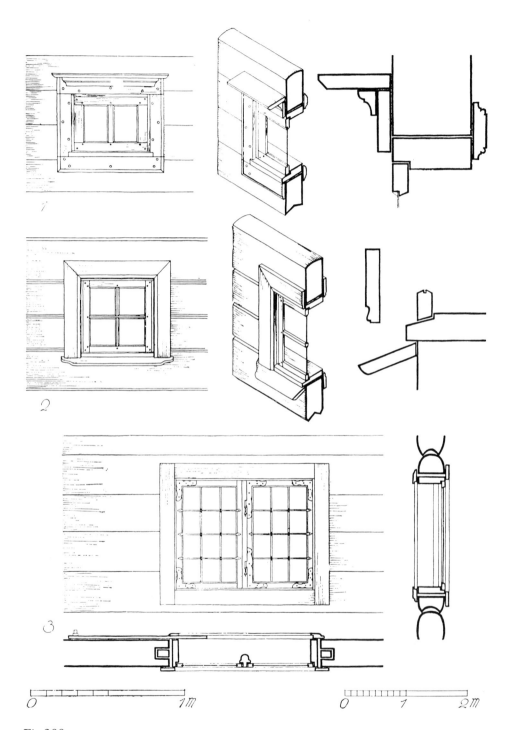

Fig 300
Light window framing from Scandinavia. To keep the wall
logs from moving out of alignment, splines are sometimes
inserted into the logs at the sides of the opening (3). In
items **1** and **2**, great care has been taken to provide for
runoff of driven rain from the sill. To prevent water from
entering the joints of the cover boards, the vertical trim on
the first window shown fits over the sill member.

Fig 301
Swedish light window framing from the *Laxbrostugan*, now in Skansen, Stockholm. These window units swing outward to open. An interesting feature is the blending of the window styling with that of the trim boards. On the inside, the sill is chamfered to create as smooth a transition as possible to the vertical surface.

1

2

0   1 m

0   0,5 m

Fig 302
Windows of the *Laxbrostugan* or Laxbro house from Västmanland, now in Skansen, Stockholm (*cf.* Fig **301/1**).

Fig 303 (opposite)
Heavy wood-frame windows from Bavaria: **1** from Wegscheid near Lenggries (from 1758); **2** from Niederneuching (from 1581); **3** from Greiling; **4** from Schlegldorf near Lenggries.

In **1** and **4**, the frames are fastened in place with skew pegs and are set into a rabbet cut out of the inside of the log wall, meaning that trim boards were only needed on the interior. In this instance, it was necessary that the logwork have fully settled before the frame was installed. In **2** and **3**, the frames are held on both sides by trim boards.

303

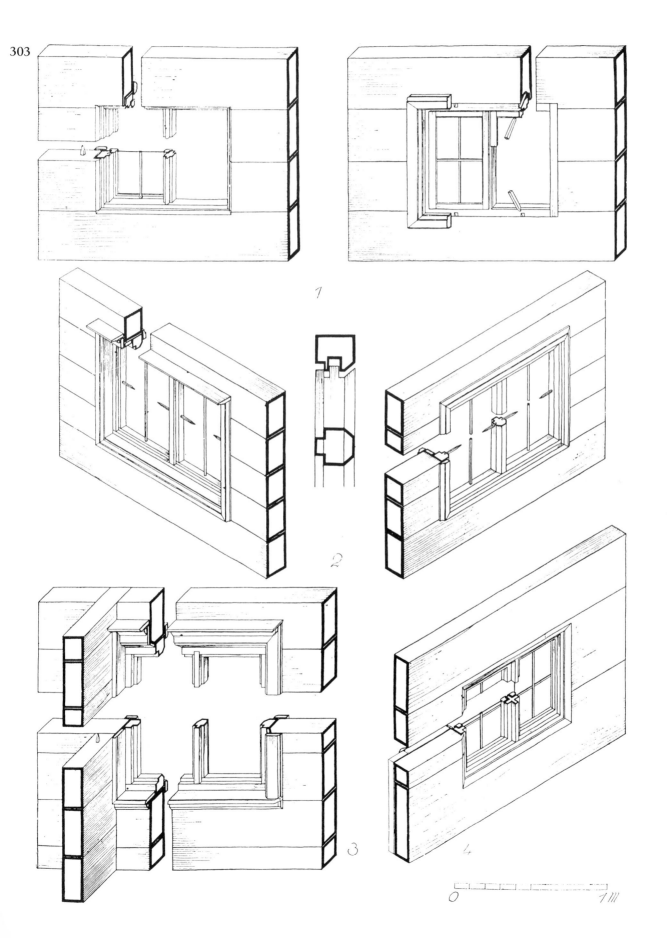

1

2

3 4

0 1 m

● 237

Fig 304
Heavy wood-frame window, set into a rabbet in the wall
and secured by angled pegs. From Wegscheid near
Lenggries, Upper Bavaria, Germany. This unit was only
installed once the logwork had settled.

Fig 305
Heavy-framed window of the so-called *hirtenhaus* near
Erding in Upper Bavaria. The trim boards and the shutters
were both correctly fastened to the frame. The entire
window unit thus remained independent of the
deformation which occurred in the log wall.

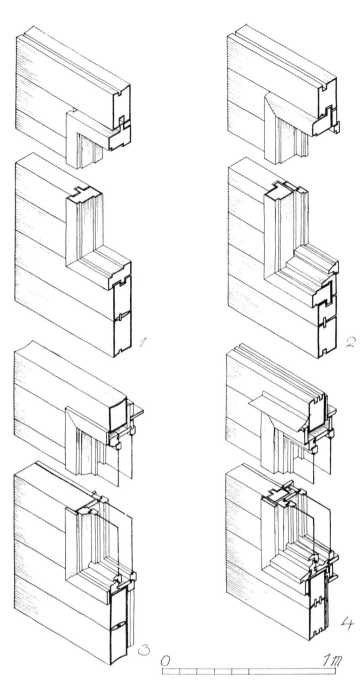

Fig 306
Modern-day heavy-frame windows: **1** from a ski chalet
owned by Max Meier and A.H. Steiner, both architects,
Zürich, Switzerland; **2** from the recent log buildings of
Brunold Brothers BSA., Arosa; **3** from a summer house of
the architect Max Schön in Lenggries; **4** from a ski cabin
of the architect Adolf Schuhmacher, Basel.

Items **1** and **2** show an interesting attempt to fit a tongue
on the frame into a mortised groove all the way around the
opening, installing the window unit as the walls were built
and leaving space for settling at the lintel log. This skillful
joinery makes trim boards superfluous, takes the place of
splines or trimmers, and assures effective runoff. In **3** and
4, the window units were added subsequently. These are
of a more intricate design than the previous ones, and
beautifully executed by a skilled craftsman.

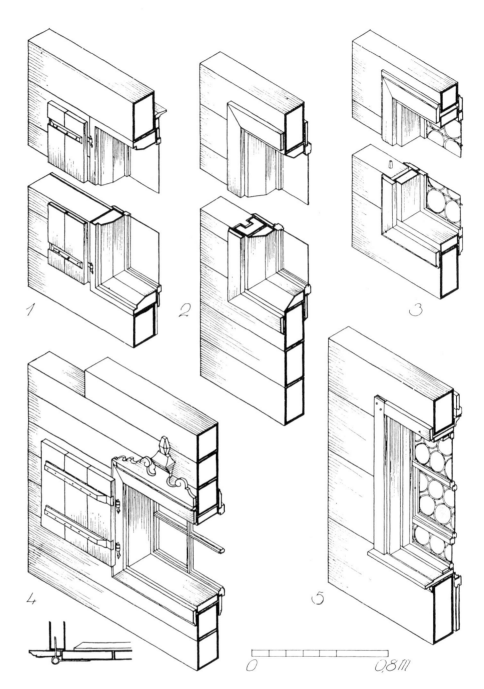

Fig 307
Heavy-frame window units from Alpine areas: **1** from
Neuhofen near Kraiwiesen, Salzburg, Austria; **2** from
Berg near Söllheim, Salzburg; **3** from Erding, Upper
Bavaria; **4** from Steegen, Oberösterreich province,
Austria; **5** from Hirschegg, Vorarlberg.

In **1** and **2**, the joint between the log wall and the frame
is only covered by trim on one side, while the others
feature trim on both sides. All show an exterior rabbet to
take the shutters, either cut out of the actual frame itself
(**1**) or formed by the frame and trim-boards together. With
the exception of **2**, where a trimmer was added. dowels
were the only means used to reinforce the openings cut in
the log walls.

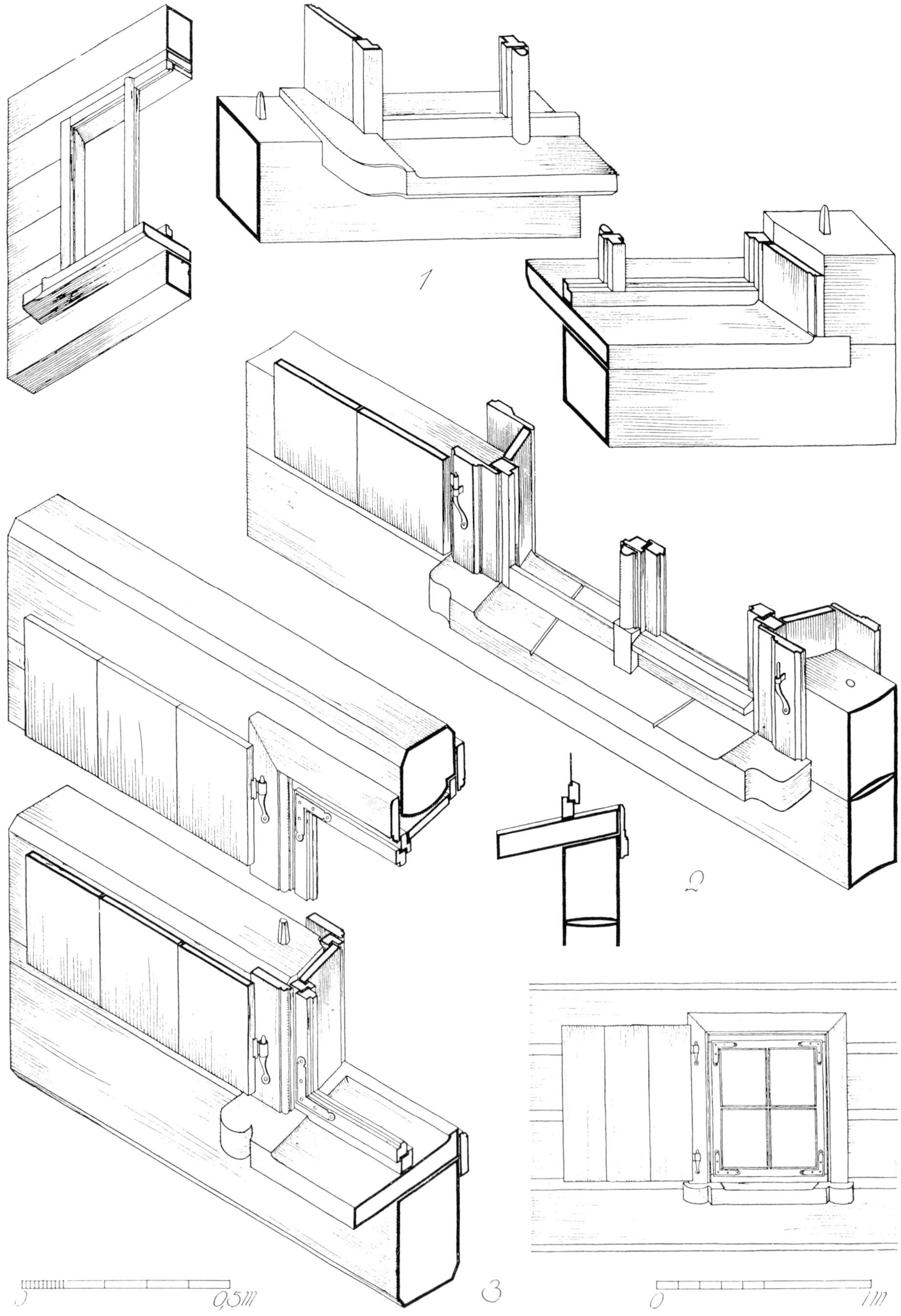

Fig 308
Window joinery from Silesia: **1** from Goldentraum;
2 from Zillertal; **3** from a farmhouse at the museum in
Hirschberg. The most salient feature of this style of
window framing, which extends into the adjacent areas
of Bohemia and Saxony as well, is the stout, boldly
protruding sill, upon which rest the side frames.

To facilitate the runoff of heavy rains, the sill slopes gently
outward. In addition, it is sometimes dished out with sides
angled toward the middle of the sill, much as a gutter. Not
infrequently, window makers would chisel grooves into
the sill to permit condensation to escape beneath the
bottom sash bar.

310

311

Fig 309
Window of a farmhouse at Hirschberg, Silesia, showing
the heavy tilted sill characteristic of houses in the
Riesengebirge mountains. Notice too the method of
chinking (*cf.* Fig **69/23**).

Figs 310 and 311
Exterior window trim from Obermillstatt in Kärnten, and
Arzbach near Lenggries in Upper Bavaria. In Fig **310**, the
top and bottom trim boards are dovetail-lapped into the
side ones. In addition to leaving the end grain exposed,
the horizontal members may not remain level because of
differences in settling. In Fig **311**, these problems are
eliminated as the trim boards are mitred at the corners.

● 241

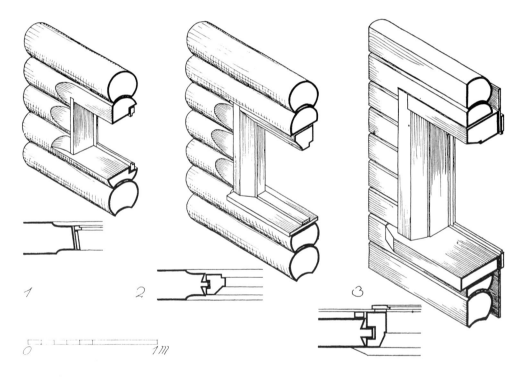

Fig 312
Window framing on log buildings in the village of
Tritschuny, White Russia. In item **1**, only one wall-log has
been completely cut away. Here, the rabbet against which
the window closes has been cut into the logwork proper.
The sides of the opening are formed by solid frames
mortised into both sill and header. Single-unit frames are
installed in **2** and **3**, with a tongue on the logwork being
fitted into a groove in the sides of the frame. Notice as well
the protruding sill.

Fig 313 (opposite)
More recent window construction from Upper Bavaria.
1 by Vinzenz Bachmann, Master Carpenter, Mettenham
(Chiemgau); and **2** by Max Schön in Munich. In both
cases, the window units have been installed after erection
of the log walls. Item **1** represents a first attempt at
creating a tightly sealed unit using a two-piece trimmer
and two splines, one into the logwork and the other into
the frame. Bolts with oversize heads have been used to
hold the system together. In **2**, the frame sits in a broad
rabbet cut into the logwork, as is not uncommon in Upper
Bavaria. Because of the need to leave space for settling, the
lintel log is unsupported over the entire width of the five-
window unit, with the result that it can easily sag in the
middle. To counter this problem, an S-profile steel
reinforcement strip was screwed to it.

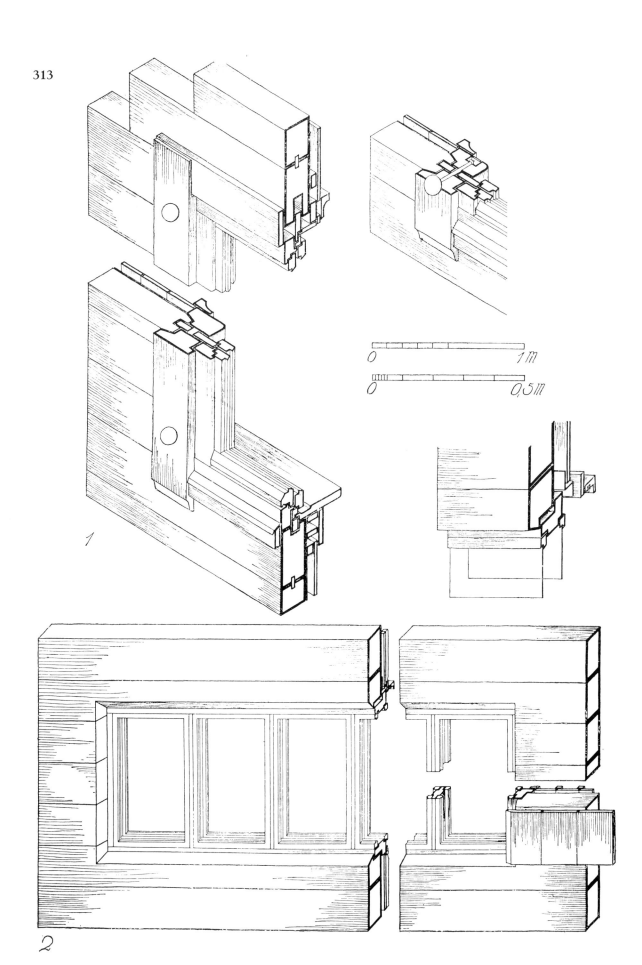

1

2

0   1m

0   0,5m

Balconies, Walkways and Other Protruding Features

Balconies and exterior walkways separate from interior floor or ceiling systems may readily be included in log buildings by extending wall logs at the corners or the intersection of partition walls to provide the structural support (Figs 314, 315, and 316). If, instead of a partition wall, beams or joists are extended to furnish this support, they are best braced by suspended brackets so as to remain unaffected by settling (Figs 317 and 318/1). In Switzerland, rigid diagonal bracing was also coupled with log-work consoles to support balconies, although this is only feasible on buildings which have already settled (Fig 318/3 to 318/6). Only when the extent of settling was so slight that it could be disregarded (*e.g.*, over the height of a single log only) did builders venture to include bracing in the form of integral timber brackets, added as the main structure was erected (Fig 318/2). As far as balustrade construction is concerned, the bottom rail is generally notched and fitted, pegged or even mortised into place.

In constructing balconies, special arrangements must be made to secure the balustrade. To do this, vertical pillar-like members, relatively slender in section, are usually tenoned into the bottom rail (Figs 314, 316 and 319). Overhead, they are customarily half-lapped, either to rafters (Fig 314/1 and 314/2), purlins (Fig 316), logwork consoles (Figs 314/6, 316/1 and 316/2) or beams extended expressly for this purpose (Figs 316/2, 319/1, 320 and 321). In a number of styles, these uprights became true columns carrying a top plate on which the rafters could then rest (Figs 314/3 and 316/4). In Norway, these upright supports may assume the form of half-logs gracefully drawn in at the middle (Fig 314/4) or of rounded pillars (Fig 315/1). In both instances, the upright is mortised out to take the top plate and bottom rail.

The many and varied timberwork styles of Switzerland include several in which the handrail of the balcony is notched right into wall logs extended well beyond the corner (Fig 319/2). Also found in Norway, Sweden, Finland and on down into Switzerland are ancient balconies partially enclosed by solid log walls, into which are cut openings for light in a variety of sizes and shapes (Fig 315).

For the upright posts to be erected right at the balcony corners, some appropriate framing must be available to receive them. Should it happen that a rafter is directly above the corner (Fig 316/3), a post may be brought up to meet it. As a generality, however, this opportunity will not be available and the upright cannot be positioned at the corner proper (Fig 316/1 and 316/2). When balconies are run only along the sides of buildings, the wall logs of the gable-end would sometimes be extended right out to the corners of the balcony, where stub walls of logwork would be notched into

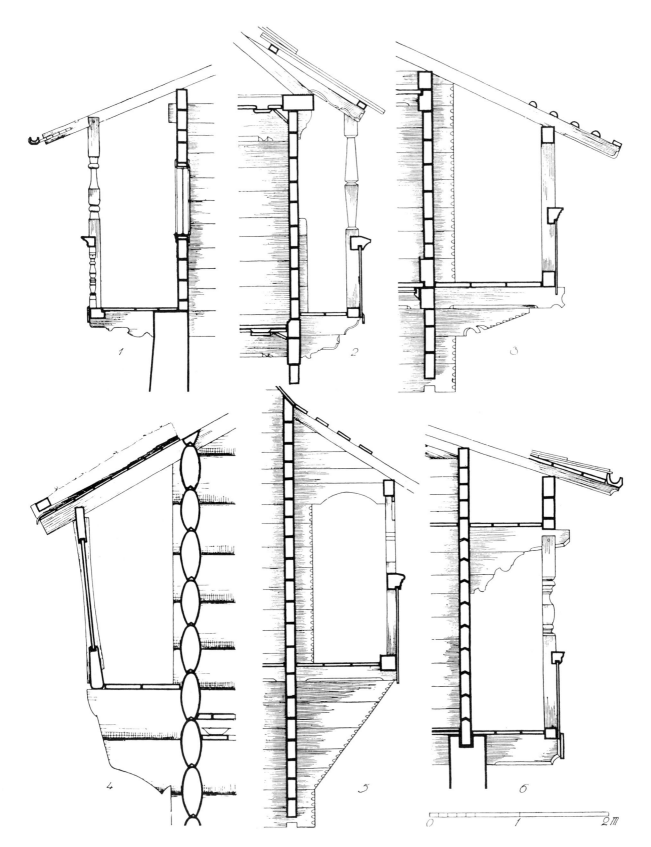

Fig 314

Columns on side balconies or walkways, providing upright support for the balustrades. **1** Fridolfing, Upper Bavaria; **2** Feistritz, Kärnten; **3** Wittigen near Meiringen, Canton Bern; **4** Dale, Setesdal, Norway; **5** Fürsten near Summiswald, Canton Bern; **6** Schliersee, Upper Bavaria.

Originally, the balustrade was held upright by vertical members, half-lapped into the rafters overhead (**1** and **2**). Strictly speaking, then, the word columns should not be applied here. Only when a plate or header is added atop the uprights is the term column appropriate (**3**, **4**, **5**). Where circumstances permit, this vertical member may also be half-lapped into the end of an extended beam (**6**), in which case it too should not be confused with a column, just as in **1** and **2**. In Norwegian log construction, the function of balustrade support is provided by the so-called *stolper*, which are sometimes inclined slightly outward so as to shed the rain. In addition, this keeps them from being affected by the settling of the log walls.

them to provide structural support which settled with the main walls (Fig **315/2**). Should the builder wish to add the upright posts when the building is first erected, resort must be taken to wedges, which can be backed off as appropriate during the settling of the structure (Fig **322**).

As a rule, the handrails of balconies are half-lapped into the upright posts and pegged in place, although tenoning is often used in Scandinavia. A distinctive style developed in Switzerland, with the railing being through-mortised and partially cut away, so that it could be fitted into the upright then slid down into a locking configuration mortised out of both sides of the post (Figs **323/1**, **323/2**, **323/3** and **324**). Alternatively, the railing would be fitted into the post then forced upward into a locking configuration (Fig **324/3**). The reverse also occurs, with the upright being mortised and tenoned to take the top and bottom rails (Fig **323/5**).

Originally, riven boards would be used to close in the area between the upper and lower railings, being held by a groove in the handrail at the top, and pegged to the lower rail at the bottom (Fig **317**). Eventually, riven boards gave way to sawn lumber

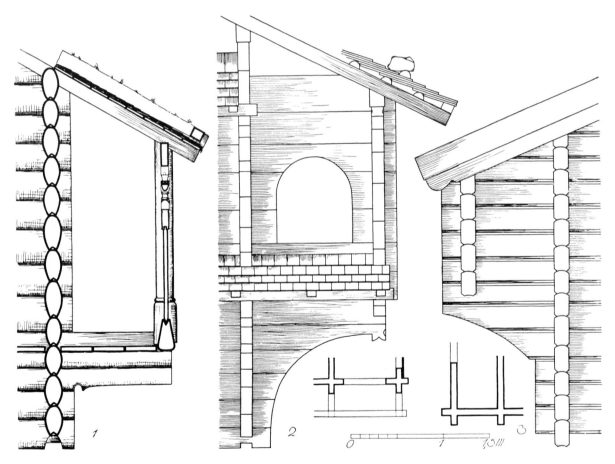

Fig 315
Side balcony arrangements: **1** from Haugen, Setesdal, Norway; **2** from Rothenturm, Canton Schwyz; **3** from Lundsjö, Sweden.

On the balcony at left, the corner posts are used to take the planking which encloses the exterior of the *sval* and to support the plank header. In items **2** and **3**, this function is performed by the logwork itself. In the first instance, provision must be made for settling of the log walls, whereas the stub walls of the other two structures settle

with the main logwork.

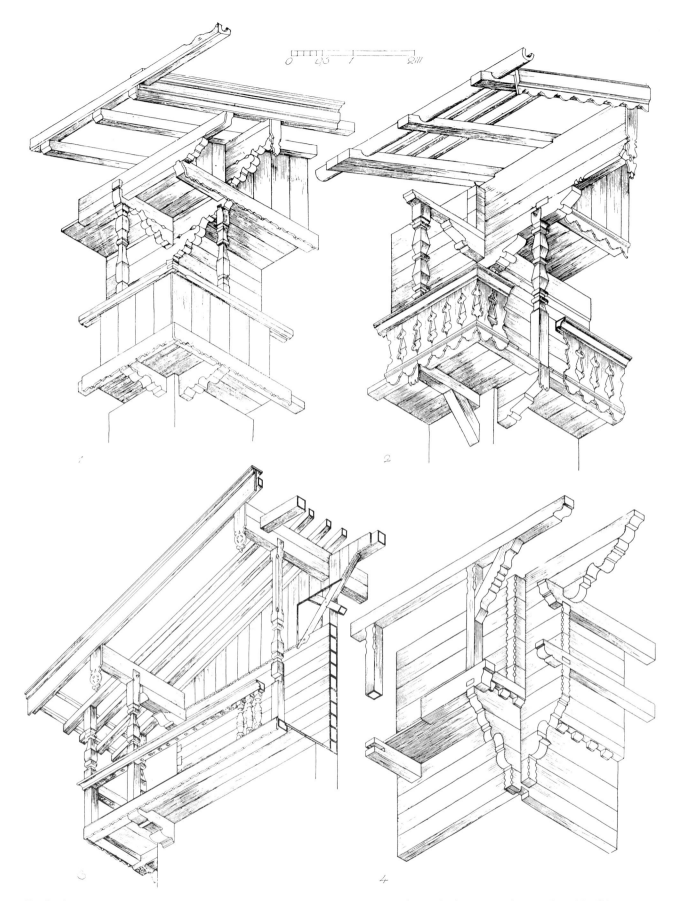

Fig 316

Framing detail on side balconies; Upper Bavaria, Austrian Tirol and Switzerland: **1** from Greiling near Tölz; **2** from Kirchbichel, Kufstein district; **3** from Fridolfing, Ruperti-Winkel; **4** from La Forclaz.

In items **1** to **3**, the bottom rail of the balcony is notch-fitted, whereas it is mortised in **4**. The difference between the styles extends to the upright posts as well, which are

tenoned into the bottom rail in **1** to **3** and half-lapped to protruding beams or purlins at the top. By contrast, **4** features uprights tenoned at the bottom, while being tenoned at the top as well to carry a log plate. In **3**, it is interesting to note the manner in which the ornamental work on the uprights has been expertly used to balance their different lengths.

and wooden pegs were replaced by iron nails (Figs **323** and **325**). In Norway, the technique of timber-frame and staving, known as *reisverk*, involves fitting vertical planking into grooves running completely around the perimeter of a timber frame. There, this system was also applied to balustrade construction, with boards being groove-fitted into both top and bottom railings, or top and bottom plates, depending upon the style (Figs **315**, **326** and **327**). To prevent water from entering the groove, the bottom rail or log sloped sharply down and away (Fig **326/1**). The advent of iron nails led to the addition of drip boards (Fig **326/2** to **326/5**), which however warp easily and hence tend to leak. In addition, they deteriorate rapidly when exposed to the elements. Being the beguiling mechanism that it is, nailing even induced builders in more recent times to create the groove itself by adding strips of wood (Fig **326/6**).

Iron also did its damaging work on the Alpine structures already illustrated. Instead of grooving out the underside of the handrail, for example, it was simply rabbeted (Figs **323/6**, **323/7** and **325/7**). For that matter, carpenters even gave up the practice of running the vertical boards down over the bottom rail; the most effective way of keeping out rain. Instead, the boards were set into a rabbet (Figs **323/9** and **325/1** and **325/6**). This meant that a covering strip or facer board had to be added. The result was frivolous forms of little durability.

New impetus, unfortunately destined to have the gravest of consequences, was provided by the stone architecture of the Baroque era, with its balustrades of luxuriant design. Carpenters and joiners began modelling their wooden balusters after those in stone, tenoning them into the rails at top and bottom (Fig **325/2** and **325/11**). Withal, the workmanship itself remained reasonably sound, with builders adopting proportions suitable to wood.

Once in a while, an attempt would be made to simplify things by rip sawing balusters turned on the lathe, so that only a half-spindle would be showing (Fig **325/2**). Eventually, the contours of full-spindle balusters were transposed to boards, since the saw heedlessly follows any pattern (Figs **323/5**, **323/9** and **325/9**, **325/10**). Meanwhile, there developed another approach to decorative embellishment, this time not focussing on the actual baluster boards themselves, but rather on a patterned motif formed by cutting away certain parts of two adjacent boards (Fig **325/3** and **325/8**). Figs **328** to **333** provide a photographic illustration of this development. However, the

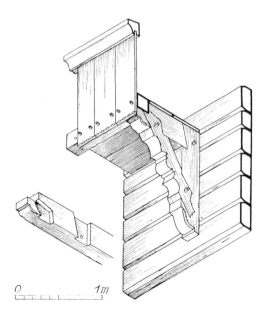

Fig 317
Suspended brace or bracket on the balcony of a farmhouse in Kärnten's Nockgebiet region. This feature has the advantage of being unaffected by the settling of the log walls. Initially used on the battlements of old fortified castles, this type of joinery later found its way to all-timber construction.

248 ●

0   1m

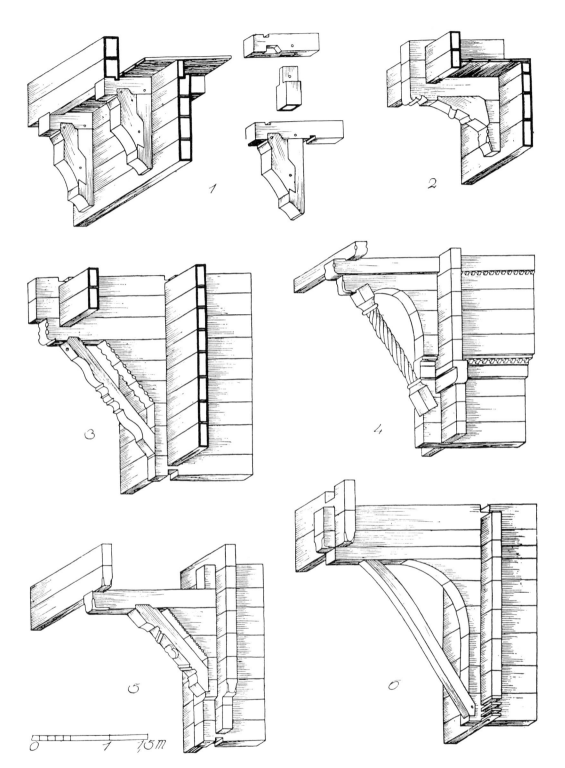

Fig 318

Cantilevered features supported by brackets and diagonal bracing. **1** Niederlungwitz near Glauchau, Sachsen-Altenburg; **2** to **6** from Switzerland.

On the issue of settling, item **1** shows a bracket combined with a suspended brace, providing a slip joint with the log wall. In **2**, the builders were able to include the bracket at the same time as the main logwork was erected because of the small amount of height involved in a single log. In **3** to **6**, however, the bracing had to wait until after settling. In **3**, the lower end of the brace was first tenoned into the end grain of the wall log, then driven into a locking recess on the underside of the upper log and pegged. In **4**, the top of the brace fits into a mortise, while the bottom is half-lapped into the extended log ends. In **5**, the top of the brace, which includes a locking shoulder, was driven in from the side, while in **6**, the brace is tenoned at the top. The lower joint is a pegged half-lap.

● 249

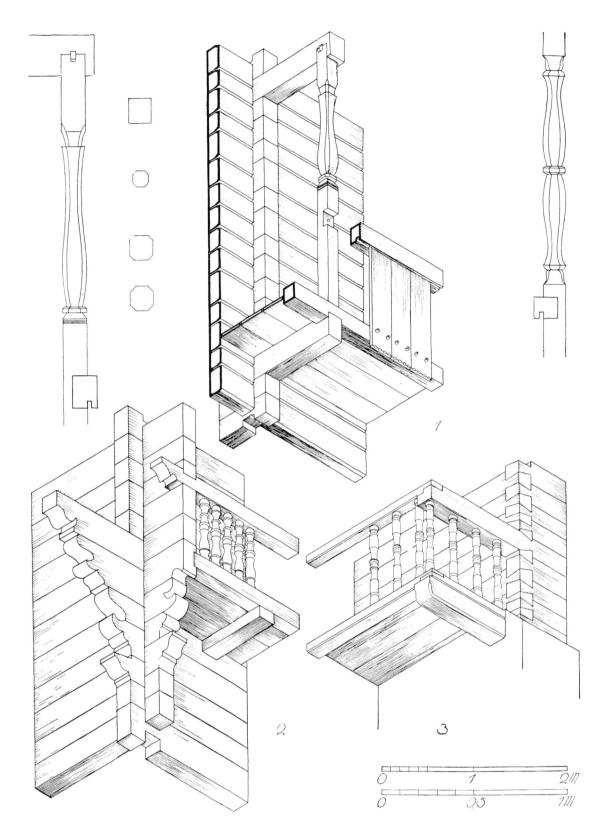

Fig 319
Upright balcony support systems: **1** from the Forstau region on the border between Salzburg and Steiermark provinces, Austria (at left from 1660; right from 1762); **2** from Champery. Canton Valais (from 1778); **3** from Steegen, Oberösterreich province, Austria (1758).

To provide upright support for the balustrade, special posts half-lapped into extended beams may be used (**1**).

The support may also be provided at handrail height by tieing the railing into the protruding cornerwork (**2**). Another alternative is to extend a log well out beyond the corner to perform this function (**3**). Evidence of the drawknife having been used as a shaping tool is visible on the uprights, as is that of the saw, although this has been confined to crosswise cuts.

Fig 320
Farmhouse in the Forstau region, Salzburg. Here, the balustrade of the balcony is kept upright by posts half-lapped into extended beams (*cf.* Fig **319/1**).

Fig 321
Farmhouse in the Forstau, Salzburg. Both balustrades are held upright by slender posts, secured to purlins, brackets and a single protruding beam.

use of sawn boards with sawn-out edgework, fastened moreover with iron nails, eventually spawned exaggeratedly quaint designs which give the observer, even though he may not be an expert in the field, a contrived and unhealthy impression.

To shed driving rain, balustrade boards must always be vertical. If placed horizontally, water can no longer run off as rapidly, a problem further complicated by warping. However, the most serious error in this regard is to further promote deterioration due to exposure by cutting ornamental designs into the boards (Fig 325/12). Even a design such as that shown in Fig 325/13 is inadvisable, since it allows rain to penetrate at the very spot where wood is most vulnerable, *i.e.*, where the end grain is exposed.

In addition, the creative design mind of early log builders also produced some delightful work in the restful wooden balustrades completely enclosed by plain boarding alone. In Kärnten, for example, the aim was at times to create an effect in the larger sense by extending the baluster boards below the lower edge of the balcony in a dovetail shape for a distance of about a meter in from the corners (Figs 334 and 335). On a different note, one farmhouse in the Isartal valley featured religious motifs placed here and there on the reposeful woodwork, as if they were delicate ornaments on their own (Figs 336 to 338). In similar fashion, the date of construction forms the decorative motif on a farmhouse near Lake Tegernsee (Figs 339 to 341).

Fig 323 (opposite)
Balustrade construction from log building areas of Switzerland. **1** part of a foot-bridge dating from the Middle Ages, Lucerne; **2** from Gladbach; **3** from a corn granary of the *Lüthi-Hof* farm in Waldhaus, Canton Bern; **4** from Gladbach; **5** from a fruit storehouse in Schwarzenburg, Canton Bern; **6** from a corn granary in Schnottwil, Canton Solothurn; **7** from a granary in Golderen; **8** from a house in Epagny, Canton Freiburg.

In items **1** to **5**, the tops of the balustrade boards fit into a groove cut out of the handrail, while the bottoms are pegged to the sill rail. Vulnerable spots are protected from the wet, and driven rain is able to run off freely. In **6** and **7**, the railing is rabbeted rather than grooved. In the latter instance, the sill rail has also been rabbeted to take an added trim board lower down. Here too, provision was made for runoff of heavy rains, although this aspect has been neglected in **8** and **9**. Here, the bottoms of the balustrade boards also sit either in a groove (**8**) or in a rabbet and moulding strip combination (**9**). Both allow moisture to enter, thus promoting deterioration from weathering. Moreover, the contouring of the railings does not really give that ''natural wood'' look. The connection between railing and post is unique, with the railing being through-mortised and partially cut away, so as to fit into and down onto corresponding notches in the post (**1** to **3**) or into it and upward, as in **4**. This produced some singular joinery configurations on the uprights, as shown in **1** to **3**. In **5**, part of the post was cut away into a tenon, onto which the railing was set. In **6** to **8**, the handrails are notched into the uprights.

Fig 322
Upright including wedges which can be tapped out gradually as the building settles.

323

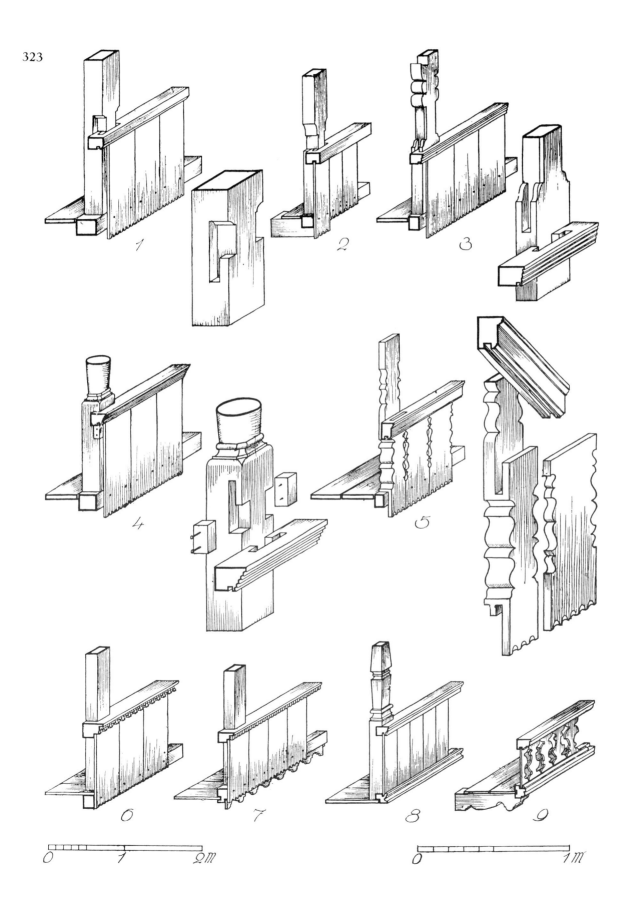

1 2 3

4 5

6 7 8 9

0 1 2m

0 1m

● 253

Fig 324
Balcony posts on a granary in Waldhaus, Canton Bern. In order to be able to cut out the mortises for the opposed tenons of the handrail and to fit them into place, the post above the joint had to be narrowed for a distance equal to at least the thickness of the railing. This was then carried on upward and worked back into the original form by way of a gentle undulation (cf. Fig 323/3).

Fig 325 (opposite)
Balustrades from log building areas of southern Germany, eastern Germany and Austria: **1** Fischhausen, Upper Bavaria; **2** Kiefersfelden, Upper Bavaria; **3** Garmisch, Upper Bavaria; **4** Gilge, Labiau district, East Prussia; **5** Ellenau, Tirol; **6** Söll, Tirol; **7** Alpbach, Tirol; **8** Maishofen, Salzburg; **9** Salzburg; **10** Pinzgau, Salzburg; **11** Mittersill, Salzburg; **12** Salzburg; **13** Obsmarkt, Salzburg.

In **5**, the boards are fitted into a groove in the handrailing and nailed to the bottom rail, as with the Swiss items illustrated. Unlike these, however, the boards here do not extend down below the lower rail to form a drip shield but rather leave a portion of the lower edge exposed. In **4**, as in the Swiss styles, the boarding is protected at the handrail, but in this case by a board nailed in place. However, this is of limited durability only, in addition to the fact that the boards must be nailed top and bottom. In **12**, the boarding has been applied horizontally, thus placing the edges of the boards at right

angles to any water being shed. This encourages the absorption of moisture. Because they are only nailed at long intervals, these boards are prone to warping. Finally, the decorative cutout-work reduces the strength of the wood. This untoward tendency to decorative effect also produced a horizontal trim board added over the boarding along the lower rail (**1**, **6**, **7** and **8**), a feature which gives rain an opportunity to attack the woodwork. In **3**, moulding strips are used to form a rabbet for the boarding. When balusters began to emulate the forms of Baroque stone architecture (**2** and **11**), any kind of

defence against rain at the lower rail was abandoned. Something like this was only possible because of the protection afforded by the roof over the balustrade. To reduce labour, lathe-turned balusters were sometimes re-sawn into two halves (**2**). From these spindle-like balusters there arose the custom of sawing balcony boards into decorative shapes, either individually (**9** and **10**) or combined to form cutout patterns (**3** and **8**). At times, the craftsman would lose himself in a form which, while highly picturesque, was nonetheless an outright invitation to problems from weathering (**13**).

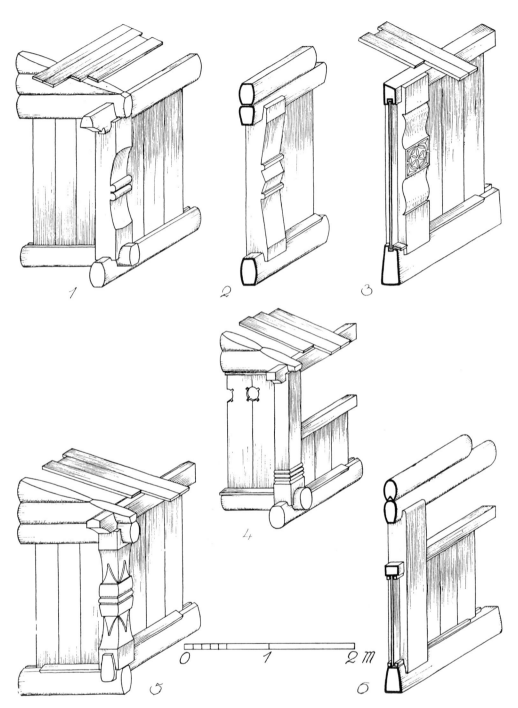

Fig 326
Balustrade and staving detail in the Norwegian log
building style. The items are all originally from
Gudbrandsdalen, now in Sandvig's outdoor museum in
Lillehammer (courtesy of Anders Sandvig). They show
extensive adaptation of these distinctively North
Germanic features. Whereas the staving boards in items **1**
to **5** are groove-fitted top and bottom in the old traditional
manner, they are held by strips of wood nailed on back
and front in **6**. The latter is a fairly recent feature, as
indicated by the fact that the strips have been saw-cut and
fastened with iron nails.

Fig 327
The Setesdal grouping (*Setesdalhof*), now in Bygdö,
Oslo, including two houses and accompanying *lofts*
(storehouses). The *loft* at left was originally in Valle
(second half of the 17th century), while that in the middle
is from Austad (*c.* 1700). The balconies on the granaries
and houses are of so-called *reisverk* construction, with
posts and vertical staving.

328

329

Figs 328 to 333
Balustrades of farmhouses from the Forstau region
(Salzburg), Pförn on Lake Tegernsee, Schladming
(Steiermark) and the Isartal valley near Tölz. Fig **328**
shows the traditional style of boarding, while Figs **329**

and **330** illustrate balustrades modelled after stone
architecture. Figs **331** to **333** show the influence of turned
balusters on balcony boarding. Fig **329** Corner of a
balustrade with turned balusters from Pförn near Egern on
the Tegernsee (from 1776).

Fig 330
Balustrade and balusters of a farmhouse in Greiling, near Tölz.

Fig 331
Balustrade of a farmhouse from Schladming, Steiermark province (Austria). The boards enclosing the balcony are cut out in the shape of turned balusters. At the top, they are let into the handrail, while being fitted into a rabbet and nailed at the bottom.

Fig 332
Boarded balustrade on a farmhouse in Greiling near Tölz.

Fig 333
Boarded balustrade on a farmhouse in Greiling near Tölz.

Fig 334
Corner styling of a balustrade from Patergassen in the Nockgebiet region of Kärnten, Austria. The vertical boarding, which fits into a groove in the handrail, is fastened at the bottom with protruding wooden pegs. The corners of the balustrade are highlighted by four boards, extended below the lower edge of the others and cut into a dovetail pattern. This motif is characteristic of Kärnten.

● 259

Fig 335
Corner portion of the balustrade on a farmhouse in
Radenthein, Kärnten.

336

Fig 336, 337 and 338
Farmhouse in Wegscheid near Lenggries (Upper Bavaria),
showing balustrade adorned with religious motifs. In
depicting a church, cutouts have been used to represent
the spire, the door and the windows. Incised carving and
colour have been used to indicate the main part of the
building.

337

338

Fig 339
Farmhouse near Gmund on the Tegernsee, with the year
of construction cut into the balustrade.

Fig 340
Corner detail, balustrade of a farmhouse near Gmund.
The numerals and the fancy cutouts are actually within the
baluster boards. This afforded greater scope for creative
work than if a design were interrupted by the line between
two boards.

Fig 341
Corner design of the balustrade on a farmhouse near
Gmund. The cutout six shown here illustrates the hazards
of cutting away part of a board without adequate regard
for potential warping and splitting.

Gable Sheathing

When the log walls do not continue on up into the gable area (Fig **342/2** to **342/4**) or if the building is enclosed by boarded staving (Fig **342/1**), some form of vertically installed sheathing must top off the main logwork if we are to stay with wood. This necessitates a contrast to the horizontally laid logs and the dissimilar character which they embody. This vertical sheathing material is fastened to the rigid timber frame with wooden pegs (Figs **342/3**, **342/4**, **343** and **344**) or iron nails (Figs **342/2** and **345**). In Norway, gable boarding was frequently groove-fitted (Fig **342/1**).

A distinctive form of timberwork evolved where the Alemannic people, bringing with them their traditional post-and-beam construction (Fig **346**), pushed into areas where Celtic-style log building prevailed. When these newcomers found that solid log walls were much better able to withstand the severity of wind and weather high up in the mountains than were those of boarded-in timber framing, they gradually adopted logwork for living quarters and sheltering livestock. However, they retained their native framing in the gables and in mow areas. And just as events themselves may in the course of time flow from the heroic to the lyric, the austere post-and-beam gable eventually gave way to elegant and intricate framing systems such as those shown in Fig **347**. To prevent roof purlins from shifting out of place, diagonal bracing was added, as were tie beams between the uppermost pair of purlins, which also served to carry a king post and struts. Even in early post-and-beam construction, the planking, which was about half the thickness of the wall, was applied flush with the inside surface, leaving the timber frame clearly visible. This custom lived on in a sense with the practice of applying gable boarding to the inside of the more intricate framing styles which evolved. Now since the structure in the larger sense had taken a turn to the picturesque, not even the graceful timber struts were able to retain their simple square-edged form, being obliged instead to take on ornamental contouring. Whatever the tools used to produce this, be it drawknife, chisel or the unfeeling saw, the results were fairly much appropriate to the character of wood and the functional role of the various items of timberwork.

It is interesting to notice how gable walls, which need not fulfill the major functions of those enclosing living quarters, also came to include picturesque designwork when the sheathing was applied exterior to the timber frame. In Germany's East Prussia, for example, the gable might jut out the thickness of a log (Fig **342/2**). In Kärnten, Austria, the quaint effect was at times produced by offsetting the boarding at collar-beam height, shifting it outward beyond the plane of the house wall or balcony railings to that of a pair of rafters pushed forward at the gable (Fig **342/3** and **342/4**).

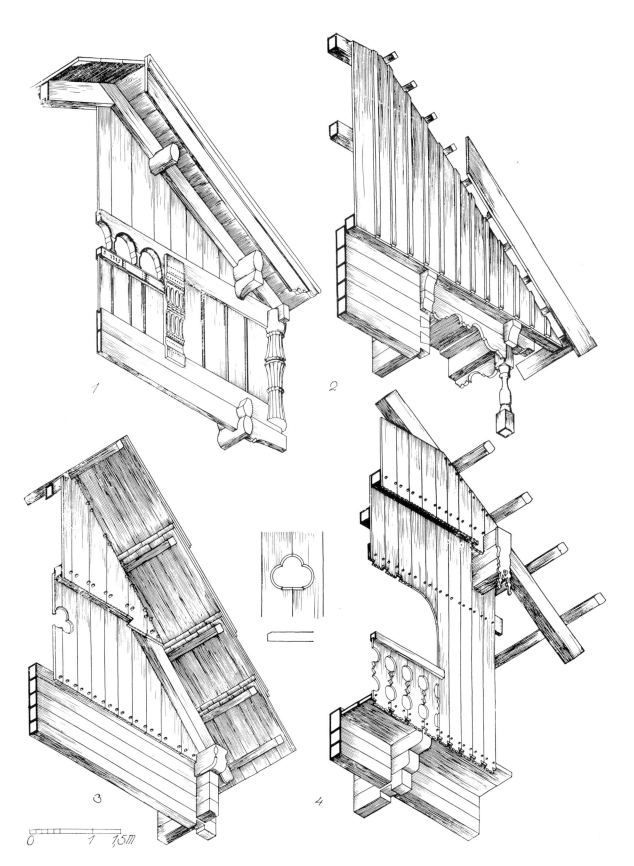

Fig 342
Boarded gables: **1** on a *loft* from Telemark, Norway; **2** on
a farmhouse in Gilge, Labiau district, East Prussia; **3** from
Obermillstatt, Kärnten; **4** from Fanning, Lungau,
Salzburg.

In **1**, the boarding is groove-fitted; pegged in **2** to **4**.

While the middle of the rafter underside accepts the
boarding in **1**, the three subsequent items show use of one
or both sides of the outermost pair of rafters for fastening
the sheathing. In itself, this produced an extraordinarily
effective exuberance, underscored in miniature by the
protruding wooden pegs and slender battens.

265

Fig 343
Hay barn with boarded gable from Radenthein, Kärnten.
The boarding has been fastened with visible wooden pegs,
affording striking embellishment to the structure as a
whole. No iron nails were used, except on the handrail
covered by two boards.

Fig 344
Farmhouse in St. Oswald, Kärnten. The sheathing boards
on the gable and the boarding of the balustrade have been
simply applied side by side. To provide a decorative
accent, several boards were extended below the bottom
edge-line and cut into a dovetail pattern.

Fig 345
Farmhouse in Wegscheid near Lenggries. The joints
between the boards covering the gable are hidden by
battens; a technique which has developed only since the
advent of the iron nail.

● 267

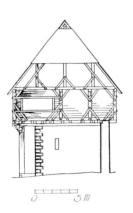

Fig 346
House from Pfullendorf, Germany, in West Germanic
post-and-beam construction and dating from the late
Middle Ages.

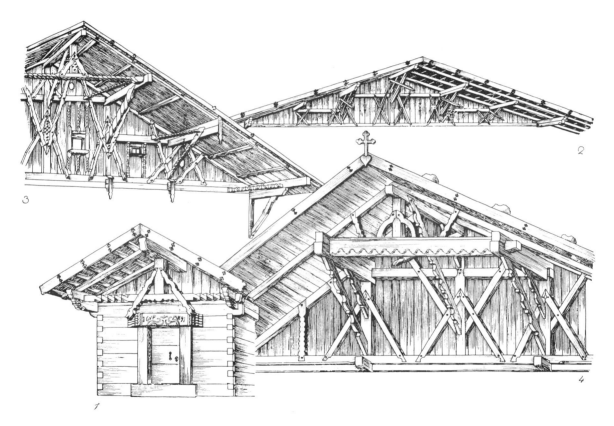

Fig 347
Gable-end framing, showing intricate timberwork and
vertical boarding: **1** from Vals near Schule in the Valsertal
valley, Tirol; **2** from Garmisch, Upper Bavaria; **3** from
Stuben in Tirol; **4** from Heiligkreuz near Hall, Tirol. These
picturesque framing techniques evolved from Alemannic
(*i.e.*, ancient West Germanic) post-and-beam construction
(Fig 346). On gables, this in time became a rich and
graceful form of timber framing. The doubled purlins
facilitated the extension of rafters beyond the gable, either
with or without a tie beam, where even open framing
might be incorporated (**1**, **3** and **4**). A favourite practice
involved cutting ornamental light openings into the
sheathing boards (**2**) or placing small windows inside the
timberwork framing (**3**). Volume II will provide a more
detailed look at this type of framing.

Flared Log-end Treatment

In its earliest form, flared cornerwork was an outgrowth of the protruding log end. Here, as with other architectural features, the creative impulse of the old-time log builder soon made its mark, producing a multitude of alternatives to resolving the transition from the vertical to the horizontal. The most striking of these emerged where the saw was left untouched or used only sparingly (Figs **348/1**, **348/4**, **350**, **351**, **352**, **353** and **354**) or where used moderately in a manner consistent with the nature of wood (Figs **314/3**, **314/5**, **315/2**, **355**, **356** and **357**). One interesting feature encountered from Scandinavia on down into Switzerland is the short downward return taken by the vertical line of the projecting log ends or the keyed cornerwork just before the outward flare begins (Figs **348/1** to **348/3**, **349**, **350** and **351**). Where the saw assumed the dominant role in shaping and forming, much of the natural character of wood is lost. Despite powerful contrasts, features so formed have less of an expressive impact than those previously described, nor do they have the same heart and soul; something which must be especially emphasized (Figs **348/3** and **356/2**).

However, these saw-cut designs are the very ones at the forefront of things today, making it especially timely that we contrast them with others created by tools which showed greater regard for the essential nature of wood. A demonstration of this kind not only points the way to proper craftsmanship, but also discloses unsuspected beauty and fineness which may be evoked from wood, quite literally, with a flick of the wrist.

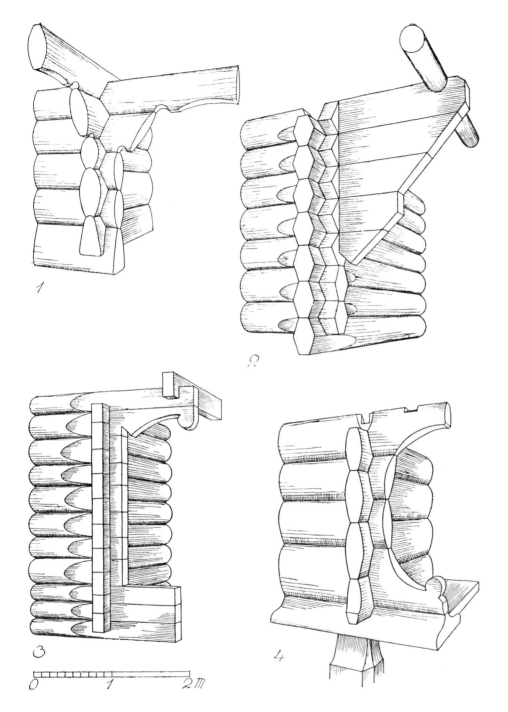

Fig 348
Flaring endwork from Norway and Sweden:
1 Nordgarden, Åseral, Norway; **2** Mora, now in Skansen, Stockholm; **3** Karelia, formerly Sweden; **4** Rjukan, Telemark, Norway.

In item **1**, the basic shape of the logs is largely retained despite the outward flare of the log-ends. An interesting feature is the manner in which various builders sought to make the transition from the vertical line of the log ends to the horizontal just at the point where the logs begin to flare outward. In **2** to **4**, a number of logs combine to create a single design feature. This is further accentuated in **2** and **3** by the fact that the logs have been hewn in contrast to their original round shape. The Norwegian styles shown here are more in keeping with the natural character of solid timber than are those from Sweden. Except for the reversal of direction where the bottom of the flared endwork meets the vertical in **2**, this design might be imagined in stone as well. In **3**, the indentations appear too extreme, doing undue violence to the logs. To appreciate this, compare **3** with the Norwegian logwork above it.

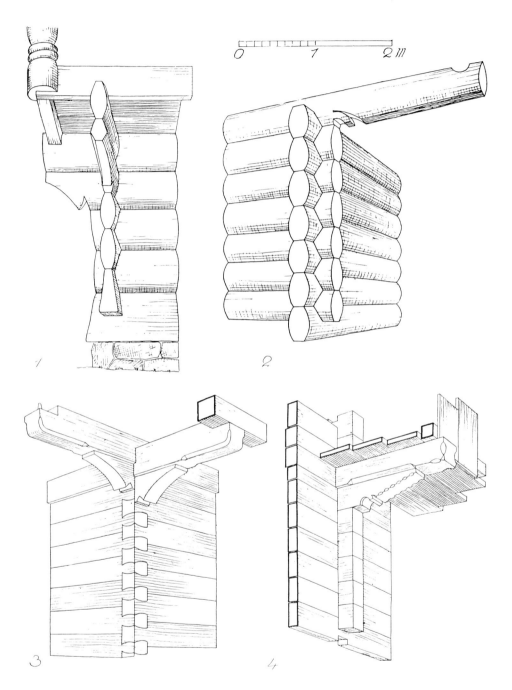

Fig 349
Cantilevered endwork from Norway, Sweden, Upper
Bavaria and Switzerland, showing similar decorative
styling. **1** from Torslid, Fyresdal; **2** from the *Mora-Hof*,
now in Skansen; **3** from the *Spiegelhof* near Tölz; **4** from
Wittigen. All four show the notch in the lowermost of the
protruding logs, a feature which arrests the upward line of
the cornerwork and ushers in any number of configurations
leading to the outermost log end. Even here there are
similarities of approach, as evidenced by **1** and **3**, for
example, or **2** and **4**.

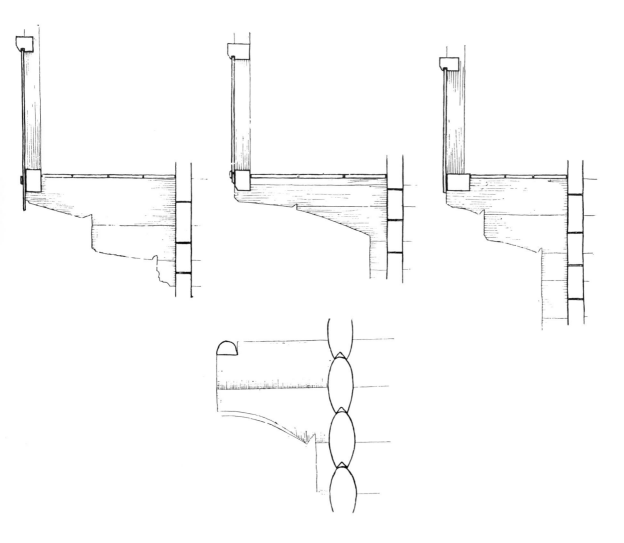

Fig 350
Flared endwork on farmhouses in Alpbach (Tirol)
contrasted with that of a *loft* from Mannpann, Valle
(Setesdal), Norway. Both styles show the same flat arch
and the same notch to begin the flare. The notch
originated with the old carpenter's practice of notching to
indicate the ending of the log beneath. In addition to this
decorative feature, further characteristics may be found in
the Alpbachtal valley which point to a Nordic (in this case

East Germanic) architectural heritage.

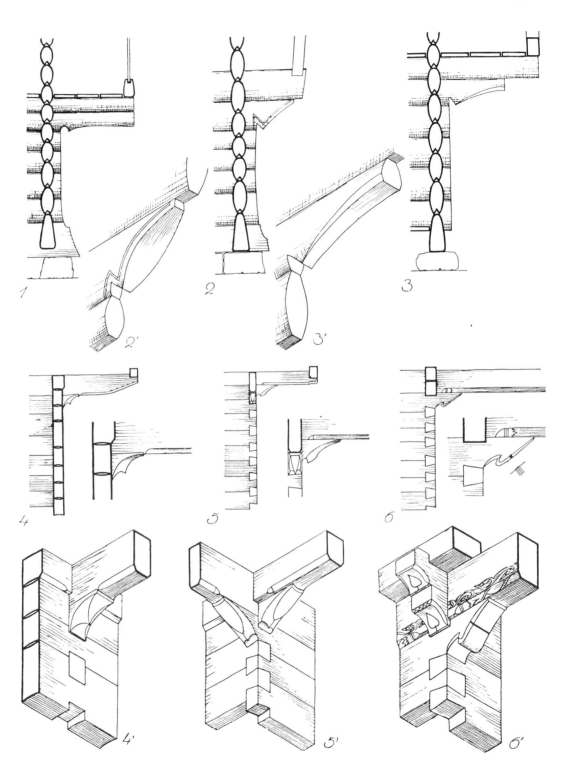

Fig 351

Extended log-end configurations: **1** to **3** on log houses (*arestue*) and granaries from Norway; **4** dwellings from Lain near Lenggries; **5** dwellings from Wackersberg near Tölz; **6** a *kasten* from Niederneuching near Erding, dating from 1581, now on the grounds of the *Staatsgut Grub* near Munich.

The Norwegian timberwork, done without the aid of a saw in the styles of the Middle Ages, is untouched by the influences of stone architecture, whereas the Bavarian work shows features which had their origins in the so-called "diamond-cut" quarry stone on the one hand, and the consoles of solid masonry construction on the other. This notwithstanding, application of the drawknife here has produced a craftsmanlike re-working in wood. In these latter three items, cutting across the grain was done by saw.

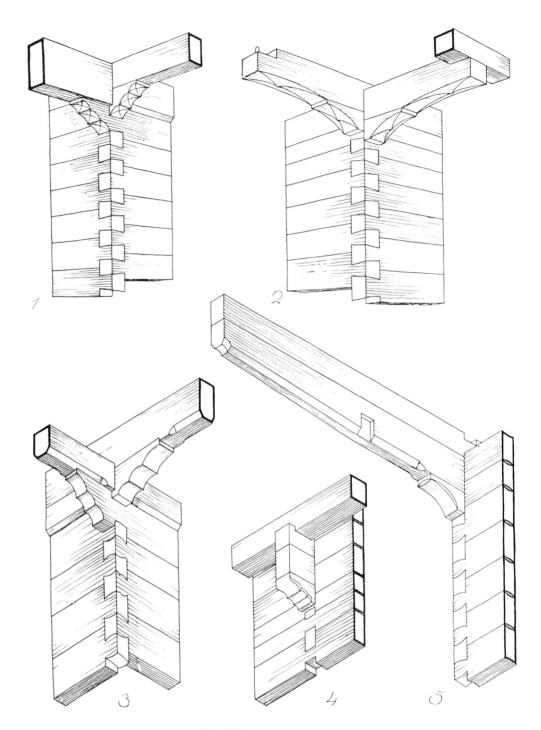

Fig 352
Cantilevered log-end designs from the log building area of
Upper Bavaria. **1** Wackersberg near Tölz; **2** Fischhausen
on Lake Schliersee; **3** Arzbach near Lenggries; **4** Erding;
5 Mettenham near Marquartstein. All of the logwork
clearly shows evidence of drawknife carving. Although
the diamond-cut stonework popular during the
Renaissance has had some impact on item **2**, the builders
were still sufficiently in touch with the nature of wood to
produce a craftsmanlike re-working in timber. Most
beautiful and expressive in appearance is **5**, where the
form seems to flow naturally, as it were, out of the grain of
the wood.

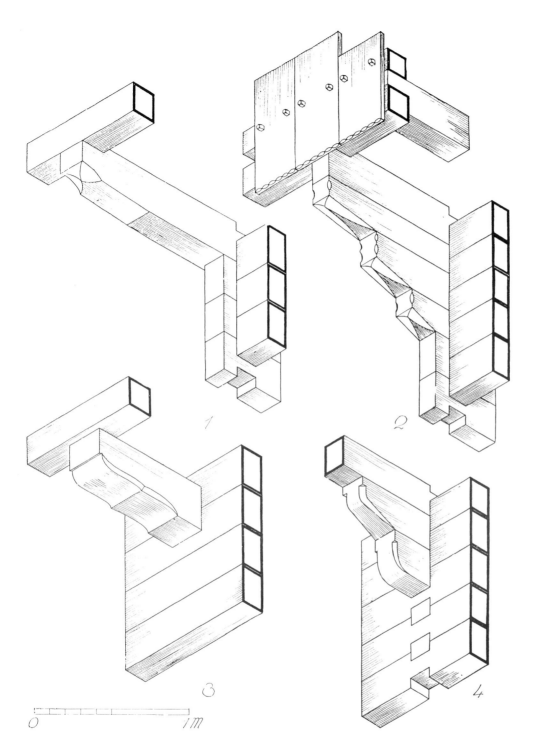

Fig 353
Log ends worked with drawknife, *klingeisen* and gouge; all
from Kärnten province, Austria. **1** St. Lorenzen; **2** to **4**
Ebene Reichenau. As in Fig **352**, we again see the intimate
tie between the craftsman and wood, and with it the most
sensitive matching of the tool to the nature of the material.

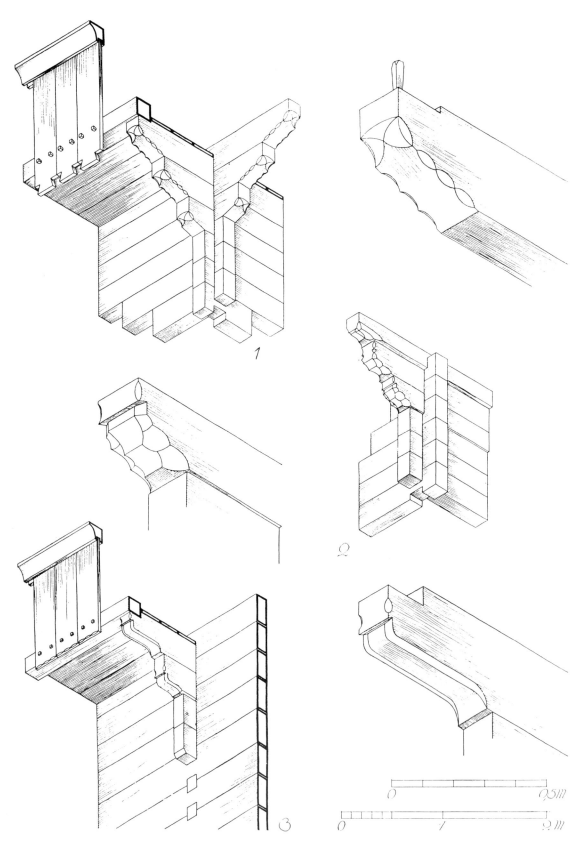

Fig 354
Logs ends worked with drawknife, *klingeisen* and gouge;
Kärnten province, Austria. **1** St. Oswald; **2** Ober-
Millstatt; **3** Radenthein. Here, every stroke of the hand
tool has been accompanied by a deep sense of intimacy
with the natural character of wood. This is what makes
these forms so alive and timeless in their beauty. The

design itself developed as the work went along, *i.e.*, it
evolved organically out of the basic design contour. Such
craftwork vanished with the adoption of the saw, which
can be used without regard for the structure or the special
qualities of wood, and with which the builder quite
arbitrarily sets the design in advance.

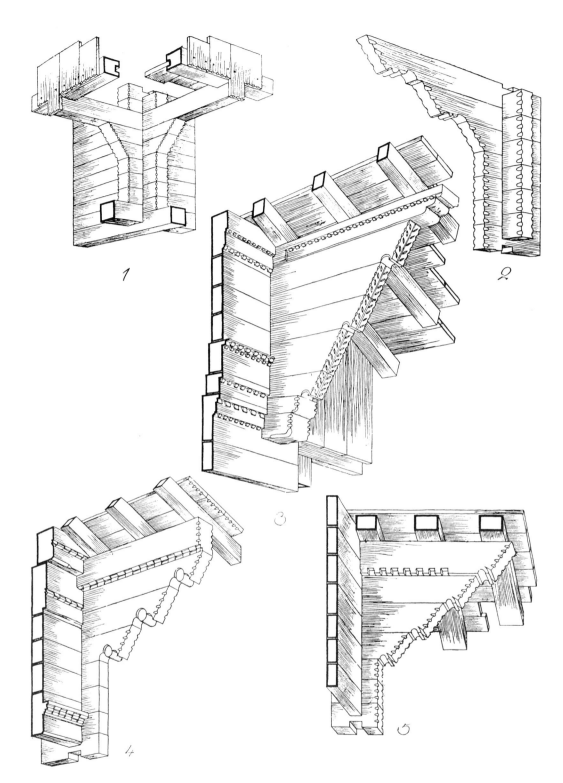

Fig 355
Cantilevered endwork designs from the log building
region of Switzerland. **1** Grindelwald; **2** Frutigen, Canton
Bern (from 1555); **3** Rougemont, Canton Vaud (1623);
4 Bernese Alps; **5** Rüti, Bernese Alps.

On the one hand, the saw cuts on each of these reflect
the structural function in an obvious manner, with no
attempt at concealment. On the other, the character of the
logwork, which lies in the horizontal motion suggested by
it, is expressed in the stepped design.

● 277

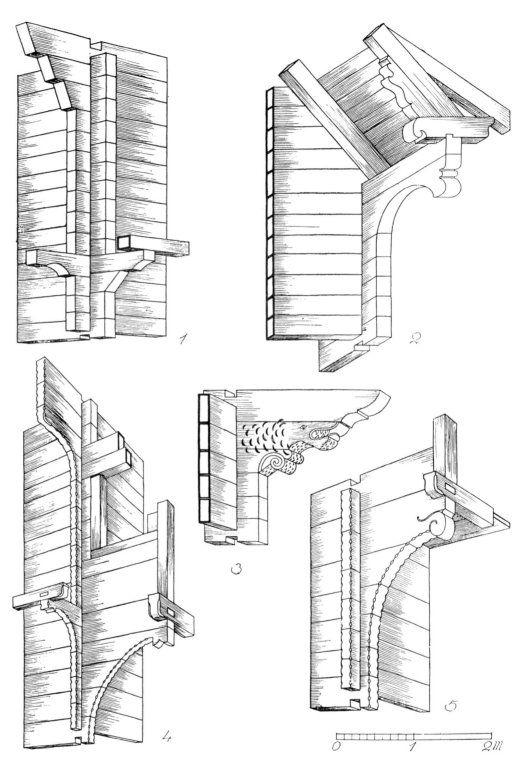

Fig 356
Detail of extended cornerwork from log building areas in Switzerland and the Austrian Vorarlberg. **1** Rüti, Bernese Alps; **2** Rheintal, Vorarlberg; **3** Luvis ob Ilanz, Canton Grisons; **4** Lungern, Canton Unterwalden; **5** Weggis, Canton Lucerne.

We feel the work of the saw in each of these examples; still a freehand operation in item **1**, but following a pre-marked line in the others. As long as care is taken to keep the saw lines simple, as in **4** and **5**, the result is an acceptable design, since the cut lines reflect the structural function in an obvious manner. However, once the saw cuts become too contrived, while at the same time ignoring the essential nature of logs, as is the case in **2**, our emotional attachment to the wood is disrupted. Despite the richness of the design lines, the feature as a whole loses vitality. In **3**, the unaffected dragon's head motif adds a novel note to the overall picture, without being able to efface the previously noted faults.

Fig 357
Section of a storehouse from Egiswyl, Canton Bern.
Although the construction is of half-round logs, the
projecting log ends seem to form a single unit. The
decorative gougework helps accentuate the linking of the
individual ends into a visual whole.

Columns and Uprights from across Europe's Log Building Areas

With the exception of Scandinavian columns, which were frequently round in keeping with the natural shape of the tree trunk (Figs **358/6**, **358/11** to **358/13** and **359**), upright supports were generally fashioned from square-edged timber (Figs **360**, **361**, **358/1** to **358/5**, **358/7** to **358/10** and **362** to **366**). By virtue of its uplifting lines alone, this most elegant of architectural forms obliges comparison with the living tree of the forest. Following from this, as from the nature and character of wood itself, is the imperative that this feature be largely retained when the material is worked or shaped by the craftsman. The column shown in Fig **358/9**, for example, must be considered deficient, in that the horizontal has been overly emphasized at the base, detracting from the unity of the whole.

Under the woodworker's skilled hand, there developed all manner of variation in column design. If a tapered or drawn-down effect was desired, the craftsman might begin working in from both ends, rough-shaping at first with a broadaxe, then moving to a drawknife or shave for the final smoothing. This led to the practice of leaving a decorative band of wood around the middle of the column, as shown in Figs **358/1** to **358/5**, **359** and **360/1**. Where builders wished to give a moulded contour to the top and bottom of an upright, the temptation to forsake the existing lines of the natural log proved too great. This trend in turn meant a need to blend the ends of a column or pillar into the tapering shaft, giving rise to the bulged-out design, and with it the most dynamic form of expression attainable on an upright (Figs **358/6** to **358/8** and **361/1**).

Fig 358 (opposite)
Wooden column designwork from a number of log building areas. **1** East Prussia; **2** Setesdal, Norway; **3** Switzerland; **4** East Prussia; **5** Switzerland; **6** Norway; **7** and **8** Tirol, Austria; **9** Switzerland; **10** Tirol; **11** Setesdal; **12** Telemark, Norway; **13** Norway; **14** Tirol.

Items **1** to **4** feature drawn-in styling, **6** to **9** show the bulging or bowed-out design, while **5** and **10** to **14** combine both drawn-in and bulged-out lines. The uprights would first be rough hewn, following which the finer detail would be added with drawknife and chisel. The various items illustrated show how the nature of wood stirred the creative imagination, right from the very first application of the tool. At the narrowest part of a drawn-in column, for example, some woodworkers fashioned a band around the upright. Elsewhere, the bulged motif was repeated in the form of rings (**6**). Another possibility lay in the counterpoint created by dishing out the ends of the column in chalice-like fashion (**7**). The drawknife simply invited bevelled edges (**8** and **9**). With curved drawshave in hand, the craftsman might also indulge his fancy by transforming bevels into fluting (**12**), which could also be cut with a heavy gouge (**13**). Smaller gouges came into play for working edge designs (**2** and **11**). Of paramount importance in all of this was that the basic shape of the round log or squared timber be largely retained. Failing this, the result is an affront to the character of wood (**9**).

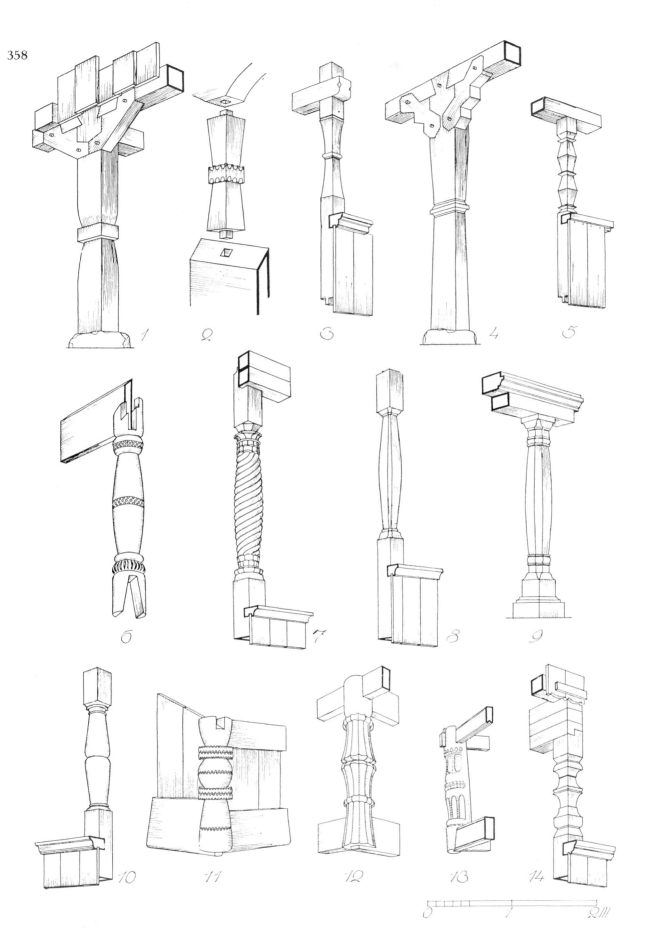

1   2   3   4   5

6   7   8   9

10   11   12   13   14

0   1   2 m

This occurred where the design comprised features stacked horizontally; something characteristic of stone architecture. Conveying as it does a sense of force being applied, the bulging design is most dynamic in the impression it creates. In this connection, we must not lose sight of the fact that the bulging shaft on the columns of classical antiquity first appeared on pillars of wood, only subsequently being transposed onto stone. Stone, however, is a lifeless building material, and of itself could never have inspired masterpieces of entasis.

● 281

In the push for ever-greater variety of design, attempts were also made to combine the two styles just described (Figs **358/5**, **358/11**, **358/14** and **361/2**) or to simply enliven the thickest part of the bulge by drawing it in sharply (Fig **358/10** and **358/12**).

The timberwork shown in Fig **360/2** strikingly illustrates how unique architectural forms can evolve simply from the function performed by an upright; a situation which applies equally to the column in Fig **364**. In the former case, the balustrade boarding is inclined somewhat, because the support pillar is drawn in slightly toward the middle, although retaining its squared configuration at top and bottom. When saw-work was included in more desirable designs, it was confined to nothing more than indentations at right angles to the long dimension of the upright (Fig **360/1**).

Finally, we have the arrival on the scene of decorative edgework, applied with curved gouge, V-gouge or skew chisel. The Renaissance saw the spread of the spindle even to

Fig 359
Corner view of a storehouse on posts, part of the *Aelvroshof* farmstead, now in Skansen, Stockholm. One of the uprights supporting the porch is rounded, while the other is squared. Both have been embellished by recessing a portion, yet leaving some material for decorative effect. While the corner posts have been mortised in place, the middle upright is tenoned in the manner of the doorposts.

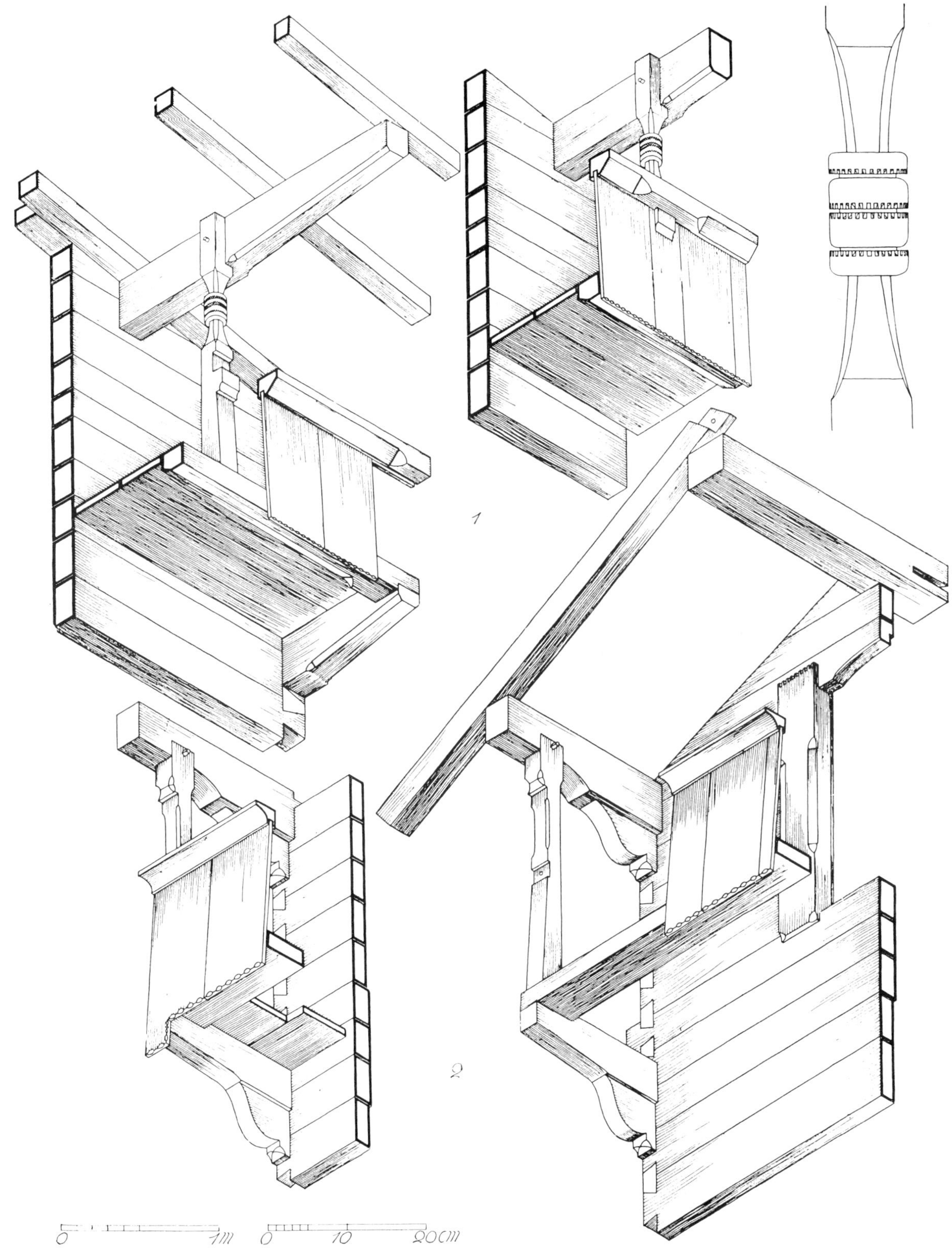

Fig 360
Balcony framing from the Chiemgau, Bavaria (Germany).
1 from Buchberg, built in 1698; and **2** from Schleching
(1675). A distinctive feature of both is the manner in
which the pillars have been worked from the solid timber,
and how each includes a console-like projection: one at
handrail height, the other at the top. In the latter instance,
this followed naturally from the post being drawn in at the
middle where the railing was located. The balustrade
boarding is set into a groove in the handrail and fastened
to the lower railing with iron nails.

● 283

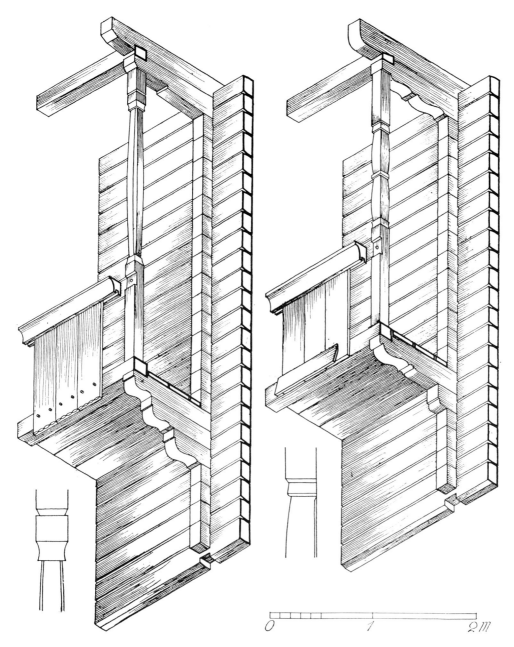

Fig 361
Balcony framing from two houses in St. Oswald, Kärnten,
Austria. The vertical column-like members serve to keep
the balustrade upright. They are tenoned into the sill
railing and half-lapped into the saddle provided by the
extended log-end. Notice the slender form in keeping
with their function. The finely executed swelling, which
occurs once on the right hand upright, but twice on the
other, lends both a robust and at the same time a dignified
appearance. The balustrade boards are groove-fitted into
the inset handrail in age-old fashion, and are either
pegged to the sill railing (left) or fastened with iron nails

(right). Being driven below the surface of the boarding,
the heads of the iron nails are not affected by exposure to
rain. Moreover, nailing in this manner is quick and easy.
This is what gave rise to the idea of applying a covering
board over the lower edge of the boarding where the end
grain was prone to weathering. Subsequently, this feature
became adopted as a natural part of balustrade framing.
Also noteworthy here is the manner in which the volutes
borrowed from stone architecture have been kept shallow
as befits the nature of the solid log, while seeking to
conform as much as possible with its fundamental shape.

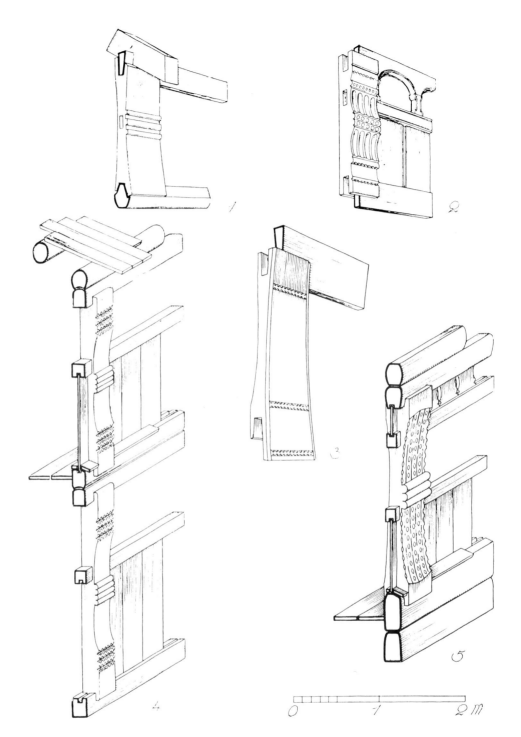

Fig 362

Balustrades in the Norwegian log building tradition. 1 to 3 from Telemark; 4 and 5 from Gudbrandsdalen. These balustrades developed in conjunction with the *sval* or covered walkway.

The rafters extended well out beyond the log wall (1) or, in the case of a purlin roof, beyond the last purlin (4), rest upon a plate log. This is carried by distinctive supports known as *stolper*, which perch atop the sill by virtue of a finely-done mortise, while holding the plate in a mortise as well. Out of the profound empathy which marks Scandinavian timberwork, the creative mind of the log builder sought to highlight the feeling of firm grip by enlarging these posts both top and bottom (3). These uprights would first be rough hewn to the shape of a parallelepiped, from which the desired artistic design would then be fashioned. In the course of this process, woodworkers began to see in a number of features the suggestion that these purely random forms be transformed into decorative designwork, an item which in time became the subject of strict rules of placement and proportion. The initial result was embellishment in the middle of the *stolper* (1, 4 and 5) which then spread over the full height of the post (2). The balustrade boarding is groove-fitted both top and bottom. The boards may be butted flush against one another (4 and 5) or tongue-and-groove fitted (2). To prevent water from entering the joint, a gently sloping drip board was nailed on at the sill (4 and 5).

Fig 363
Barn and storehouse from the *Aelvroshof*, now in Skansen, Stockholm. The date 1566 is carved into one of the uprights of the second storey. These members are mortised out on both ends. The two decorative rolls follow naturally from the upright being drawn in toward the middle.

Fig 364
Portion of a storehouse from Waldhaus, Canton Bern. Opposed tenons cut out of the handrail fit into corresponding mortises in the upright, which itself is tenoned into the purlin.

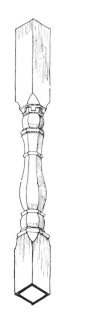

Fig 365
Pillar from the walkway of the *kasten* (storehouse) in Niederneuching (1581). In addition to chisel and drawknife, the handsaw has been used to fashion this post, although only for cuts at right angles to the long grain of the wood. This lends a striking note to the spots where the saw was used; a feature in keeping with the nature of this tool.

Fig 366
Second floor walkway or balcony of the *kasten* from Niederneuching.

the surfaces of columns and pillars. Particularly when applied to wood, however, this contouring must be kept extremely shallow. Figs **365** and **366** show a sample of work from this period; one which strikingly reveals the depth of the craftsman's innate feel for the essential quality of wood. Without the saw-toothed indentations on the top, we might almost imagine that we have before us a naturally grown feature. To best appreciate the essential character of the uplifting wooden pillar, it is helpful to contrast it with stub-log supports such as those pictured in Figs **367** and **368**.

Fig 367
Double door of a barn from Hofgastein, Austria.

Fig 368
Stub-log supports on a shed in St. Lorenzen, Kärnten, Austria. The lower one has been given a corbel-like taper with a drawknife.

Moulded Contouring

It was in the area of moulded contours that stone architecture exerted its strongest influence upon building with timber. The process began as far back as the late Romanesque period, paralleling the appearance of the cross-ribbed vault and leading carpenters to try transposing the bold contouring of stone ribs onto solid wooden beams, despite their fundamentally different nature. Next to appear on the scene were stone cornices. The result was that artisans building in wood began vying with stone in their timberwork, producing an undesirable coarseness in moulded contouring.

In Norway, where stone architecture lives much in the shadow of log and timber structures, the age-old styles of grooving and moulding natural to timberwork persisted longest. These may well serve us as guideposts, showing us the way home from our wayward wanderings. It goes, of course, without saying that this whole issue can best be appreciated by viewing the examples discussed here in their native setting. At first glance, it may seem improbable that grooving and contouring of such delicate proportions as that found in Norway could possibly affect in a major way the appearance of the timberwork on which it occurs. In fact, however, it not only affords an air of considerable refinement, but a cleanness of line as well. We might well look on such work as a naturally occurring feature, since none but a few slivers were removed from the surface of the wood to fashion it (Figs 369, 370, 371, 372 and 373).

Bevelling, which because of its usually indiscriminate and crass use in our architecture has been the cause of many a misdeed, is seldom included in Norwegian grooving or contouring work. When it is used, it is either kept shallow (Fig 371/6) or steep (Fig 371/8), and accompanied by the most delicate grooving. Even on more massive timberwork, the individual members are often adorned with delicate grooving, assuring a fineness of proportion (Fig 372/3). Even the oval-hewn logwork

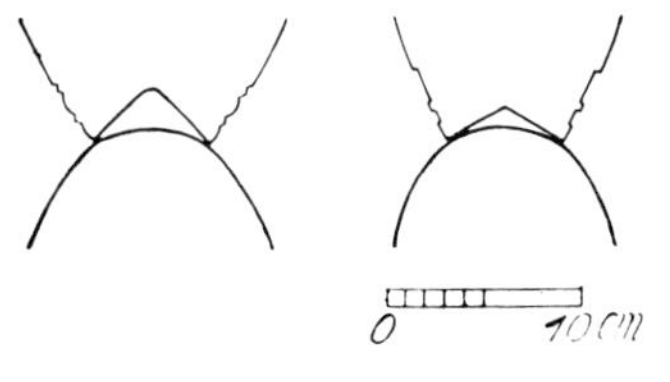

Fig 369
Fitted logwork, Norwegian style. The underside of the top log is V-grooved in each case, while the lower log is convex on top. The resulting space was packed with oakum or woolen material stained blue and red and so laid that its jagged ends visibly protruded on the exterior, giving a gay effect. This chinking, combined with the weight bearing down on a gently arched surface along a ridge, assured the best seal between the logs.

0   10 cm

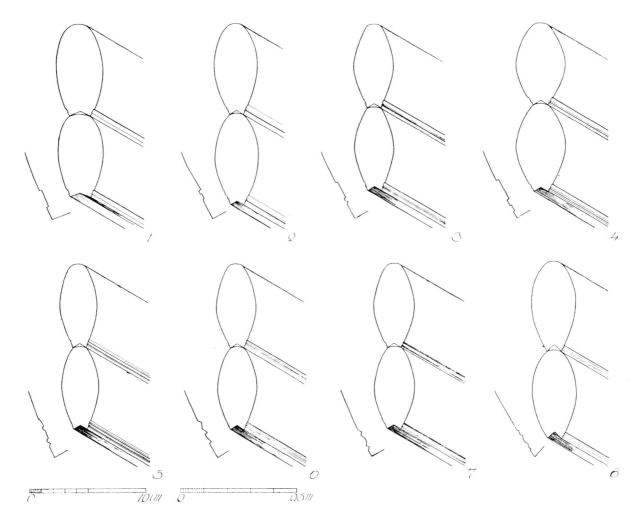

Fig 370
Decorative grooving on Norwegian logwork. **1** Vindlaus,
Eidsborg; **2** Snartland, Fyresdal; **3** Vaa, Rauland;
4 Berge, Rauland; **5** Brokka, Skaffå (1565); **6** Grovum,
Nissedal (1616); **7** Fladeland, Vraadal (1773); **8** Austad
(c. 1700).

The exceptionally delicate grooving gives the oval-hewn
logwork an elegant appearance. Since the logwork evokes
an impression of strain imposed by a load, the decorative
grooving could not properly run anywhere but along the
edges of the joints between the logs. The embellishment
helps the eye better see the logs (which resemble muscles)
as individual members. Fig **5e** shows the tool used for this
type of work in its most rudimentary form.

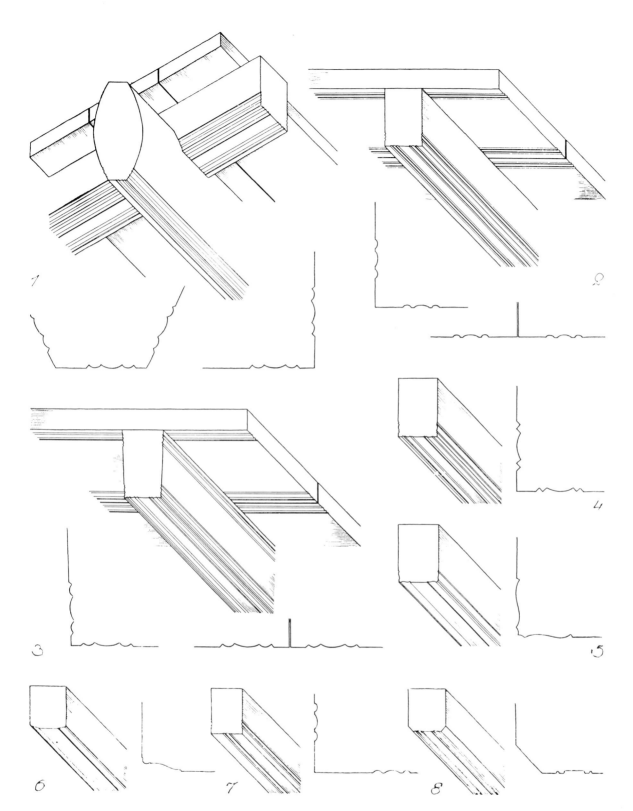

Fig 371
Finely grooved embellishment on Norwegian log
structures. **1** Austad, Setesdal; **2** Nordgarden, Åseral;
3 Austad; **4** Lovvik i Stafsaa; **5** Nerstol, Eiken; **6** Grösli,
Numedalen (1633); **7** Austergarden, Åseral; **8** Rolstadt,
Gudbrandsdalen.

Here, the profiling has been kept extremely shallow and
delicate. As only a very few slivers have been removed by
the chisel or gouge, it appears to have grown so naturally,
lending an air of refinement to the various members.
Notice how the log purlin in item **1** has been more richly
embellished on the inward-facing side than toward the
wall. When fluting began to appear on the scene in the
Renaissance, log builders adapted this practice brought
from abroad to their own native grooving techniques,
producing a shallow and delicate profile (**6**). In the case of
bevelling, which likewise appears to have been brought
from abroad, Norwegian craftsmen refined the
proportions and softened the severe indentation by
running delicate side grooving along the edges (**8**).
Moulded contours found in our present-day wooden
architecture are for the most part overly coarse and
lacking in feeling; quite the reverse of those shown above.

● 291

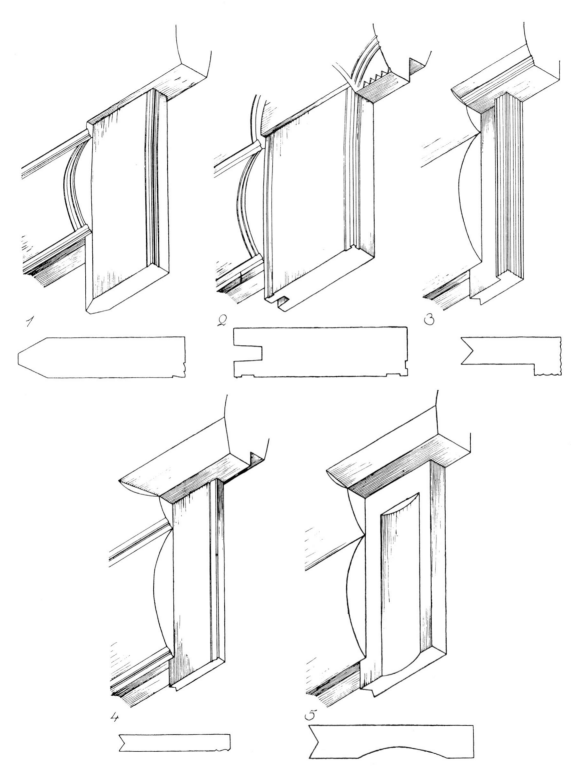

Fig 372
Doorpost profiling from Norwegian log building areas.
1 Midgarden, Rauland; **2** Vindlaus, Eidsborg; **3** Dale,
Valle.

The profiling has been fashioned out of the grain of the
wood with great sensitivity and feeling for the nature of
the material. Worthy of special note is **3**, where both the
outer face of the pilaster-like projection and the side of the
doorpost have been covered with vertical grooving, which
in proportion and design matches that along the lower
edge of the lintel. In the larger sense, the forms maintain
their powerful language; in fact, the taughtness is
enhanced by the refinement of the profiling. The builder
of **5** went his own way, but even here we sense the effort to
take away as little as possible from the basic shape.

was given this fine embellishment (Figs **369** and **370**), lending it an appearance of such elegance, particularly on the interior, as to preclude any thought of panelling or other finishwork on the inside walls.

On protruding log ends and the juncture of doorposts with the logwork, decorative grooving was also run on over the end grain or across the lengthwise surface of the logs at their ends (Fig **372/1** and **372/2**). Tongue and groove planking was also embellished in this fashion (Fig **373**). Here, as otherwise the case, this grooving was frequently applied along edges, to which the eye is particularly drawn.

The doorposts of log buildings in Switzerland show similar features, although with slightly less fine proportions (Fig **374**). Here, too, individual slivers were chiselled out and an attempt made to keep the decorative work in harmony with the nature of solid wood. In Upper Bavaria, this type of grooved work is only found where log builders fell somewhat under the influence of the cabinetmaker's craft (Fig **375/1** and **375/2**). It was in Switzerland, however, that decorative work in log building found its most lavish expression. In addition to the purely longitudinal grooving just described, Swiss craftsmen sought to heighten the effect still further by conjuring forth rich incised ornamentation (Figs **376/5**, **376/6** and **377/5** to **377/8**). Invariably, however, the embellishment begins with lengthwise grooving along the grain, followed by chiselwork from this beginning (Fig **378**).

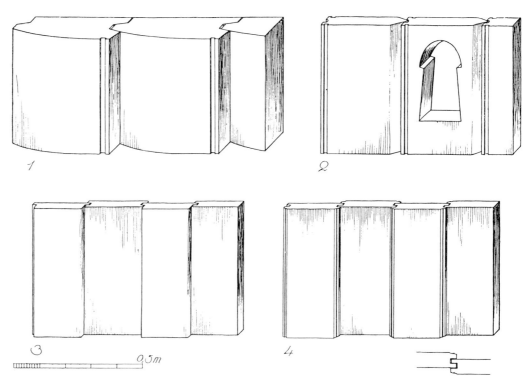

Fig 373
Norwegian planking styles: **1** from a stave church in Gol (c. 1200); **2** a *loft* in Haugen, Sandnes, Setesdal (Middle Ages); **3** a *stabur* (raised storehouse) in Haugeland, Telemark; **4** a dwelling in Manspann, Valle, Setesdal.

Like logs and beams, planking was also embellished with exceptionally delicate grooved edgework. The planks of early examples show a slightly rounded exterior (**1**). All visually accentuate the individual plank as a separate entity, giving walls in this style an exuberant, yet powerful appearance.

293

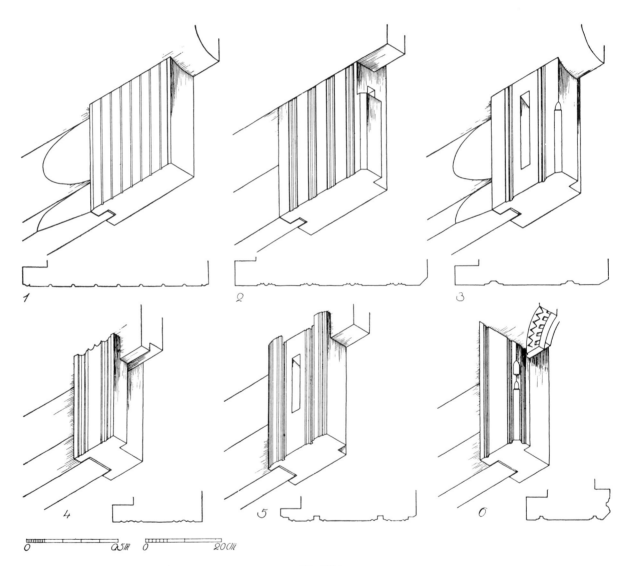

Fig 374
Doorpost profiling on log buildings from Switzerland.
1 Eggiswyl; **2** Ried (1772); **3** Waldhaus (1701); **4** Naters;
5 Ried (1772); **6** Naters (1609). **1**, **2**, **3** and **5** are from
Canton Bern; **4** and **6** from the Valais. As in the wooden
architecture of Scandinavia, here too the profiling is
beautifully in keeping with the nature of wood, with only a
very few slivers removed. The post in item **1** is of oak, the
fibres of which do not separate as readily as spruce, of
which the others are made – a fact which also allows for
the design comprising small individual grooves.

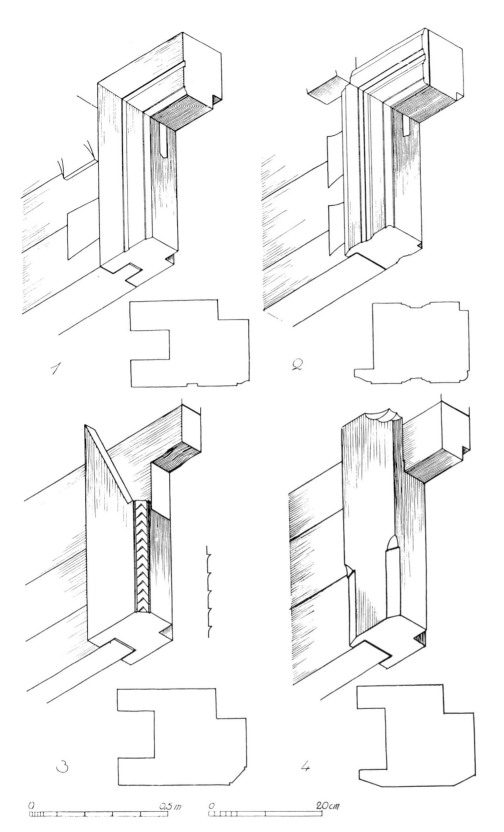

Fig 375
Doorway contouring from Upper Bavaria and the Tirol.
1 from Lein near Lenggries; **2** from Greiling near Tölz;
3 from Villanders near Klausen; **4** from Zell in the
Zillerthal. The profiles have been kept finely proportioned
throughout and are very appropriate to timberwork. An
attractive feature is the manner in which the shallow
chamfer in **4** blends easily into the exterior face of the
doorpost, and how strikingly its top has been adorned
with three scoops of the *klingeisen*. Even the skew-chisel
ornamentation on the chamfer in **3** strikes us as natural.

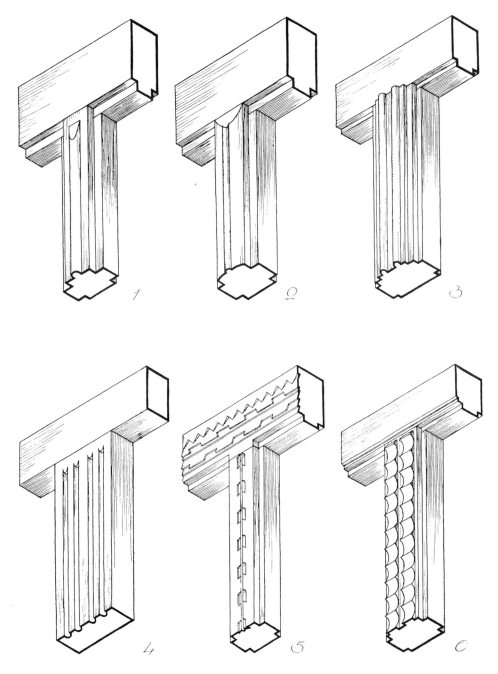

Fig 376
Beautifully executed designwork on window frames from
log buildings in Switzerland. **1** from Fruttigen (1805);
2 from Grindelwald; **3** from Rütt (1600); **4** from La
Forclaz, Canton Vaud (1671); **5** from Stalden in the
Valais; **6** from Willigen near Meiringen (1796).

Each bespeaks an intimate matching of the design with
the longitudinal fibres, which are broken only in **5** and **6**
by cuts across the grain.

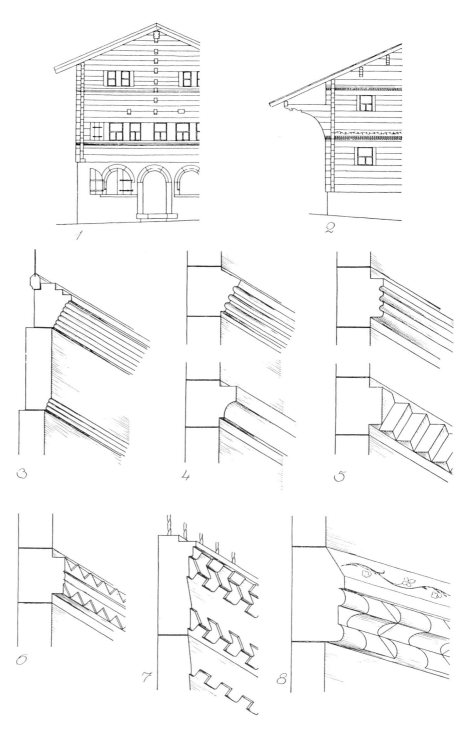

Fig 377
Decorative courses on Swiss log buildings. **1** Kippel, Canton Valais (1543); **2** St. Gallenkirchen, Vorarlberg (1776); **3** Wittigen, Canton Bern; **4** to **6** Kippel (16th century); **7** Matten near Interlaken (1750); **8** St. Gallenkirchen (1776).

With the exception of the lower item in **4**, all of these moulded styles are properly in keeping with the nature of wood. In some instances, the obvious approach was taken, with slivers being chiselled out along the grain (**3**, **4** and **5** above). Alternatively, the craftsman first fashioned a basic contour, into which further patterns were then chiselled, cutting the grain at an angle in rhythmic succession (**5** below; **6**, **7** and **8**). From this there naturally followed a vast array of varied styles.

Fig 378
Partial view of a dwelling in Interlaken.

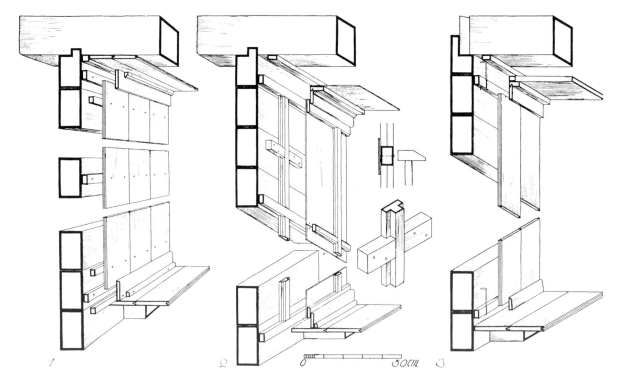

Fig 379
Because of shrinkage in the logwork, interior panelling
must be applied so as not to interfere with settling. In **1**,
this was achieved by having only the middle piece of
strapping forming a fixed connection between the
panelling and the log walls. The upper and lower lengths
of strapping are not fastened to the wall, and serve only to
support the panelling nailed to it. In **2** (from Vinzenz
Bachmann), the panelling rests on a full framework of
strapping, with rabbeted vertical members which, while
held by small notched blocks of wood, are still free to
move. In **3** (from Brunold, Arosa), horizontal strapping is
held by iron clips, which allow the required movement.

Fig 380

Wall panelling and wainscoting. **1** Flush panelling of tongue and groove boards, which should be narrow in consideration of warping and shrinkage. **2** Flush panelling of chamfered, tongue and groove boards, a style which inevitably looks unattractive and should be avoided. **3** Board-and-batten style. To avoid a makeshift appearance, the battens should be fitted against a horizontal board both top and bottom, thus making the outer layer of woodwork a unified whole. **4** Wainscoting, with strips of woodwork covering the joints between the boards and the same design principle as in the previous example. **5** Full-panel wainscoting, without additional dividers. **6** Groove-edged wainscoting with plywood panels. **7** Plywood wainscoting, with splines between the panels. Strips of wood are placed under the splines for fastening to the framework of strapping. The panels may be 10 to 20 mm in thickness and 1.5 to 5.0 meters in width and may also be joined as shown in **1** and **4**. The most distinctive feature of plywood panels is seen in the great widths possible.

● 299

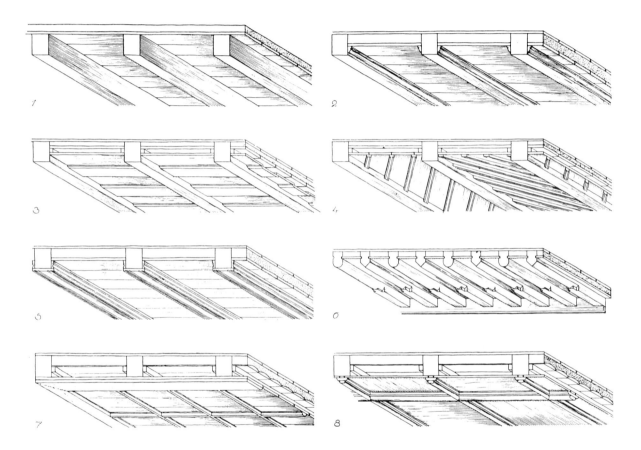

Fig 381
Beam ceilings, with beams exposed (1 to 6) and concealed
(7 and 8). 1 Full tongue and groove plank ceiling with
exposed beams, over which a layer of earth has been
applied as insulation against the cold. 2 Lowered or false
ceiling with plain sections between the beams; 3 with
lapped ceiling boards between the beams. 4 Diagonal
board and batten ceiling. 5 False ceiling, with beams
boxed in to conceal unsightly checking. 6 Multi-beam
ceiling, with only a single board between each of the
beams. 7 False ceiling, with nailed-on dividers.
8 Panelled ceiling with panels of plywood. The moulding
or contouring of individual members must blend with the
overall design, and should be appropriate for wood. The
builder must resist the desire to chamfer or bevel all edges,
and in this context, beams may frequently be left
unprofiled. In 6, the profiles of the beams have been
influenced by the stone ribs of Gothic arches, a feature still
acceptable in this instance because of the lowered position
of the ceiling boards.

Interior Finish Work

The settling of the log walls must be allowed for in the interior joinery as well. At times, builders will not wish to wait until the walls have fully settled, preferring to apply interior cladding as soon as the main logwork is up. Here, care must be taken to assure that such interior work is not adversely affected by settling. Fig **379** shows three different methods of keeping exterior walls independent of interior cladding.

The panelling or wainscoting itself may be applied in a variety of different styles (Fig **380**). The simplest is a plain panelling of tongue and groove boards. On no account should the edges of the boards be chamfered, as is the common practice today, since this is ugly in appearance. To preclude checking, narrow boards should be selected. Needless to say, the boards should be well seasoned prior to application. With lapped or board-and-batten panelling, a suitable moulding or similar piece of wood-work should be added, either at floor or ceiling – much in the manner of a plinth or frieze (Fig **380/2** and **380/3**). Whereas the aforementioned styles accentuate the vertical, groove-edged panelling also permits horizontal divisions, with panels of ply-wood affording the greatest scope in terms of width (Fig **380/4** and **380/5**). In recent years, craftsmen have adopted the practice of joining such plywood panels with splines, which produces a clean and uncluttered surface (Fig **380/6**).

At the ceiling, beams may either be left exposed or concealed from view by cladding. In either case, as Fig **381** illustrates, a broad range of design alternatives exists, as is the case with wall claddings. In this regard, the false or lowered ceiling offers the architect a particularly rewarding outlet for design. With the individual members visually close at hand, contouring and profiling demands an especially fine touch. In this regard, the woodworker should proceed very warily with bevelling; never at an angle of 45°.

The various natural colours of native European woods provide broad latitude in terms of colour composition. If the species available are inadequate to provide the desired colour effect, individual details may be done in colour, although here the colours used must always be in sharp contrast to the warm tones of wood. In this regard, distinctive and pleasing effects can also be achieved simply with black and white alone. For a pleasant and homey atmosphere, the floor colour should be markedly in contrast to that of walls and ceilings. Otherwise, it is possible to actually create the impression of being closed inside a wooden box. In like manner, furniture should also blend harmoniously with the whole in colour, quite apart from its design.

Accessory items of other materials such as iron must similarly be suited to the nature of wood. Iron lighting fixtures must not be overly heavy in detail, as is unfortunately not uncommon today. It is notable that in Norway, where, as we have already seen, pure solid timber construction endured longest, iron door hardware on log buildings shows exceptionally delicate detail. In fact, even surfaces are embellished with finely chased ornamentation.

Chimneys and ventilation pipes must not be fastened rigidly to the structure, right up through the roof, nor should central heating equipment be fastened to the walls. The fire hazard which may be created by hot pipes is inherently precluded by hot water heating. In consideration of fire, stairs should be of oak as much as possible.

In bathrooms, special care must be taken to keep water away from the wood, as it too can be a problem. The solution here is to use a water repellant panelling, applied so as not to be affected by the working of the log walls. This applies to floor coverings as well.

Fig 382
The Fjeldgard house from Gudbrandsdalen, now at the outdoor museum in Lillehammer, Norway. Windows did not come to the Scandinavian house until the arrival of the chimney, *i.e.*, relatively late. The thin slab of stone over the chimney weighted down with a rock is characteristic of Norway.

A Selection of Log Structures
from Scandinavia to the Southern Alps
and Carpathians

To round out this in-depth survey, it will be useful to now examine the structures in Figs **382** to **419**, which stretch from Scandinavia to the southern portions of both the Alps and the Carpathians, in light of what has been discussed.

The reader of this book will have his eyes opened to much that is unfamiliar by the highly detailed studies presented herein, unveiling a world otherwise on the brink of disappearing. Thereupon follows the realization of the freshness and vigour inherent in architectural structures beautifully in harmony with the special nature of wood, accompanied by the discovery that such exquisite items have a majesty transcending the fashionable style of any period.

The book reveals by way of concrete illustration just how readily unique structures can be created from an intimate contact with solid timber and how, furthermore, as go the creative sensibilities of the craftsman, so goes the structure as a whole.

We have thus in our early wooden architecture a resource of inestimable value, one which can also extend its benefits to building with other materials as well. As Goethe himself phrased it during his third tour of Switzerland:

> "In the village of Uhwiesen, I found timberwork emulating stonework. What are we to make of such a thing, considering that just the reverse is the basis of our native architecture's outstanding beauty".

Fig 383
Two-storey storehouse from Dalarna, Sweden. Notice the overhanging upper storey.

Fig 384
Storehouse from Mora. In the background, a hostel from Nas, both in Dalarna, Sweden.

Fig 385
Stabur (storehouse) from Telemark. The sawn decoration on the barge board of the right hand structure is a later addition and out of character for Scandinavian building.

Fig 386
Stabur and barn from Numedalen. The storehouse at left,
of pure log construction, is the most recent of the
buildings. An interesting feature is the stained exterior,
with the white of the end grain standing out in contrast.

Fig 387
Rolstadloft from Söndre Fron in Gudbrandsdalen, dating
from the late Middle Ages.

Fig 388
Stabur from Telemark. A beautiful example of the
extensive use of grooved or moulded edgework, at times
even run onto the end grain.

Fig 389
Stabur from Rauland in Telemark. The original planking
has been removed from the porch of the lower floor and
the *sval* (balcony or walkway) of the upper storey, clearly
revealing the timber framing and the main logwork.

Fig 390
A solid timber structure known as the *Kasten*, dating from
1581. Originally in Niederneuching (Upper Bavaria), now
on the *Staatsgut Grub* property near Munich.

Fig 391
Side elevation of the *Kasten* from Niederneuching.

Fig 392
Farm house from the Isartal valley near Lenggries.

Fig 393
Farm house from the Isartal valley near Lenggries.

394

395

Figs 394 and 395
Storehouse from Schleching (Chiemgau, Germany) with
built-in baking oven, dating from 1675.

396

397

Figs 396 and 397
Two modest log cottages, built as accommodation for
retired farm people (Hofgastein, Austria). In both cases,
the chimney is built so as to be independent of the settling
of the log walls.

Fig 398
Farm house not far from Millstatt in Kärnten (Austria)
showing roofed-in balcony on the gable end.

Fig 399
Hay barn near Schladming in Austria's Steiermark
province.

Fig 400
Troadkasten or granary from St. Oswald, Kärnten, with broad overhanging roof apron.

Fig 401
Troadkasten from Arriach, Kärnten province.

Fig 402
Three storey storehouse from the *Schmiedhof* farmstead in
Arriach, Kärnten, Austria.

Fig 403
Three storey storehouse near Millstatt, Kärnten (Austria).

404

405

Figs 404 and 405
Granary or *troadkasten* from Winkel near Ebene
Reichenau and near Patergassen, both in Kärnten
province. A comparative look at the two clearly illustrates
the delightful expressiveness of the purely timber
structure vis-a-vis the plastered one.

Fig 406
Granary from Arriach, built around 1880 by Peter
Hauptmann, a farmer. This structure may well be one of
the last to be built by a non-professional carpenter, as was
the custom going back to earliest times.

Fig 407
Storehouse from Eggiswyl in Canton Bern, with a later
addition.

Fig 408
Storehouse building from the *Lüthihof* farmstead,
Waldhaus, Canton Bern, from 1629.

Fig 409
Storehouse of the *Lüthihof*, Waldhaus, showing the braces
supporting the side balcony.

Fig 410
Vertical tie logs providing wall support on a storehouse
from Münster (Valais), Switzerland, built without support
posts beneath.

Fig 411
Multi-storey storehouse without the foundation of
support posts, from Münster in the Valais.

Fig 412
Storehouse from Münster, Valais.

Fig 413
Storehouse with lower floor used as stable, from the
Nikolaustal valley, Valais, Switzerland.

Fig 414
Storehouse with overhanging upper storey from Münster in the Valais. A vertical tie-log provides bracing on the gable wall.

Fig 415
Multi-storey storehouse with stable on ground level. Gable and side walls have been braced with vertical tie beams.

Fig 416
Log dwelling in Naters, Valais.

Fig 417
Residential dwelling, Stalden, Valais, Switzerland.

Fig 418
East Germanic storehouse from the Transylvanian
Erzgebirge.

Fig 419
East Germanic dwelling from the *Erzgebirge* of
Transylvania.

Source References of Figures

Fig 43: sketch at lower right from A. Dengler, ''Der Aufbau des Holzes'' in *Handbuch der Holzkonservierung*, 1916.

Fig 44: from Hempel and Wilhelm, *Waldbäume*.

Fig 45: from A. Dengler, ''Der Aufbau des Holzes'' in *Handbuch der Holzkonservierung* by E. Troschel.

Fig 46: from F. Kollman, *Die Technologie des Holzes*.

Fig 48: from Nördlinger. *Die technischen Eigenschaften der Hölzer*.

Fig 64: redrawn from Axel Hamberg, *Redogörelse för Nordiska Musseets utveckling och förvaltning*, 1925, p. 179.

Fig 78: from Sigurd Erixon, *Folkliv* 1, 1937.

Fig 81: from Master Carpenter Vinzenz Bachmann, Mettenham, Germany.

Fig 85: from Dethlefsen.

Fig 92: from G. Midttun, *Setesdalen*, Kristiania (Norway), 1919 and G. Boëthius (Sweden).

Fig 95: items 1 and 2 from Gladbach, 3 and 4 from Dethlefsen.

Fig 96: item 1 from Eigl; 3 from Dethlefsen, 8 from Eigl; 9 from Gladbach.

Fig 97: item 2 from Soeder; 3 to 7 from Gladbach.

Fig 99: items 1, 2 and 4 taken from *Nordiska Museet, Fataburen* (Stockholm: 1904, 1918 and 1929/30); 3 from *Setesdalen* (Oslo: 1919); 5 and 7 taken from *Das Bauernhaus in der Schweiz* (Zürich: 1903); 6 from J. Meyer, *Fortids Kunst i Norges Bygder* (Oslo: 1922); 8 from *Vest-Agder II* (Bergen: 1927).

Fig 100: item 1 taken from *Das Bauernhaus in Österreich – Ungarn* (1906); 2 and 5 from *Das Bauernhaus in der Schweiz* (1903); 4 from Gladbach, *Charakterische Holzbauten der Schweiz* (1896); 3 from a photo by the author.

Fig 103: redrawn from H. Reinerth, *Die Wasserburg Buchau*, 1928, p. 45, Fig 11.

Fig 107: items 1 to 5 from Ossian Elgström, *Karesuandolaparna* (Stockholm: 1922), pp. 170, 168, 128, 140, 158.

Fig 109: from Sigurd Erixon and Andreas Lindblom, *En bok om Skansen*, 1933.

Fig 110: photo by Neupert, Oslo.

Fig 115: item 3 from Gladbach, 5 to 12 from Dethlefsen.

Fig 116: watercolour by Karl Kunz, Herzogswalde, East Prussia.

Fig 117: left, taken from D. Gilly, *Handbuch der Landbaukunst*; and right, from Fauth, *Das Lehmschindeldach*.

Fig 120: items 1, 2, 4 and 6 redrawn from *Nordiska Museet*, 1922/24 (p. 141); 1917 (p. 183); 1902 (p. 48) and 1912 (p. 224); 3 from Erixon, *Führer durch Skansen*, p. 47; 5 from a photo by Helge Hoel.

Fig 142: photo: Olsson, Ljungbyhed.

Figs 142 and 143: commercial photos.

Fig 163: illustration at left from Gladbach.

Fig 171: items 2 and 3 from Gladbach.

Fig 173: redrawn from J. Meyer, *Fortids Kunst i Norges Bygder*.

Fig 174: item 1 from *Setesdalen* (1919); 2 from *Vest-Agder II* (1927); 3 from Johan Meyer, *Fortids Kunst 1* (1920); 4 from *Vest-Agder II*.

Fig 175: item 1 from *Das Bauernhaus in der Schweiz*; 2 from a photo by the author; 3 from *Nordiska Museet, Fataburen* (1912).

Fig 176: redrawn from photos by Gerda Boëthius in *Timmerbygnadskonsten*, p. 203.

Fig 177: redrawn from photos of the *Höhere Technische Lehranstalt*, Beuthen, Upper Silesia (now Poland).

Fig 178: redrawn from E. Gladbach, *Charakterische Holzbauten der Schweiz*, p. 10.

Fig 179: redrawn from photos in Gerda Boëthius, *Timmerbygnadskonsten*, p. 104.

Fig 180: redrawn from photos in *Das Bauernhaus in der Schweiz*, Bern No 5 and Valais No 2.

Fig 181: items 1 and 3 redrawn from E. Gladbach, *Der Schweizer Holzstil* (I, Plate 28 and II, p. 21); 2 from a photo by the author.

Fig 183: redrawn from S. Erixon, *Skansens kulturgeschichtliche Abteilung*, Fig 92; *Fataburen, Kulturhistorisk Tidskrift*, 1910, p. 118, Fig 4 and 1925, p. 80, Fig 13.

Fig 184: redrawn from *De sandvigske sammlinger*, 1907, p. 84, Fig 143.

Fig 185: redrawn from *De sandvigske sammlinger*, 1907, p. 122, Fig 231.

Fig 186: *ibid.*, p. 54, Fig 96.

Fig **187**: *ibid.*, p. 140, Fig 262.

Fig **188**: from a commercial photo.

Fig **189**: redrawn from the book *Setesdalen*, 1919, Pl. 23.

Fig **190**: photo by Neupert, Oslo.

Fig **191**: from a commercial photo.

Fig **192**: redrawn from a photo of the *Höhere Staatliche Gewerbeschule* in Villach, Austria.

Fig **193**: redrawn from *Bauwerke der Schweiz*, 1896, Plate 32.

Fig **194**: redrawn from *Das Bauernhaus in der Schweiz* and *De sandvigske sammlinger*, 1907, p. 24, Fig 33.

Fig **195**: redrawn from *De sandvigske sammlinger*, 1928, p. 145.

Fig **196**: redrawn from *Nordiska Museet, Fataburen*, 1912, p. 224, Fig 16 and *Der Baumeister*, 1934, p. 26.

Fig **196a**: photo by Richard Schimann, Innsbruck.

Fig **196b**: photo by Richard Schimann, Innsbruck.

Fig **198**: item **1** taken from *Das Bauernhaus in Deutschland*; **2** from *Das Bauernhaus in der Schweiz*.

Fig **199**: item **1** taken from *Das Bauernhaus in Österreich-Ungarn*; **2** from Baumeister, *Das Bauernhaus des Wallgaues*; **4** to **6** from Gladbach, *Der Schweizer Holzstil*; **7** from Deininger, *Das Bauernhaus in Tirol und Vorarlberg*.

Fig **200**: items **1** and **2** taken from *Das Bauernhaus in Deutschland*; **3** from A. Gut, *Die Denkmalpflege*, 1923; **4** to **6** from Dethlefsen; **7** from Deininger.

Fig **201**: from W. Souslov, *Monuments de l'ancienne architecture russe*, Petersburg, 1901.

Fig **202**: item **1** taken from *Die Denkmalpflege*, 1923; **2** from Gladbach; **3** from *Das Bauernhaus in Deutschland*.

Fig **204**: both from photos by the author.

Fig **205**: item **1** from Midttun, *Setesdalen*; **2** from photos by Arne Berg in *Norske Bygder, Vest-Agder*.

Fig **209**: items **1** to **5** from photos taken by the author at Skansen; **6** from Gerda Boëthius.

Fig **211**: redrawn from Johan Meyer, *Fortids Kunst i Norges Bygder*, 1920, 1922.

Fig **212**: above, redrawn from G. Boëthius, *Studier i den nordiska timmerbygnadskonsten*, 1927; below, redrawn from *Nordiska museets och Skansens Årsbok, Fataburen*, 1931.

Fig **213**: item **1** redrawn from Gisle Midttun, *Setesdalen*, 1919; **2** from *De sandvigske sammlinger*, 1928; **3** from Gerda Boëthius, *Timmerbygnadskonsten*, 1927.

Fig **215**: photo: Norsk Folkemuseum.

Fig **217**: item **1** taken from G. Boëthius; **2** from Gisle Midttun, *Hus og huskunad*, 1913; **3** from Georg Raschke, *Die Entdeckung des frühgeschichtlichen Oppeln*, 1931; **4** from *Das Bauernhaus in der Schweiz*, 1903; **5** from a photo by the author.

Fig **222**: see also Phleps, ''Ostgermanische Spuren im Gefüge des westgermanischen Ständerwerks'', in *Brauch und Sinnbild*, F. Herrmann and W. Trautlein (ed.), 1940, Plate 32.

Fig **225**: *cf.* also G. Raschke, *Aus Oberschlesiens Urzeit*, No. 17, 1932, p. 9.

Fig **230**: photos by the author.

Fig **238**: from photos by the author.

Fig **241**: from photos by the author.

Fig **244**: from photos by the author.

Fig **251**: from photos by the author.

Fig **253**: from a photo by the author.

Fig **258**: from photos by the author.

Fig **261**: from photos by the author.

Fig **262**: from photos by the author.

Fig **263**: photos by the author.

Fig **264**: photo by Dr. Moro, Villach, Austria.

Fig **265**: photos by the author.

Fig **266**: photos by the author.

Fig **267**: photos by the author.

Fig **268**: photos by the author.

Fig **270**: photos by the author.

Fig **271**: photos by the author.

Fig **272**: from a photo by Peter Schwarz, Ulm.

Fig **278**: photo by the author.

Fig **282**: item **3** redrawn from *Das Bauernhaus in Deutschland* and **4** from *Tegninger af aeldre nordisk architektur*, Copenhagen, 1872–1879.

Fig **283**: taken from Emil Ekhof, *Svenska Storkyrkor*, Stockholm, 1914–1916.

Fig **284**: photos by the author.

Fig **285**: item **1** photo by the author; **2** from *Das Bauernhaus in Deutschland*, p. 308.

Fig **287**: from photos by the author.

Fig **288**: item **1** taken from *Das Bauernhaus in Österreich-Ungarn*; **2** from Deininger, *Das Bauernhaus in Tirol und Vorarlberg*; **3** from *Das Bauernhaus in Österreich-Ungarn*.

Fig **289**: photos by the author; particulars provided by the museum staff at Skansen have been used for the sketch of the Swedish item.

Fig **292**: redrawn from A. Bielenstein, *Die Holzbauten und Holzgeräte der Letten*, 1907.

Fig **297**: item **1** taken from *Das Bauernhaus in der Schweiz*, Schwyz Plate 2; **2** from Uri Plate 2 in the aforementioned work; **3** from *Das Bauernhaus in Österreich-Ungarn*, Tirol Plate 4; **4** from the same work, Kärnten Plate 1; **5** from *Das Bauernhaus in Deutschland*, p. 308.

Fig **298**: item **1** taken from Gladbach, *Der Schweizer Holzstil*, Plate 7; **2** from *Das Bauernhaus in der Schweiz*, Bern Plate 11.

Fig **299**: item **1** from a photo of the Akademischer Architektenverein, Munich; **2** and **3** photos by the author; **4** from *Das Bürgerhaus in der Schweiz*, Vol IV, 1913, p. 93; **5** photo by the author.

Fig **300**: items **1** and **2** from photos by the author taken at the outdoor museum, Skansen (Stockholm); **3** from a photo by Helge Hoel, Oslo.

Fig **301**: photos by the author.

Fig **303**: items **1** to **3** from photos by the author; **4** from a photo by Max Schön of Munich.

Fig **306**: item **1** taken from *Der Baumeister*, 1934; **2** from *Das Werk*, 1932; **3** and **4** from *Moderne Bauformen*, 1933.

Fig **307**: items **1**, **2** and **4** taken from *Das Bauernhaus in Österreich–Ungarn*; **3** from *Bayerischer Heimatschutz*, 1913; and **5** from a photo by Peter Schwarz.

Fig **308**: items **1** and **2** photos by the author; **3** from a photo by the architect Pulver of Hirschberg.

Fig **312**: from H. Soeder, *Das Dorf Tritschuny im litauisch-weissruthenischen Grenzgebiet*, 1918.

Fig **314**: item **1** taken from *Alte bayerische Zimmermannskunst*, Akademischer Architekten-Verein, Munich, 1926; **2** from *Das Bauernhaus in Österreich-Ungarn*; **3** from *Das Bauernhaus in der Schweiz*; **4** from *Setesdalen*; **5** from *Bauwerke der Schweiz*, 1900; **6** from *Das Bauernhaus in Deutschland*.

Fig **315**: item **1** taken from Gisle Midttun, *Setesdalen*; **2** from *Das Bauernhaus in der Schweiz*; **3** from *Skansens Vårfestbok*, 1924.

Fig **316**: item **1** from *Das Bauernhaus in Deutschland*; **2** from *Das Bauernhaus in Österreich-Ungarn*; **3** from *Alte bayerische Zimmermannskunst*, Akademischer Architekten-Verein, Munich; **4** from Gladbach.

Fig **318**: item **1** taken from *Das Bauernhaus in Deutschland*; **2**, **3** and **6** from Gladbach; **4** and **5** from *Das Bauernhaus in der Schweiz*.

Fig **319**: item **1** from a photo by the author; **2** from Gladbach; **3** from *Das Bauernhaus in Österreich-Ungarn*.

Fig **323**: items **1** and **3** from photos by the author; **2**, **4** and **5** from Gladbach; **6** from *Das Bauernhaus in der Schweiz*; **7** and **8** from Graffenried and Stürler; **9** from Anheisser.

Fig **325**: items **1** and **2** taken from *Das Bauernhaus in Deutschland*; **3** from Carl Schäfer; **4** from Dethlefsen; **5**, **6** and **7** from Deininger, **8** to **13** from Eigl.

Fig **327**: photo by staff of the Norsk Folkemuseum, Oslo.

Fig **342**: item **1** taken from Johan Meyer, *Fortids Kunst, Telemarken V*; **2** from Dethlefsen; **3** photo by the author; **4** from *Das Bauernhaus in Österreich-Ungarn*.

Fig **347**: items **1** and **3** from *Das Bauernhaus in Österreich-Ungarn*; **2** from Karl Schaefer; **4** from Deininger, *Das Bauernhaus in Tirol und Vorarlberg*.

Fig **348**: item **1** from Midttun, *Vest-Agder II*; **2** and **4** from photographs; **3** from Gerda Boëthius.

Fig **349**: item **1** from J. Meyer, *Fortids Kunst i Norges Bygder*; **2** and **3** photos by the author; **4** from *Das Bauernhaus in der Schweiz*.

Fig **351**: item **1** from G. Midttun, *Setesdalen*; **2** from Meyer, *Telemarken V*; **3** from Midttun, *Vest-Agder II*; **4** to **6** photos by the author.

Fig **352**: items **1**, **3**, **4** and **5** photos by the author; **2** from *Das Bauernhaus in Deutschland*.

Fig **353**: photos by the author.

Fig **354**: from photos by the author.

Fig **355**: items **1**, **2**, **4** and **5** taken from Gladbach; **3** from Anheisser.

Fig **356**: item **1** from Gladbach; **2** from Deininger; **3** from Anheisser; **4** from *Bauwerke der Schweiz*, 1896; **5** from Neumeister and Haberle.

Fig **358**: items **1** and **4** from Dethlefsen; **2** and **11** from Midttun; **3** and **5** from Gladbach; **6**, **12** and **13** from Johan Meyer; **7**, **8**, **10** and **14** from Deininger; **9** from *Architecture suisse*.

Fig **360**: from photos by Albert Jäkle.

Fig **361**: from photos by Dr. Moro, Villach, Austria.

Fig **362**: items **1** to **3** from *Fortids Kunst i Norges Bygder*; **4** and **5** from Anders Sandvig.

Fig **370**: items **1** to **7** from Johan Meyer; **8** from Gisle Midttun.

Fig **371**: items **1**, **2**, **3**, **5** and **7** taken from Midttun, *Setesdalen* and *Vest-Agder II*; **4** from Meyer in *Fortids Kunst*; **6** and **8** from photos by the author.

Fig **372**: items **1**, **2** and **4** from J. Meyer; **3** and **5** from G. Midttun.

Fig **373**: item **1** photo by the author, **2** and **4** from G. Midttun; **3** from Johan Meyer.

Fig **374**: from photos by the author.

Fig **375**: photos by the author.

Fig **376**: items **1**, **3**, **4** and **6** taken from Gladbach; **2** from Grafenried and Stürler; **5** from a photo by the author.

Fig **377**: items **1**, **2**, **4**, **5**, **6**, **7** and **8** from Gladbach; **3** and **7** from *Das Bauernhaus in der Schweiz*.

Fig **382**: photo by Neupert, Oslo.

Fig **383**: photo by Grombergs Nya Aktb., Stockholm.

Fig **386**: photo by Neupert, Oslo.

Fig **387**: staff photo, Bygdoe museum.

Fig **388**: photo by Neupert, Oslo.

Fig **389**: photo by Neupert, Oslo.

Bibliography

Alte Bayerische Zimmermannskunst. Akademischer
    Architekten-Verein, Munich. 1926.
Architecture suisse.
Baumeister. *Das Bauernhaus des Wallgaues.*
Bauwerke der Schweiz. 1896 and 1900.
Bayerischer Heimatschutz. 1913.
Berg, Arne. *Norske Bygder, Vest-Agder.*
Bielenstein, A. *Die Holzbauten und Holzgeräte der Letten.*
    St. Petersburg – Petrograd 1907 – 1918.
Boëthius, Gerda. *Studier i den nordiska*
    timmerbygnadskonsten. Stockholm, 1927.
Deininger. *Das Bauernhaus in Tirol und Vorarlberg.*
Dengler, A. ''Der Aufbau des Holzes'' in *Handbuch der*
    Holzkonservierung, 1916 by E. Troschel.
Der Baumeister, 1934.
De sandvigske sammlinger, 1907 and 1928.
Das Bauernhaus in der Schweiz. Zürich, 1903.
Das Bauernhaus in Deutschland.
Das Bauernhaus in Österreich-Ungarn, 1906.
Das Bürgerhaus in der Schweiz. Vol IV, 1913.
Das Werk, 1932.
Eckhof, Emil. *Svenska Storkyrkor.* Stockholm, 1914–1916.
Elgström, Ossian. *Karesuandolaparna.* Stockholm, 1922.
Erixon, Sigurd and Lindblom, Andreas. *En bok om*
    Skansen. 1933.
Erixon, Sigurd. *Folkliv 1.* 1937.
——. *Führer durch Skansen.*
——. *Skansens kulturgeschichtliche Abteilung.*
Fataburen, Kulturhistorisk Tidskrift. 1910 and 1925.
Fauth. *Das Lehmschindeldach.*
Gilly, D. *Handbuch der Landbaukunst.*

Gladbach, E. *Charakteristische Holzbauten der Schweiz.*
    1896.
——. *Der Schweizer Holzstil.*
Gut, A. *Die Denkmalpflege.* 1923.
Hamberg, Axel. *Redogörelse för Nordiska Musseets*
    utveckling och förvaltning. 1925.
Hempel and Wilhelm. *Waldbäume.*
Kollmann, F. *Die Technologie des Holzes.* 1936.
Midttun, Gisle. *Hus og huskunad.* 1919.
——. *Setesdalen.* Kristiania, 1919.
——. *Vest-Agder II.* Bergen, 1927.
Meyer, Johan. *Fortids Kunst 1.* 1920.
——. *Fortids Kunst, Telemarken V.*
——. *Fortids Kunst i Norges Bygder.* Oslo, 1920 and 1922.
Moderne Bauformen. 1933.
Nordiska Museet, Fataburen. Stockholm. 1902, 1904, 1912,
    1917, 1918 1922/24 and 1929/30.
Nordiska museets och Skansens Årsbok, Fataburen. 1937.
Nördlinger. *Die technischen Eigenschaften der Hölzer.*
Phleps, Hermann. ''Ostgermanische Spuren im Gefüge
    des westgermanischen Ständerwerks'' in *Brauch und*
    Sinnbild, ed. F. Herrmann and W. Trautlein 1940.
Raschke, Georg. *Aus Oberschlesiens Urzeit,* 17, 1932.
——. *Die Entdeckung des frühgeschichtlichen Oppeln.* 1931.
Reinerth, H. *Die Wasserburg Buchau.* 1928.
Skansens Vårfestbok. 1924.
Soeder, H. *Das Dorf Tritschuny im litauisch-*
    weissruthenischen Grenzgebiet. 1918.
Souslov, W. *Monuments de l'ancienne architecture russe.*
    Petersburg, 1901.
Tegninger af aeldre nordisk architektur. Copenhagen,
    1872–1879.

Index to Figures

apertures for light, etc., in log walls (*see also* loop-holes), Figs **293**, **294**.

arched-ceiling interior, Figs **196**, **196a**, **196b**.

architectural designwork on doorposts, Fig **288**.

architectural styling on window frames, Fig **297**.

arestue, open hearthed cabin (Norway), Figs **189**, **215**.

auxiliary rafter, use on sod roof, Fig **108/10**.

axes, Fig **7**.

balconies, Figs **314–321**, **324**, **360**, **361**, **366**, **398**.

balustrades (*see also* balconies), Figs **319–321**, **323**, **325**, **326**, **328**, **329**, **332–341**, **360–362**.

barge boards, Figs **115**, **124**, **139–141**, **385**.

barns, Figs **65–68**, **118**, **125–127**, **162**, **173**, **194**, **218**, **219**, **221**, **223**, **224**, **273–275**, **343**, **363**, **386**, **399**.

Bavarian door framing (*see also* skew pegging), Figs **252–272**.

beam ceilings, Figs **203**, **381**.

beam ends, treatment, Fig **36**.

bearer poles, to secure roofing, Figs **111/5**, **118**, **119**, **124**, **129**, **130**.

birch bark, in roofing, Figs **109**, **121**, **122**, **171**.

boarded roofs, Figs **109**, **118**, **119**, **158–161**.

boring tools, Fig **91**.

bowed-out doorposts (Scandinavian), Figs **213–216**.

bracing for log walls, additional, Fig **95**.

brackets, support, Figs **36**, **105**, **106**.

butted timber joints, Fig **96**.

cantilevered construction (*see also* flared endwork), Figs **204**, **205**, **314–319**, **348–357**.

ceiling and beam framing, Fig **199**.

ceilings (*see also* open-ceiling structures), Figs **202–205**, **381**.

Celtic door framing, Figs **226–228**.

chapels, Figs **194**, **195**.

cheese shed (Switzerland), Fig **181**.

chisels, Fig **22**.

columns, Figs **21**, **24**, **27–29**, **31**, **34**, **216**; on balconies, Figs **314**, **330**, **358–366**.

contouring, Figs **29**, **35**, **41**, **375**, **381**.

cornerboards, on square-hewn logwork, Fig **85**.

cornerwork, Figs **9**, **18**, **20**, **33**, **62**, **71**, **73–83**, **90**, **93**, **99**, **100**, **204**, **209**.

crooked wooden stops, for retaining roofing, Figs **108/5**, **109/A**, **120**, **176**, **184**, **186**.

crook-ended rafter, Figs **42**, **171**, **176**.

cross-walls, *see* stub walls.

domed huts, Laplander's, Fig **107**.

doorposts, Figs **94**, **208**, **209**, **211–214**, **217**, **218**, **226–238**, **241**, **244**, **251**, **252**, **256–263**, **265–272**, **276**, **277**, **282–292**, **372**, **374**.

doors and doorways, Figs **23a**, **24**, **206–218**, **225–231**, **243–250**, **251**, **257–272**, **276–292**, **375**.

double-forked mortising, Figs **222**, **251**, **277**.

dovetailed corners, Figs **73**, **77**.

dovetail pattern on balcony, Fig **335**.

dovetails, pegging, Figs **93**, **101**; scribing, Fig **81**.

dowelling (*see also* pegs and pegging), Figs **206**, **252**.

drawknife decoration, Figs **351–353**.

eaves framing, Figs **198–201**.

eavestroughs, wooden, Figs **124**, **144**, **145**.

eldhus, Swedish cabin or interior with central hearth, Fig **179**.

felling, Figs **51–56**.

flared endwork (*see also* cantilevered construction), Figs **33**, **201**, **348–357**.

floor and ceiling construction, Figs **202–205**.

foundation construction, *see* sill construction.

fruit storehouse (Switzerland), Fig **178**.

gables, Figs **342–347**.

gable boards, *see* barge boards.

gable and roof systems, Fig **174**.

grain storehouses, *see* granaries.

granaries, Figs **192**, **204**, **231–243**, **245**, **251**, **286**, **289–291**, **327**, **400–407**.

groove-edged shakes and shingles, Figs **123**, **132**.

grooved edgework, decorative, Figs **6**, **24**, **30**, **211**, **238**, **241**, **298**, **369–374**, **377**, **388**; old tool for applying, Fig **5e**.

grooves, lateral for fitting logwork, Fig **69**.

gutters, *see* eavestroughs.

hold-downs, for roofing material, *see* bearer poles.

interior finish work, Figs **379–381**.

joints, used in log and timber building, *see* notches, butted timber joints, doors and doorways, windows, cornerwork, partition walls.

klingeisen (curved drawshave), Figs **84, 353, 375**.
krokraptr, crooked wooden stops on Norwegian sod roofs, Figs **108/5, 109/A, 120, 176, 184**.
kronstänger, suspended beams or rods, as room dividers in old Swedish log cottages, Fig **188**.

lapped timber joints, Fig **96**.
Latvian log house, door framing of, Fig **292**.
loft (Norwegian storehouse), Figs **220, 221, 342, 387**.
log walls, *see* wall construction, partition walls.
loop-holes, apertures for light, etc., in log walls, Figs **293, 294**.
loose-laid shakes and shingles, Figs **124–128, 180**.

mouse guard, on granary, Fig **192**.

nailed-shingle roofing, Figs **132, 134–157**.
notches, *see* cornerwork, partition walls.

open-ceiling log structures, Figs **176–196**.
oval-hewn logwork, Figs **24, 26, 71, 173, 174, 176, 179, 184–187, 189, 194, 195, 211, 213, 216, 218, 295, 314, 315, 348, 349, 351, 369, 370**.
overhanging construction (*see also* cantilevered construction), Figs **204, 205**.

panelling, interior, Figs **379, 380**.
partition walls, Fig **86**.
pegs and pegging (*see also* skew pegging, dowelling), Figs **40, 88, 89, 93**; on roofs, Figs **124, 131, 168, 171, 197**; on balconies, Figs **317, 318, 323, 334, 335, 361**; gables, Figs **342, 343, 361**.
pegs, crooked wooden, for retaining sod roofing, Fig **108**.
pillars, *see* columns.
planes, tools, Figs **60, 61**.
profiling, *see* grooved edgework, contouring.

rafters, roof, *see* roof framing.
reisverk (Norwegian timberframe and vertical staving), Figs **184, 327**.
retaining planks, at eaves of roof, Figs **121, 122, 171**.
roof framing, description and types, Figs **165–168**.
roofing techniques from Sweden, Figs **109, 120**.
roofs, *see* sod roofs, tamped-thatch roofing, thatch-tiled roofing, wooden roofing, boarded roofs, shingled roofing.

saddle boards, on roofs, Fig **176**.
saddle logs, on roof, Fig **179**.
saddle poles, on roof, Figs **109, 112, 115, 120**.
saws, Fig **58**.
Scandinavian door framing, Figs **208–210, 217, 218**.
scissor poles, with thatched roofing, Fig **111**.
shakes, wooden, *see* shingled roofing, shingles.
sheaf-thatched roofing, Fig **115**.
shed roof styles, Fig **171**.
shingled roofing, Figs **124–157, 192**.
shingles, making of, Figs **123, 133**.
sill construction, Figs **99–103, 105, 106**; decorative sills, Fig **377**.
skew pegging, Figs **252–275, 285, 303**.
sod roofs, Figs **108–110**.
spiral grain, traditional Bavarian carpenter's method of determining, Fig **50**.
splines, as reinforcement in log walls, Fig **92**.
stabur (raised Norwegian storehouses), Figs **385, 386, 388, 389**.
stave churches, Figs **135–138**; columns from, Figs **27, 28**.
stolper (Norwegian) support posts, Figs **314/4, 362**.
stone, differing material from wood, Fig **26**; as roofing material, Figs **162–164**; as roof weighting, Figs **124–127, 180**.
storehouses (*see also* granaries and lofts), Figs **193, 197, 204, 220, 221, 327, 357, 359, 364, 383–385, 394, 395, 407–415, 418**.
stub walls, Figs **95, 165, 315**.
support props or piers, wooden, under Swiss granaries, Fig **20**.
sval (Norwegian), porch or elevated balcony or walkway, Figs **187, 221, 315, 389**.
swelling and shrinkage of timber, Figs **47, 48**.

tailpieces, rafter, Fig **200**.
tamped-thatch roofing, Figs **111–118**.
thatch-tiled roofing, Fig **117**.
tie logs, vertical, as wall bracing, Figs **95, 97, 251**.
timberframing, Figs **32, 41**.
tools, involved in log building, Figs **91, 123**.

vapour barrier on sill, Fig **101**.
verge boards, *see* barge boards.
vertical tie logs (beams), *see* tie logs.

wainscoting, *see* panelling.
walkways, elevated, *see* balconies, *sval*.
wall construction (*see also* cornerwork, bracing for log walls), Figs **62, 69**.
well tops, decorative wooden casings, Fig **23**.
window apertures, *see* loop-holes, apertures.
windows, Figs **296–313, 376**.
window sills, to deal with runoff of rain, etc., Figs **299, 300, 308, 309**.
wölbi, sloped interior ceiling (Switzerland), Figs **169, 181, 182**.
wooden roofing (*see also* boarded roofs), Figs **118–122**.